Science Background to Engineering

Science Background to
Engineering

R L Timings

LONGMAN

Addison Wesley Longman Limited
Edinburgh Gate, Harlow
Essex CM20 2JE, England
and Associated Companies throughout the world

First published 1996

British Library Cataloguing in Publication Data
A catalogue entry for this title is available from the British Library

ISBN 0-582-25414-1 ✓

Set by 31 in 10/12 pt Times
Produced through Longman Malaysia, TCP

Contents

Preface

Science Background to Engineering has been written to cover the City and Guilds of London Institute (CGLI) Basic Competence unit 2010-02-032, comprising:

- Basic Physical Quantities
- Structures and States of Matter
- Mass, Force, Weight and Acceleration
- Mass per Unit Volume
- Forces and Moments of Forces
- Centre of Gravity, Equilibrium and Stability
- Friction
- Pressure
- Electricity and Magnetism
- Principles of Tool Construction and Materials Technology

Although this is an optional endorsement to the basic General Engineering Competence, it is essential for those students who wish to proceed to the more advanced Main Competences.

Science Background to Engineering complements the companion text *General Engineering* by the same author. It also complements the 'underpinning knowledge and understanding' elements of the Engineering Training Authority's basic training units. Since most persons studying for a CGLI certificate in Basic Engineering Competences will also be undergoing practical skill training to EnTra standards, they should also find the commonality of subject matter and approach particularly helpful.

Science Background to Engineering is student centred and, although it can be used as a conventional text, it is designed particularly for self-learning situations where students can work with a minimum of supervision and tutorial support. It is therefore suitable for NVQ and GNVQ courses organised on an open-learning, flexi-time basis. The text has been written in a less formal style than that normally adopted for technical texts and the author hopes that, as a result, the reader will find it more enjoyable.

R.L. Timings
1996

Acknowledgements

The publishers are grateful to the following for permission to reproduce copyright material:

Gaumont Watch Company Limited for our Fig. A6.5; Addison Wesley Longman for our Fig. J4.1A from *Engineering Materials Volume 1* by R.L. Timings; Edward Arnold (Publishers) Limited for our Figs M4.2A & M4.2R from *Vehicle and Engine Technology Volume 1* by Heinz Heisler.

EnTra Publications for permission under a reciprocal agreement to reproduce and adapt some of their material.

The author thanks the Dension Mayers Group for their assistance during the preparation of the text.

Introduction – how to use this book

- This book consists of a number of *Modules* subdivided into short *Sections*. You must work through these Sections in the order in which they appear in the book. Never move onto the next Section until you are satisfied that you understand the Section that you have just completed.
- The end of each Section provides a 'natural break'. This enables you to study at times convenient to you. Sometimes you will only have time to complete one Section. Sometimes you may have time to complete several Sections.
- Each Module deals with a major subject area. For example **Module A** deals with the SI system of units and how to use them.
- Each Section within a Module deals with a separate topic. For example **Section A1** is the first topic in Module A; it deals with physical quantities.
- You will find a complete list of Modules in the Contents list at the front of the book.
- Each Section consists of text, worked examples, and one or more *Activities*. You should respond to all the Activities as you come to them. They are an essential part of the learning process. You will quickly come to recognise an Activity since they are designed to stand out from the text. Here is the Activity heading for Activity A1.1:

Activity A1.1

- Having completed the Activity you will be told to **Now check your response**. (If you reach the bottom of a page without being told to check your answer, then the Activity continues on the next page.) You should check your solution against my model *Response* at the back of the book. You should always do this, even if you are confident your solution is correct. Sometimes I expand on the solution in order to develop the topic further, and sometimes I use my Response to provide a 'lead-in' to the next Section.
- You will know when you have come to the end of the Response because you will be told to **Now return to the text**. If you reach the bottom of page without seeing this message, then my model Response continues on the next page.
- If your solution is incorrect, hopefully my model Response will clear up any misunderstanding. If you are still unsure of your ground, **consult your Tutor**. Never move on until you have thoroughly understood the Activity you have just completed.

- At the end of each Module there is an *Assignment* for you to complete and hand to you Tutor. This will enable your Tutor to check your progress and help you with any residual difficulties.
- Finally, to complete the Activities and Assignments you will require:

  1. A loose leaf folder with a supply of lined paper and graph paper.
  2. A 'scientific' calculator.
  3. Normal drawing instruments.

I am sure you will soon get used to using this book.

Now turn to the first page of the text

Introduction to the SI system

A1 Physical quantities

If you have not already read the Preface and the Introduction at the front of this book, please do so now before proceeding with the first Activity. Here is the first Activity. It is very simple and it is mainly intended to show you how this book should be used.

 Activity A1.1

In your notebook write down any whole number you like between **1** and **9** inclusive.

When you have done this, turn to the response section at the end of this book and check your response. It will be headed **Response A1.1**

Now check your response

Let's summarise what you have learnt from your first Activity:

- A physical quantity = a number × a unit.
- You have learnt how to recognise and complete an activity.
- You have learnt how to check your response.

A2 SI base units

SI stands for Système International and is the universally adopted international system of physical units used in science and technology. Table A2.1 lists the **base units**.

Table A2.1

Physical quantity	Unit name	Unit symbol
length	metre	m
mass	kilogram	kg
time	second	s
plane angle	radian	rad
amount of a substance	mole	mol
electric current	ampere	A
luminous intensity	candela	cd
solid angle	steradian	sr
thermodynamic temperature	kelvin	K

For the moment we are only concerned with the first three quantities and their units:

length (metre)

mass (kilogram)

time (second)

Try and find the information to complete the statements in the next activity.

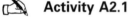 **Activity A2.1**

Copy the following statements into your notebook and complete them by inserting the appropriate information into the spaces provided:

(a) The maximum mass of a letter which can be sent under a first-class stamp is _____ kilogram (kg).

(b) The time taken for planet Earth to rotate once is _____ seconds (s).

(c) The pitch of an ISO M10 fine thread is _____ metres (m).

Now check your response

As you saw from my response, the base units are not always convenient to use when large or small quantities are involved. For this reason we often use **multiples** or **submultiples** of the base units. For example, it is more convenient to state the pitch of an M10 fine thread in millimetres rather than in metres. That is, as 1.25 mm rather than 0.00125 m. Let's now consider the multiples and submultiples of some of the more commonly used units.

A3   Multiples

Figure A3.1 shows the geographical locations of Aberdeen and Penzance.

Fig. A3.1

The distance from Aberdeen in Scotland to Penzance in Cornwall is 1 128 000 metres by road. For such long distances it is more convenient to use kilometres instead of metres. Since 1 kilometre equals 1000 metres, the distance between Aberdeen and Penzance becomes 1128 kilometres (km). The prefix **kilo** is a multiple. It makes the unit bigger. For example:

    1 kilogram (kg) = 1000 grams (g)
    1 kilometre (km) = 1000 metres (m)

Table A3.1 provides a list of multiples in common use.

Table A3.1

Prefix	Symbol	Multiplying factor
deca-	da	10^1 ($\times 10$)
hecto-	h	10^2 ($\times 100$)
kilo-	k	10^3 ($\times 1000$)
mega-	M	10^6 ($\times 1\,000\,000$)
giga-	G	10^9 ($\times 1\,000\,000\,000$)
tera-	T	10^{12} ($\times 1\,000\,000\,000\,000$)

Don't worry about the very large multiples at this stage. They are mostly used in electronic engineering and stress calculations. Now for some simple calculations involving multiples.

 Activity A3.1

Write down and complete the following calculations in your notebook. To give you a start, I have completed the first calculation for you. Express:

(a) 14 kilometres in metres   14 km $\times$ 1000 = **14 000 m**
(b) 14.3 kilometres in metres
(c) 25 kilograms in grams
(d) 12 decagrams in grams
(e) 1.75 hectometres in metres
(f) 12 tonnes in kilograms
(g) 3 megatonnes in tonnes
(h) 0.5 megatonnes in kilograms

Now check your response

In Activity A3.1, calculation (h) gave a very large answer. It is very easy to make a mistake when writing down so many place-holding zeros. For this reason we often use **standard form** when dealing with large and small numbers. For example:

$$100 = 10 \times 10 \text{ which is the same as } 10^2$$
$$1000 = 10 \times 10 \times 10 \text{ which is the same as } 10^3$$

So 2500 can be written as 2.5 $\times$ 1000 which is the same as **2.5 $\times$ 10³**.
And 2 500 000 can be written as 2.5 $\times$ 1 000 000 which is the same as **2.5 $\times$ 10⁶**.

For multiples, note how the power to which the 10 is raised is equal to the number of zeros in the multiplying factor. So, when we reduce a number to standard form, we express it as a quantity in which only the numbers from 1 to 9 inclusive lie to the left of the decimal point multiplied by 10 raised to some power. This power is equal to the number of zeros in the multiplying factor.

Referring back to Activity A3.1, my worked example (a) expressed in standard form would be as follows:

$$14\,000 \text{ m} = 1.4 \times 10\,000 \text{ m} \text{ which is the same as } \mathbf{1.4 \times 10^4 \text{ m}}$$

Now it's your turn to convert some quantities into standard form.

 ## Activity A3.2

Convert your answers to the calculations in Activity 3.1 into standard form where this is appropriate.

Now check your response

In the next activity I have reversed the procedure. You have to convert from smaller units to larger units. Therefore you have to divide by the conversion factor. For example:

$$51\,000 \text{ grams} = \frac{51\,000}{1000} \text{ kilograms} = \mathbf{51 \text{ kg}}$$

Sometimes you will end up with a decimal fraction and this makes life rather more complicated. For example:

$$51\,000 \text{ grams} = \frac{51\,000}{1\,000\,000} \text{ tonnes} = \mathbf{0.051 \text{ t}}$$

This really needs to be expressed in standard form, but how do we deal with the decimal fraction? Again we write down the quantity with only a single number of 1 to 9 inclusive appearing to the left of the decimal point and, again, we multiply by 10 raised to some power. This time the power will be negative; it will be given a minus sign. This tells us that we have divided by the conversion factor. 0.051 t expressed in standard form becomes $\mathbf{5.1 \times 10^{-2}}$. The power is 1 greater than the number of zeros to the **right** of the decimal point. So

$$5.1 \times 10^{-2} = \frac{5.1}{10^2} = \frac{5.1}{100} = \mathbf{0.051}$$

 ## Activity A3.3

Write down and complete the following calculations in your notebook. To give you a start, I have completed the first calculation for you.

(a)   Without using standard form, express:
    (i)   1 450 000 grams in kilograms

$$\frac{1\,450\,000 \text{ grams}}{1000} = \textbf{1450 kg} \text{ (Don't forget the units)}$$

    (ii)   27 000 grams in kilograms
    (iii) 3 000 000 grams in tonnes
    (iv) 2.5 metres in decametres
    (v)   75 hectometres in kilometres
    (vi) 2.7×10^5 metres in kilometres
(b)   This time express your answers to the calculations in part (a) in standard form where appropriate.

Now check your response

A4 Submultiples

Sometimes quantities are too small to be measured conveniently using SI base units. For example, it is more convenient to write down the thickness of a piece of sheet metal as 0.5 mm than it is to write it down as 0.0005 m. In this example I have used the millimetre. The prefix **milli-** means 'the thousandth part of' the unit that follows it. Since the unit reduces the size of the base unit, such a prefix is called a **submultiple**.

Table A4.1 provides a list of submultiples in common use.

Table A4.1

Prefix	Symbol	Multiplying factor
deci-	d	10^{-1} $(\times 0.1)$
centi-	c	10^{-2} $(\times 0.01)$
milli-	m	10^{-3} $(\times 0.001)$
micro-	μ	10^{-6} $(\times 0.000\,001)$
nano-	n	10^{-9} $(\times 0.000\,000\,001)$
pico-	p	10^{-12} $(\times 0.000\,000\,000\,001)$
femto-	f	10^{-15} $(\times 0.000\,000\,000\,000\,001)$
atto-	a	10^{-18} $(\times 0.000\,000\,000\,000\,000\,001)$

Again, don't worry about the very small submultiples. They are mostly used in electronic and telecommunications engineering.

Note

- The symbol for the prefix **micro** is μ. This is the Greek letter **mu**.
- The power to which 10 is raised is the number of decimal places in the conversion factor when it is written in full.

Activity A4.1

Write down and complete the following calculations in your notebook. To give you a start, I have completed the first calculation for you.

(a) Without using standard form, express:
  - (i)   15 millimetres in metres   15 mm $\times$ 0.001 = **0.015 m** or
                                   (15 mm)/(1000) = **0.015 m**
  - (ii)   5.7 millimetres in metres
  - (iii) 5.0 microseconds in seconds
  - (iv)   1.7 nanoseconds in seconds

(b) Express your answers to part (a) in standard form.

Now check your response

Now let's reverse the calculations. This time we are going to convert quantities in large units into quantities in small units that is, quantities using submultiples.

Activity A4.2

Write down and complete the following calculations in your notebook. To give you a start, I have completed the first calculation for you. Express:

(a) 0.0012 metres in millimetres   0.0012 m $\times$ 1000 = **1.2 mm**
(b) 0.017 metres in millimetres
(c) 1.57×10^{-2} metres in millimetres
(d) 0.000 08 seconds in microseconds
(e) 9.4×10^{-8} seconds in microseconds

Now check your response

A5 # Derived units

These are units derived from the SI base units. The base units may be combined together by multiplication or division. This is best understood by looking at some examples.

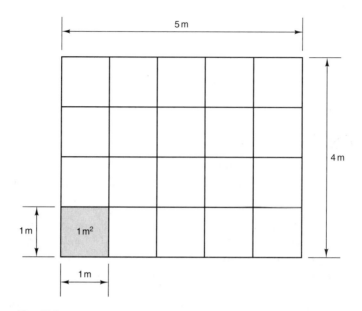

Fig. A5.1

Figure A5.1 shows the floor plan of my office. I told you earlier that it is 5 m long. I have now included the width, 4 m. Since the plan is rectangular, the area is found by multiplying its length by its width:

$$
\begin{aligned}
\text{area} &= \text{length} \times \text{width} \\
&= 5 \text{ m} \times 4 \text{ m} \\
&= 5 \times 4 \times \text{m} \times \text{m} \\
&= 20 \times \text{m} \times \text{m} \\
&= \mathbf{20 \ m^2}
\end{aligned}
$$

In Fig. A5.1 I have marked out the length and width in metres (the base unit). This gives me 20 squares of area 1 m² each.

$$\text{total area} = 20 \times 1 \text{ m}^2 = \mathbf{20 \ m^2}$$

I could have worked in millimetres and square millimetres or in kilometres and square kilometres. However, for this size of rectangle, metres were the most convenient. Because I have multiplied two base units together (m × m), I have obtained a **derived unit**, the unit of area (m²). The calculations in the following activity are relatively easy. I want you to pay particular attention to using the correct units.

Activity A5.1

Copy the following table into your notebook and complete the calculations.
To give you a start, I have done the first one in each group.

Table A5.1A

Length	Width (breadth)	Area
5 m	4 m	5 m × 4 m = **20 m²**
3 m	2 m	–
12 m	–	36 m²
50 mm	5 mm	–
15 mm	–	45 mm²
10 km	2 km	–
–	20 km	800 km²
100 m	2 km	–
300 mm	0.5 m	–

Diameter	Area
5 m	$A = \dfrac{\pi D^2}{4} = \dfrac{\pi \times 5^2}{4} = \dfrac{\pi \times 25}{4} = $ **19.6 m²**
8 km	–
7 km	–
40 mm	–

Now check your response

The same principles apply when finding volumes. For a box-shaped figure,
such as the basic outline of my office, we can find the volume by multiplying
the floor area by the height as shown in Fig. A5.2. So we now have another
derived unit, the cubic metre (m³). This is a unit of volume or capacity. In
the following activity I have given you the cross-sectional area. To find the
volume of each solid, you have to multiply the area by the height or the
length.

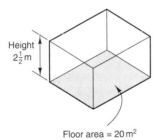

Height
$2\frac{1}{2}$ m

Floor area = 20 m²

Volume = area × height = 20 m² × $2\frac{1}{2}$ m = 50 m³

Fig. A5.2

Activity A5.2

Copy the following figure into your notebook and calculate the volumes of the solids shown.

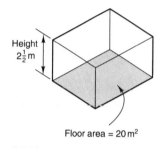

Height
$2\frac{1}{2}$ m

Floor area = 20 m²

Fig. A5.2A

Now check your response

The derived units for area and volume result from the multiplication of two or more base units.

Derived units can also result from the division of base units. For example:

$$\text{speed} = \frac{\text{distance (m)}}{\text{time (s)}}$$

$$= \text{metres per second (m/s or ms}^{-1})$$

Multiples and submultiples may also be used to keep the number to a convenient size, for example, millimetres per second (mm/s) or kilometres per hour (km/h).

Example

Calculate the speed of a body if it travels 15 metres in 3 seconds.

Solution

$$\text{speed} = \frac{\text{distance}}{\text{time}} = \frac{15 \text{ m}}{3 \text{ s}} = \textbf{5 m/s or 5 m s}^{-1}$$

 ### Activity A5.3

Perform the following calculations in your notebook:

(a)   Calculate the speed of a body if it travels 80 kilometres in 2 hours.

(b)   Calculate the speed of a body if it travels 80 millimetres in 5 seconds.

(c)   Calculate the time taken for a body travelling at 45 m/s to move through a distance of 90 metres.

(d)   A car is travelling at 45 km/h. How far will it travel in 4.5 hours?

Now check your response

When speed changes so that it progressively increases over a period of time we have **acceleration:**

$$\text{acceleration (rate of change of speed)} = \frac{\text{speed}}{\text{time}}$$

$$= \frac{\text{m/s}}{\text{s}}$$

$$= \frac{\text{m}}{\text{s} \times \text{s}}$$

$$= \text{m/s}^2 \text{ or } \text{ms}^{-2}$$

If the speed decreases over a period of time we have **deceleration** (negative acceleration). Another derived unit is the unit of **force:**

force = mass (kg) × acceleration (m/s²)

= kilogram metres per second squared (kgm/s²)

This is rather a mouthful so we call the unit of force the **newton** after the scientist and mathematician Sir Isaac Newton. Table A5.1 shows some commonly used physical quantities and units. Others will be introduced as we proceed.

Table A5.1

Quantity	Quantity symbol	Unit of measurement	Unit symbol
length	l	metre	m
area	A	square metre	m²
volume	V	cubic metre	m³
mass	m	kilogram	kg
weight	W	newton	N
force	F	newton	N
density	ρ*	kilogram per cubic metre	kg/m³
energy	Q	joule	J
power	P	watt	W
time	t	second	s
speed and velocity	v	metre per second	m/s
acceleration	a	metre per second per second	m/s²
electrical potential	U	volt	V
electromotive force (emf)	E	volt	V
electrical current	I	ampere (amp)	A
electrical resistance	R	ohm	Ω†
electrical resistivity	ρ*	ohm-metre	Ω m

*ρ is the Greek letter rho.

†Ω is the Greek letter omega.

Here are some rules you will need to remember if you are going to use the symbols and units correctly:

- The quantity symbol is always in *italic* (sloping) letters.
- The unit symbol is always in roman (upright) letters.
- Where a unit is named after a famous person the following rules apply:
  (i)   When referring to the person use a capital initial letter in the normal way (e.g. Sir Isaac Newton).
  (ii) When the name refers to a unit use lower case (small) letters (e.g. newton)
  (iii) The symbol for the unit uses the capital initial letter (e.g. N).

Example

James Watt has the unit of power, the **watt**, named after him. The symbol for the watt is **W**.

To avoid using the same letter twice, which would be confusing, sometimes a combination of capital and small letter is used for unit symbols, for instance:

- The unit of electromagnetic induction is the henry (H).
- The unit of frequency is the hertz (Hz).

 ### Activity A5.4

Rewrite the following sentences into your notebook using the correct capital and small letters. In this activity, underline any letters which should be in italics in a printed text.

(a)   The unit of force (f) is called the newton (n) in honour of the famous british scientist sir isaac newton.

Now check your response to exercise (a) before proceeding with the remaining exercises.

(b)   The unit of energy (q) is called a joule (j) in honour of the british scientist james joule.
(c)   The unit of electrical resistance (r) is called an ohm (Ω) in honour of the german scientist georg simon ohm.
(d)   The unit of electrical potential (u) is called a volt (v) in honour of the italian scientist alessandro volta.
(e)   The unit of electric current (i) is called an ampere (a) in honour of andré-marie ampère, the french physicist.

Now check your response

A6 # Measurement

Length

When I stated that my office was 5 metres long, I raised two questions:

- How do I know it is 5 metres long?
- How long is a metre?

In answer to the first question, I compared the length of my office with the scale on a steel measuring-tape similar to the one shown in Fig. A6.1.

Steel tape

In fact, all measuring processes involve the comparison of a dimension or property with a known standard. That is, measurment is always a **comparative** process.

In answer to the second question, the international standard metre is, legally, the distance between two lines on the horizontal web of a platinum–iridium bar kept at the International Bureau of Weights and Measures in Paris. The shape of the bar is shown in Fig. A6.2.

Fig. A6.1

However, for scientific and technical measurement of length this standard is no longer sufficiently accurate and the International Standard Metre has been redefined as 'the length of the path travelled by a beam of laser light in $1/299\,792\,458$ of a second.'

The laser used in such a standard is very precisely specified, as are the conditions for its operation.

My steel tape would not have been checked against such a precise standard. However, it would have been checked against precision measuring equipment which, in turn, would have been directly derived from a laser standard.

The traditional material standard of a platinum–iridium alloy bar cannot be exactly copied or replaced. Nor can it be precisely measured with sufficient accuracy for present-day requirements. Nor is it stable. Minute changes of length occur over a long period of time. Laser standards can be copied and replaced, if destroyed, without loss of accuracy. There are laser

Fig. A6.2

standards at various centres throughout the world, and manufacturers of precision measuring equipment can readily have their products checked and calibrated against them.

Mass

Mass is the quantity of matter in a body and depends upon the number and size of the atoms in that body. The base unit of mass is the **kilogram**. The standard kilogram is a platinum–iridium alloy cylinder kept at the International Bureau of Weights and Measures in Paris. A picture of the standard mass is shown in Fig. A6.3

Fig. A6.3

The mass of an object can be determined by using a **balance** as shown in Fig. A6.4. The known masses being used on the right-hand pan are directly

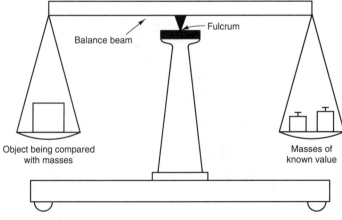

Fig. A6.4

related to the standard mass. So, again, the measurement of mass is a comparative process.

 Activity A6.1

The object shown in Fig. A6.4 has a mass of 200 g. If the object were transferred to the moon would it still have a mass of 200 g?
Answer **yes** or **no** and give reasons for your answer.

Now check your response

Time

The second of time used to be defined as a precise fraction of the solar year 1900. Unfortunately we cannot go back in time to check if the value calculated was correct. Nowadays we use the fact that a caesium isotope, 133, emits electromagnetic radiation at a precise and unvarying frequency. The second is defined as a precise number of time periods (cycles) of an atomic oscillator emitting this radiation. The stopwatch shown in Fig. A6.5 would be calibrated against a standard which, itself, would be related by comparison with an atomic clock as described above.

That concludes Module A. Before proceeding, complete the following assignment and hand it to your tutor for assessment. Don't forget to put your name and the assignment code on all your answer sheets.

Fig. A6.5

Assignment for Module A

1 A physical quantity consists of
  (a) a number
  (b) a unit
  (c) a number times a unit
  (d) a number divided by a unit

2 The SI base unit of length is
  (a) the millimetre
  (b) the centimetre
  (c) the metre
  (d) the kilometre

3 The SI base unit of mass is
  (a) the gram
  (b) the newton
  (c) the kilogram
  (d) the tonne

4 The SI base unit of time is
  (a) the second
  (b) the minute
  (c) the hour
  (d) the astronomical year

5 The prefix *kilo-* (k) in front of a unit
  indicates a multiplying factor of
  (a) 10^1
  (b) 10^3
  (c) 10^6
  (d) 10^9

6 The prefix *micro-* (μ) in front of a unit
  indicates a multiplying factor of
  (a) 10^{-1}
  (b) 10^{-3}
  (c) 10^{-6}
  (d) 10^{-9}

7 A multiplying factor of 10^6 is the same as
  (a) $\times 1000$
  (b) $\times 6000$
  (c) $\times 1000\,000$
  (d) $\times 6000\,000$

8 A multiplying factor of 10^{-3} is the same as
  (a) $\times 0.001$
  (b) $\times 0.003$
  (c) $\times 0.0001$
  (d) $\times 0.0003$

9 15 mm is the same as
  (a) 0.0015 m
  (b) 0.015 m
  (c) 0.15 m
  (d) 1.5 m

10 7.5 km is the same as
  (a) 0.75 m
  (b) 75 m
  (c) 750 m
  (d) 7500 m

11 The quantity symbol for length is
  (a) m
  (b) *m*
  (c) 1
  (d) *l*

12 The unit symbol for mass is
  (a) m
  (b) 1*m*
  (c) kg
  (d) *kg*

13 The area of the rectangle shown in Fig. AA.1 is
  (a) 1800 mm
  (b) 1800 mm^2
  (c) 1800 mm^3
  (d) 1.8 m

30 mm

60 mm

Fig. AA.1

14 The volume of the box shown in Fig. AA.2 is
  (a) 4000 mm
  (b) 400 mm^2
  (c) 4000 mm^3
  (d) 4 m

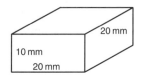

20 mm

10 mm

20 mm

Fig. AA.2

15 A rod has a circular cross-section of 10 mm^2
  and a length of 1 m. Its volume is
  (a) 10 mm^3
  (b) 100 mm^3
  (c) 1000 mm^3
  (d) 10 000 mm^3

16 A body travelling 15 m in 3 s has a speed of
  (a) 5 m/s
  (b) 45 m/s
  (c) 5 ms
  (d) 45 m/s^2

17 A car travelling at 60 km/h is travelling at the same speed as a motor cycle travelling at
(a) 600 m/min
(b) 1000 m/min
(c) 3600 m/min
(d) 6000 m/min

18 A vehicle whose speed is increasing uniformally is
(a) maintaining a constant speed
(b) stationary
(c) accelerating
(d) decelerating

19 Acceleration has units
(a) m/s
(b) ms^{-1}
(c) m/s^2
(d) m/s^{-2}

20 The formula for calculating the speed of a body is
(a) speed = distance × time
(b) speed = distance/time
(c) speed = time/distance
(d) speed = distance × time^2

MODULE B Structure and states of matter

B1 Atoms

An atom is a particle. It is a very small particle. It is so small that the ink used to print the full stop at the end of this sentence contains about one million million (10^{12}) atoms. An atom is made up of even smaller particles (subatomic particles). Some of these particles carry negative electrical charges. They are called **electrons**.

Electrons revolve around a nucleus like planets around the sun. We can't see atomic or subatomic particles but, by studying their behaviour, scientists have been able to construct large-scale models of what they think the particles look like.

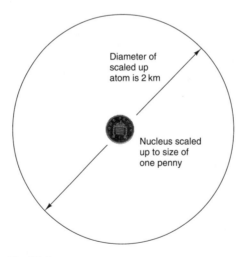

Diameter of
scaled up
atom is 2 km

Nucleus scaled
up to size of
one penny

Fig. B1.1

Figure B1.1 shows what the scale sizes would be if the nucleus were enlarged to a ball having the same diameter as a penny. The electrons would orbit

around the nucleus in a spherical envelope some two kilometres in diameter.
At this scale the electrons would still only be dots.

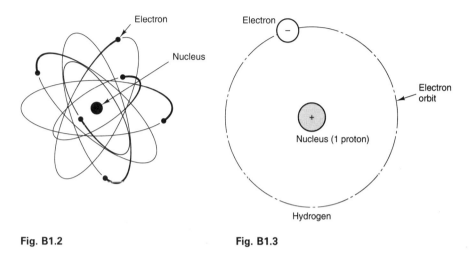

Fig. B1.2   Fig. B1.3

It is difficult to draw models of atoms because the electrons orbit around the
nucleus in a three-dimensional spherical 'cloud'. Figure B1.2 attempts to
show electrons orbiting around a nucleus. A more convenient and
informative way of drawing atoms is to use a Bohr model, in which all the
atoms are shown orbiting in a single plane. Figure B1.3 shows a hydrogen
atom drawn in this way. A hydrogen atom is the simplest atom possible
because it has only one electron.

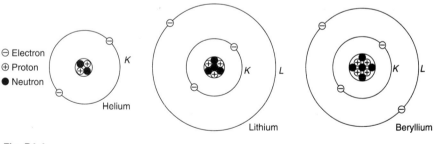

Fig. B1.4

Figure B1.4 shows some more Bohr models of simple atoms. The models
show the number of electrons, protons and neutrons in each atom. The more
protons and neutrons that are present in the nucleus, the greater will be the
mass of the atom. If you look at the diagrams carefully, you will see that:

- The number of electrons and the number of protons equal each other.
- The number of neutrons present in the nucleus is unrelated to both the number of electrons and the number of protons.

Now let's have an Activity to consolidate what you have learnt so far.

 Activity B1.1

Copy out and complete the following statements in your notebook using some of the words listed below:

(a) The number of electrons in an atom _____ the number of protons in the _____ of the atom.

(b) There is _____ relationship between the number of electrons and the number of neutrons in an atom.

(c) _____ orbit around the nucleus of an atom.

(d) The nucleus of an atom can contain either _____ alone or both _____ and _____ .

(e) Of the atoms shown in Fig. B1.4, the atom of _____ has the greatest mass.

Lithium, protons, no, a, beryllium, electrons, neutrons, helium, equals, varies from, nucleus, isotopes, ions.

Now check your response

Let's now consider the particles that make up an atom in greater detail:

Electrons   These are negatively charged particles that orbit around the nucleus of an atom. In an atom there are as many orbiting electrons as there are protons in the nucleus.

Nucleus   This is the core of an atom. It contains protons and neutrons. Since the mass of the electrons is negligible, the mass of the atom is considered to be the combined masses of all the protons and neutrons in the nucleus.

Protons   These are particles carrying a positive electrical charge. The mass of a proton is approximately 1800 times greater than the mass of an electron.

Neutrons   These have approximately the same mass as protons but they carry no electrical charge. They in no way influence the way the atom reacts with other atoms. They only increase the mass of the atom.

I said earlier that electrons orbit around the nucleus of the atom like planets orbiting around the sun. In the solar system the planets are kept in their orbits by gravitational forces. In an atom the electrons are held in their orbits by **electrostatic forces**. Let's consider this for a moment.

Electrostatic attraction depends upon the following rule:

Like charges repel each other; unlike charges attract each other.

Therefore:

- Negatively charged particles repel other negatively charged particles.
- Positively charged particles repel other positively charged particles.
- Positively and negatively charged particles are attracted towards each other. Thus negatively charged electrons are attracted to positively charged protons.
- The electrons spinning around the nucleus tend to fly out of orbit like a table-tennis ball off the rotating turntable of a record-player. The electrostatic force of attraction between the electrons and the protons keeps the electrons from doing this. The forces balance out and keep the electrons in their orbits.

The atoms we have considered so far are electrically neutral, that is, they have as many negatively charged electrons as they have positively charged protons. The charges balance out. Atoms can sometimes gain or lose electrons, causing their electrical balance to be upset. They are no longer electrically neutral. The atoms have become **ions**.

Ions These are atoms which have gained or lost one or more electrons:

- Loss of an electron makes an atom **electropositive** since there will be a positively charged proton present in the nucleus without its balancing electron. The atom has become an ion. Because of its electropositive charge, such an ion is called a **positive ion**.
- Gaining an electron makes an atom **electronegative** since there will be a negatively charged electron without its balancing positively charged proton in the nucleus. The atom has become an ion. Because of its electronegative charge, such an atom is called a **negative ion**.

Some atoms change their mass without changing their chemical properties. Atoms which do this are called **isotopes**. They are said to be **isotopic**.

Isotopes These are atoms in which the number of neutrons in the nucleus can vary. Since neutrons are electrically neutral and carry no charge, the number of electrons present in an isotope does not change. Therefore the chemical properties of an isotopic substance do not change. Only the mass changes because neutrons have approximately the same mass as protons. This change of mass leads us nicely into the topic of **atomic mass**. First, however, you must complete the next activity to consolidate the ground covered so far.

 Activity B1.2

Copy out and complete the following statements in your notebook using some of the words listed below:

(a) Electrons have _____ charges.
(b) Protons have _____ charges.

(c) Electrostatically charged particles are only attracted together if they have _____ charges.

(d) Neutrons have virtually the same mass as _____ but carry _____ charge.

(e) Electrons are held in their orbits by _____ forces.

(f) The mass of an atom is said to be the sum of the masses of the _____ and _____ in the atom.

(g) Atoms which have gained or lost one or more electrons have become _____.

(h) An atom is said to be _____ if its mass changes but its chemical properties remain _____.

(i) Protons and neutrons are only found in the _____ of an atom.

Like, unlike, electrons, protons, orbits, charges, nucleus, electrostatic, isotopic, ions, positive, negative, unchanged, no.

Now check your response

B2   Atomic mass

I have already told you that the mass of an atom is concentrated in its nucleus and that it is equal to the combined masses of all the protons and neutrons present in the nucleus. Here are some more facts concerning atomic mass:

- In any given element the number of protons present in the nucleus of an atom of that element does not change.
- The **atomic number** (Z) of an element is the number of protons present in the nucleus of an atom of that element.
- The number of neutrons in the nucleus of an atom can and does vary. Therefore the **atomic mass** can vary. We usually take the average mass of a large number of atoms of an element.
- The actual mass of an atom is very small. For example the mass of a beryllium atom is only 1.5×10^{-23} grams (0.000 000 000 000 000 000 000 015 g).
- This is inconveniently small for most purposes, so we use a special scale. This scale compares the mass of an atom with the mass of the carbon-12 atom. This is a carbon isotope whose nucleus contains 6 protons and 6 neutrons.
- The silver atom can be written $^{108}_{47}Ag$. This means that a silver atom has a **relative atomic mass** (RAM or A) of 108 units. Therefore its relative atomic mass is 9 times greater than that of carbon-12 ($9 \times 12 = 108$) using the same scale.

- The atomic number (Z) of the silver atom $^{108}_{47}$Ag is the bottom number. Therefore a silver atom has 47 protons in its nucleus.
- The number of neutrons in the nucleus is the difference between the relative atomic number (A) and the atomic number (Z). Therefore a silver atom has $108 - 47 = 61$ neutrons in its nucleus.

 Activity B2.1

Given that an iron atom can be expressed as $^{56}_{26}$Fe, write down:

(a)   its relative atomic number
(b)   how much greater is the mass of an iron atom compared to the mass of a carbon-12 atom
(c)   the atomic number for an iron atom
(d)   the number of protons in an iron atom
(e)   the number of electrons in an iron atom
(f)   the number of neutrons in an iron atom

Now check your response

B3   Molecules

Except for the noble gases such as neon (used in electric discharge tubes for advertising) and argon (used as a gas shield in some welding processes), atoms rarely occur as single particles. Atoms are usually associated with other atoms in small groups. The two atoms of hydrogen gas shown in Fig. B3.1 have joined together by sharing an electron. They have formed a **molecule**.

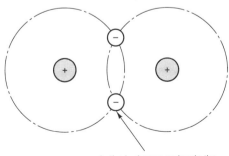

In the hydrogen molecule the electrons are shared to give a covalent bond

Fig. B3.1

Fig. B3.2

Molecules are also formed when different sorts of atoms combine together. Figure B3.2 shows a water molecule. It consists of two hydrogen atoms combined together with one oxygen atom. Hence it is give the chemical formula H_2O.

Just as the particles in an atom are held together by electrostatic charges, the atoms in a molecule are also held together by electrostatic charges. The properties of a molecule are influenced by the following factors:

- The type of atoms making up the molecule.
- The way the atoms are bonded together.
- The number of atoms in the molecule (the size of the molecule).

A large molecule (macromolecule) contains many atoms and therefore many bonds. This makes it relatively hard and brittle. A macromolecule will also have a high melting temperature and a high boiling temperature. It will also be a good electrical insulator. It will be formed from the atoms of non-metallic elements. It will be insoluble in water. A full study of molecules and their properties is beyond the scope of this book. However, there is one more grouping of atoms we must consider after you have completed the next activity.

Activity B3.1

Copy out and complete the following statement in your notebook, using some of the words listed below:

> Molecules consist of groups of _____ bonded together in different ways by means of _____ _____. The molecules may consist of the _____ type of atoms or of different types of _____. For example, a table salt (sodium chloride) molecule contains atoms of the elements _____ and _____. Very large molecules are called _____. They are hard and brittle and consist of _____ numbers of _____ atoms. They have _____ melting and boiling temperatures. They _____ _____ conduct electricity.

Atoms, same, different, electrostatic, sodium, macromolecules, charges, chlorine, large. small, metallic, non-metallic, high, low, do, not.

Now check your response

B4 Metallic Bond

The metallic bond is a bond which forms only between metallic atoms of the same element. The atoms lose electrons and become ionised. Metals do not form molecules. The metal ions arrange themselves into large, three-dimensional, geometric patterns called **lattice structures**. It is this ionic bonding together within the lattice structure that gives metals their special properties:

- Metals can be bent and formed into complex shapes in the solid condition.
- Metals readily conduct heat and electricity.
- Metals have shiny surfaces when freshly cut.

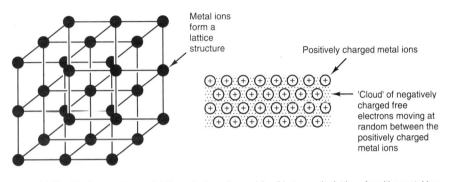

(**a**) Metal lattice structure   (**b**) Free electrons form a 'cloud' between the lattice of positive metal ion

Fig. B4.1

Figure B4.1(a) shows how the three-dimensional lattice would appear if we could see it under a microscope. Figure B4.1(b) shows a portion of this lattice in greater detail. The metal atoms have given up one or more electrons to become positively charged metal ions. The electrons which have escaped from the atoms move freely between the metal ions. We will consider this further in Section J.1. The movement of these free electrons is essential for the flow of electric current through a metal conductor. Let's now consider Fig. B4.2.

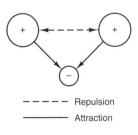

- The positive ions (denoted by the circles containing plus signs) have like charges so they tend to repel each other and keep apart.
- The positive ions are attracted to the free electron (denoted by the circle with the minus sign). This electron does not have a fixed position in the lattice. It is delocalised; it is free to move about. Remember that unlike charges tend to attract each other.
- The attractive forces between the positive ions and the electrons are greater than the repulsive forces between the ions themselves. This is because the ions are nearer to the electrons than they are to each other. The attraction between the ions and the electrons holds the ions in position in the lattice.
- Remember the lattice is three-dimensional.

Fig. B4.2

Let's now see how it is that metals can be bent and formed in the solid state.

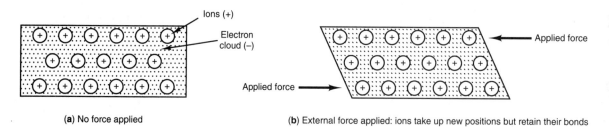

(a) No force applied   (b) External force applied: ions take up new positions but retain their bonds

Fig. B4.3

You can see in Fig. B4.3 that the metal ions are free to form bonds with any adjacent electron in the electron cloud that exists between the ions. Therefore, when an external mechanical force is applied to the metal as shown, the 'layers' of ions in the lattice are free to slide over each other. Sliding can occur without the lattice being broken. When an ion moves from its original position in (a) to its new position in (b), it is free to form a new bond with any conveniently adjacent electron. This maintains the structural integrity of the metal while allowing it to change shape.

Activity B4.1

Indicate whether the following statements are **true** or **false**. If false, explain why they are false.

(a) Metal atoms group together to form molecules.
(b) Pure metals are easily bent.
(c) Metals are good conductors of electricity.
(d) The metal atoms in the lattice lose one or more electrons and become positively charged ions.
(e) When subjected to an externally applied mechanical force of sufficient magnitude, the 'layers' of metal ions are displaced and the ionic bond is destroyed.
(f) The forces of attraction between the ions and the electrons are electrostatic.

Now check your response

B5 Elements, compounds and mixtures

Elements   These are substances containing only **one** type of atom. Copper, aluminium and pure iron are elements because no other atoms of other substances are present in them. Sodium chloride (table salt) is not an element because atoms of both the metal sodium and the gas chlorine are present in each sodium chloride molecule.

Compounds These are formed when two or more different types of atom combine together during a chemical reaction. If you have already guessed that sodium chloride (table salt) is a compound you are quite correct. Here are some rules which apply to all compounds:

- When a compound is formed, the substances from which it is made combine together during a chemical reaction to form an entirely new substance.
- This new substance will have different properties from the substances from which it is made.
- Heat is given out (but occasionally taken in) when the substances forming the compound combine together.
- Compounds can only be converted back into the substances from which they were made by chemical or electrochemical reactions.
- Compounds have fixed melting and boiling points.
- The constituent elements of any given compound are always present in the same proportions.

Example

Water is a compound formed when hydrogen gas burns in oxygen gas. The combination of hydrogen and oxygen to form water can be recognised as a chemical reaction because of the following facts:

- When hydrogen gas burns in oxygen gas, heat energy is released.
- The substance created by the reaction (water) has different properties compared with the elements from which it is made. Hydrogen and oxygen are both gases; water is a liquid. Hydrogen will burn: water will not. Oxygen supports combustion (burning); water puts fires out.
- Water can only be converted back into hydrogen and oxygen by an electrochemical process called electrolysis.
- In every 90 grams of water there is always 10 grams of hydrogen and 80 grams of oxygen.

Therefore water is a compound. It is produced by a chemical reaction.

 Activity B5.1

Given that the metal sodium will burn in the gas chlorine, explain why sodium chloride (table salt) appears to be a compound. Organise your response in a similar way to the previous example.

Now check your response

Mixtures A mixture is a close association of particles of the constituent substances in which no reaction takes place under normal conditions. Here are some facts about mixtures:

- The constituent substances in a mixture do not react together under normal circumstances and no new substances are formed. Even the mixture of chemicals in a firework will not react together until they are heated by lighting the blue touch-paper.
- The properties of a mixture are a combination of those of the individual substances found in the mixture.
- No heat energy is gained or lost when substances are mixed together.
- The substances making up a mixture can be readily separated by physical means.
- The proportions of the substances in a mixture are not fixed.
- The melting and boiling temperatures of mixtures are not constant.

Example

Let's now consider a mixture of sand and table salt.

- No matter how thoroughly we mix the sand and salt together, we will always have just sand and salt.
- If you look at the mixture of sand and salt through a magnifying glass, you can still see the individual grains of sand and salt and nothing else.
- No reaction occurs; no new substance is formed; no heat is gained or lost.
- You can mix the sand and salt in any proportions you like.
- You only require physical processes to separate the sand and salt:
  (i)   Add water to dissolve the salt.
  (ii)   Pass through a filter to remove the sand.
  (iii) Reclaim the salt by evaporation of the water.

Activity B5.2

Describe a simple method of separating iron filings and sawdust from a mixture of the two.

Now check your response

Activity B5.3

(a) List **five** important differences between compounds and mixtures.
(b) Explain why the metal zinc is an element.

Now check your response

B6   States of matter

There are **three** states of matter: **solids, liquids** and **gases**. All substances can exist in any of these states if they are made hot enough or cold enough. When a substance changes state, heat energy is taken in or given out. You have to add heat energy to water to turn it into steam. You have to remove heat energy from water to turn it into ice. We will now examine the differences between solids, liquids and gases and see how they arise.

B7   Solids

Solids can be crystalline or non-crystalline (amorphous). Most simple chemical substances are crystalline when solid. Metals are crystalline; plastics are non-crystalline; plastics are complex chemical substances. You may argue that the simple chemicals you used at school were powders or liquids. The powders were originally crystalline but the crystals had been ground down into a powder to make them more convenient for your use. Here are some facts about solids:

* All solids have a definite shape and volume.
* Compared with liquids and gases, very considerable force is required to change the shape of solids.
* The particles in a solid are closely packed together as shown in Fig. B7.1. Because of the close packing, the forces of attraction between the particles are much stronger than in liquids or in gases. The particles in liquids and gases are further apart. In solids, liquids and gases the particles are held together by electrostatic forces.

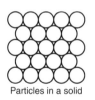
Particles in a solid

Fig. B7.1

✍ Activity B7.1

Copy out and complete the following statements in your notebook using some of the words listed below:

(a)   All substances can be solids, liquids or gases depending upon their _____ .

(b)   Heat energy is _____ or _____ during a change of _____ .

(c)   Solids have definite _____ and _____ .

(d)   Considerable _____ is required to change the shape of a solid.

(e)   The particles of a solid are _____ packed together.

Heat, state, shape, temperatures, volume, loosely, closely, force, area, gained, lost.

Now check your response

In a crystalline solid, the particles are located at fixed points in a lattice structure. They are only free to vibrate about these fixed points. They are not free to move to a different place. In theory all movement stops at about $-273\,^{\circ}C$. This temperature has never been achieved in practice.

As the temperature increases, the particles vibrate more vigorously and the solid becomes less rigid. This is why it is easier to forge steel to shape when it is red-hot. The more vigorously the particles vibrate about their fixed points, the more room they take up. To provide this additional room the metal expands. This is why metals expand when they are heated and their temperatures are raised. The opposite is also true; metals contract as they cool. This is because the particles vibrate less vigorously and take up less room. If a solid is raised to a sufficiently high temperature its particles vibrate so violently they break free from their fixed locations and the substance becomes a liquid.

 Activity B7.2

Indicate whether the following statements are **true** or **false**. If false, explain why they are false.

(a)   The particles in solids vibrate about fixed points.
(b)   These vibrations become less as the temperature increases.
(c)   Metals contract when they are heated and their temperatures rise.
(d)   Metals are more easily forged when they are heated.
(e)   Heating a metal increases the forces of attraction between its particles.

Now check your response

B8   Liquids

We finished the section on solids by saying that if the temperature is raised sufficiently, the particles vibrate so vigorously that they break free from their fixed locations. They become free to move about in a random manner in straight lines as the solid melts and becomes a liquid.

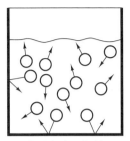

Particles in a liquid

Fig. B8.1

Figure B8.1 shows the random movement of particles in a liquid. This movement is only limited by the walls of the container and the surface tension of the surface of the liquid. Here are some facts about liquids:

- Liquids have a definite volume but no definite shape. They assume the shape of the container in which they are kept.
- The particles in a liquid are less closely packed than the particles in a solid. Thus the attractive forces between the particles in a liquid are very much weaker than those between the particles in a solid.
- Liquids are not compressible under normal conditions.
- Far less force is required to change the shape of a liquid than to change the shape of a solid.
- As the temperature of a liquid is raised, the particle activity increases. This causes the forces of attraction between the particles to become weaker. The liquid becomes more fluid, that is it becomes thinner (less viscous). The reverse is also true.

 Activity B8.1

Answer each of the following questions in your notebook with a brief statement. A simple yes or no is not adequate.

(a) Do liquids have definite shape and volume?
(b) Do the particles of a liquid vibrate about fixed points?
(c) Are the attractive forces between the particles in a liquid weaker than in a solid?
(d) Are liquids compressible?
(e) Are the particles in a liquid as closely packed as they are in a solid?
(f) Does the thickness (viscosity) of a liquid become greater as the temperature of the liquid falls?
(g) Does a liquid take up the shape of the container in which it is stored?

Now check your response

B9 Gases

If we raise the temperature of a liquid sufficiently, the particles will become so agitated that they will break through the surface tension of the liquid and escape into the atmosphere. Here are some facts about gases:

- Gases have no definite shape or volume. They will always fill the container in which they are stored.

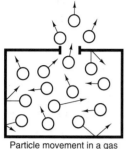

Particle movement in a gas

Fig. B9.1

- If gas particles are allowed to escape from their storage container into the atmosphere, they will disperse (spread) throughout the atmosphere indefinitely as shown in Fig. B9.1. This why cooking smells spread through a house even when there are no draughts to carry them.
- We assume that, at low pressures, there is no longer any attractive force between the particles of a gas.
- Unlike solids and liquids, gases are compressible.
- The pressure of a gas in a container is the sum of all the impacts made by the particles as they hit the walls of the container. The more gas is pumped into the container, the greater the number of particles present and the greater the number of impacts on the walls of the container in a given time. Therefore the more gas you pump into a container, the greater the pressure the gas exerts upon the walls of the container.

 Activity B9.1

Answer each of the following questions in your notebook with a brief statement. A simple yes or no is not adequate.

(a) Are gas particles free to move about at random?
(b) Are gas particles held together by strong electrostatic forces?
(c) Do gases assume the shape and volume of any vessel in which they are contained?
(d) Are gases compressible?
(e) Can unenclosed gases disperse throughout the atmosphere?

Now check your response

B10 Special properties

The properties of solids liquids and gases discussed so far are **general** properties; they apply to all solids, liquids and gases. In addition to the general properties, each solid, liquid or gas has its own **special** properties.

Example

Steel and ice are both solids. However:

- Steel is strong, has a high melting point and can be bent.
- Ice is weak, has a low melting point and is brittle.

☞   ## Activity B10.1

Following my example for solids, write down the special properties of:

(a)   the liquids **water** and **oil**
(b)   the gases **acetylene** and **carbon** dioxide

Now check your response

B11   # Cohesion and adhesion

Cohesion   This refers to the strength of the bonds between the particles within a substance and therefore the overall strength of that substance. For example, the cohesion between the particles in steel is greater than, say, the cohesion between the particles in aluminium.

Adhesion   This is the way different substances stick to each other, for example the way in which oil sticks to a metal surface. Adhesion is of great importance in the way joints can be achieved by adhesive bonding. Adhesives are being increasingly used for joining engineering components.

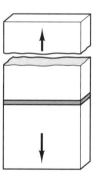

(a) Cohesive failure
of the adherend
Adhesive too strong

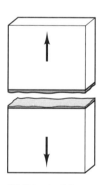

(b) Cohesive failure
of the adhesive
Weak adhesive

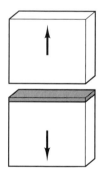

(c) Adhesive failure
*Inadequate
preparation of the
joint faces resulted in
a poor bond*

Fig. B11.1

Figure B11.1(a) shows a joint that is stronger than the material being joined. The adhesive strength of the joint is greater than the cohesive strength of the material being joined.

Figure B11.1(b) shows what happens when the adhesive strength of an adhesive is greater than its cohesive strength.

Figure B11.1(c) shows what happens when the cohesive strength of the materials being joined and the cohesive strength of the adhesive itself are greater than the adhesive strength of the bond. The joint comes unstuck.

That concludes Module B. Before proceeding, complete the following assignment and hand it to your tutor for assessment. Don't forget to put your name and the assignment code on all your answer sheets.

Assignment for Module B

1 Atoms consist of electrons orbiting around
(a) a molecule
(b) a neutron
(c) a nucleus
(d) an ion

2 Electrons have
(a) a negative charge
(b) a positive charge
(c) no charge
(d) combined charges

3 Protons have
(a) a negative charge
(b) a positive charge
(c) no charge
(d) combined charges

4 Neutrons have
(a) a negative charge
(b) a positive charge
(c) no charge
(d) combined charges

5 The number of electrons in an atom equals
(a) the number of neutrons in the nucleus
(b) the number of protons in the nucleus
(c) the number of ions in the nucleus
(d) the sum of all the protons and neutrons in the nucleus

6 The mass of an antom is taken to be
(a) the total mass of the electrons
(b) the total mass of the protons
(c) the total mass of the neutrons
(d) the combined mass of the protons and the neutrons

7 Groups of atoms combined together in gases, liquids or non-metallic solids are called
(a) molecules
(b) lattices
(c) clusters
(d) mixtures

8 An atom that has gained or lost an electron is called
(a) an isotope
(b) a lattice
(c) a molecule
(d) an ion

9 The particles of a solid, whose structure consists of a regular geometric pattern of positive ions separated by a cloud of free electrons, is said to have
(a) a covalent bond
(b) an electrical bond
(c) a macromolecular bond
(d) a metallic bond

10 A substance containing only one type of atom is called
(a) a compound
(b) an element
(c) a mixture
(d) a polymer

11 A substance consisting of two or more chemically combined elements in a fixed proportion is called
(a) a compound
(b) an element
(c) a mixture
(d) a polymer

12 A group of different substances in close association, but not combined chemically, is called
(a) a compound
(b) an element
(c) a mixture
(d) a polymer

13 A substance whose particles are closely packed together so that they can only vibrate about fixed points is called a
(a) a solid
(b) a liquid
(c) a gas
(d) a vapour

14 A substance that has definite volume but takes the shape of the container in which it is kept is called a
(a) a solid
(b) a liquid
(c) a gas
(d) a vapour

15 A substance which is compressible is a
(a) a solid
(b) a liquid
(c) a gas
(d) a plastic

16 A compound is formed by
(a) a chemical reaction
(b) careful mixing
(c) a mixture of gases only
(d) the electrolysis of a solution

17 When a chemical reaction takes place
(a) no new substance is formed
(b) gases only form new gases
(c) heat is taken in or given out
(d) a mixture is formed

18 The oil film on a metal surface remains in place because of
(a) cohesion
(b) adhesion
(c) suction
(d) keying

19 In addition to general properties, special properties apply to
(a) solids only
(b) liquids only
(c) gases only
(d) solids, liquids and gases equally

Force, weight and acceleration

C1 ## Mass

We have already considered some aspects of mass in the previous sections. Let's summarise what we have learnt so far:

- Mass is the total quantity of matter in a body. It is the sum total of the masses of all the subatomic particles in the body.
- Matter occupies space and can be solid, liquid or gaseous.
- Unless matter is added or removed, the mass of a body never varies. It is constant under all conditions. There are as many atoms in a kilogram of butter on the Moon as there are atoms in the same kilogram of butter on planet Earth.
- The base unit of mass is the kilogram. The most commonly used multiple is the tonne (1000 kg) and the most commonly use submultiple is the gram (0.001 kg). Figure C1.1 shows some relationships concerning mass and capacity.

 =  =

Platinum–iridium cylinder: standard mass 1 kg	1 dm^3 of water also has a mass of 1 kg

1 litre (l) of water equals 1 dm^3, so it also has a mass of 1 kg

Fig. C1.1 Caption

 Activity C1.1

Calculate:

(a) the mass of 5 dm^3 of water in kilograms
(b) the volume of 7 kilograms of water in litres

(c)   the mass of 5000 cm^3 of water in kilograms

(d)   the volume of 10 g of water in millilitres

(e)   the mass of 12×10^3 dm^3 of water in tonnes

Now check your response

C2   Force

Before we can discuss weight and find out how mass and weight are related, we have to consider the concept of **force**. We can't see a force; we can only see what a force can do. Here are some facts about force:

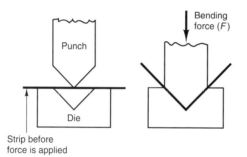

Fig. C2.1

- A force can change or try to change the shape of an object. In the example shown in Fig. C2.1, the force on the punch bends the strip of metal by pushing it into a die. A small force will only **try** to bend the strip. Bending will not be seen to take place until the force has sufficient magnitude to overcome the resistance to bending of the strip.

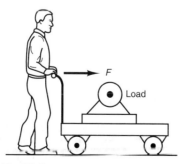

Fig. C2.2

- A force can move or try to move a body which is at rest. In the example shown in Fig. C2.2, the force (*F*) exerted on the handle of the trolley is sufficient to cause movement in the direction of application of the force (the direction in which you are pushing). If the force is too small to cause movement, it will still **try** to move the trolley.
- A force can change or try to change the motion of a body that is already moving. For example:
  (i)   The force of a strong headwind can decrease the speed of an aircraft, whereas the force of a strong tail wind can increase the speed of an aircraft.
  (ii) The force of a strong crosswind can cause a car to swerve off course.
- The effect of any force depends upon:
  (i)   The magnitude (size) of the force.
  (ii) The direction of the force.
  (iii) The point of application of the force.
  (iv) The ability of a body to resist the effects of the force.

Activity C2.1

Figure C2.2 in the text shows how a force (*F*) can move a load on a trolley. Describe what happens if:

(a)   the force (*F*) is removed
(b)   a force equal and opposite to force (*F*) is applied to the trolley

Now check your response

C3   Vectors

Quantities can be divided into two categories:

- Scalar quantities
- Vector quantities

Scalar quantities   These have magnitude (size) only. For example:

- The speed of a car is 50 km/h.
- The power of a car engine is 75 kW.
- The current flowing in a circuit is 12 A.
- The time taken to read about scalar quantities is 25 s.

Vector quantities   These have both magnitude and direction. For example, the velocity of a car is 50 km/h due north from London. I hope you can now see the difference between speed and velocity. In the case of velocity you have both the speed and the direction, therefore velocity is a vector quantitiy.

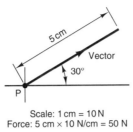

Scale: 1 cm = 10 N
Force: 5 cm × 10 N/cm = 50 N
Fig. C3.1

A force of magnitude 50 N acts on a point (P) at an angle of 30° to the horizontal as shown in Fig. C3.1. The figure is a vector diagram representing the force. A vector can represent the magnitude and direction of a force when drawn to scale. You will be drawing a lot of vector force diagrams in Module E. Here are two to be going on with.

 Activity C3.1

Draw the following vectors of forces in your notebook using a scale of 1 cm = 10 N:

(a) A force of 50 N acting due north from any point P.
(b) A force of 40 N acting at 45° to a horizontal line from a point P. Measure the angle in an anticlockwise direction.

Now check your response

C4 Weight

We have already referred several times to the unit of force, so now let's find out just how big it is. If you hold a 1 kg bag of sugar in your hand, the load on your hand will be equal to a force of approximately 10 newtons (10 N) acting vertically downwards.

On planet Earth a mass of 1 kg has a weight of approximately 10 N (to be more exact 9.81 N). It will weigh slightly more at the poles and slightly less at the equator because the Earth is not a perfect sphere.

- The **force of gravity** attracts the mass of any body towards the centre of the Earth.
- The **weight** of a body is the force of gravity acting on the mass of that body.
- Weight is a force so we measure it in **newtons**.

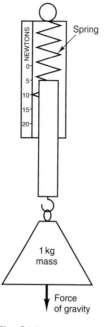

Fig. C4.1

In Fig. C4.1 the 1 kilogram mass is shown suspended from a spring balance. The mass is being acted upon by the force of gravity. The spring in the balance stretches until the force in the spring equals the force of gravity acting on the 1 kilogram mass. At this point the spring stops stretching. The force is indicated on the scale of the spring balance. Since we are measuring a force, the scale is marked in newtons. For a mass of 1 kilogram, the pointer should indicate 9.81 newtons on the scale. Remember:

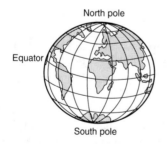

North pole

Equator

South pole

Moon

1 kg mass will weigh 9.81 N

This is an average value as the force of gravity is slightly greater at the poles than at the equator because the Earth is not a perfect sphere

1 kg mass will weigh
$\frac{1}{6} \times 9.81\,\text{N} = 1.64\,\text{N}$

The gravitational force of the Moon is approximately 1/6 that of the average value of the Earth's gravitational force

Fig. C4.2

- Mass is the quantity of matter in a body. It is constant for that body. The force of gravity acting on that body can vary. Therefore weight can vary.
- Weight is a force. It is measured in newtons. On Earth this force will be 9.81 newtons for every 1 kilogram of mass.

The Moon's gravitational force is approximately one-sixth of the Earth's gravitational force. The effect of this difference is shown in Fig. C4.2

 Activity C4.1

Copy and complete the following table into your notebook using the data given in Fig. C4.2.

Table C4.1A

Earth		Moon	
Mass	Weight	Mass	Weight
6 kg	–	–	–
–	981 N	–	–
3 tonnes	–	–	–
–	981 kN	–	–
–	–	500 kg	–

Now check your response

C5 # Force, mass and acceleration

By now you should be confident that you can calculate the weight of any mass simply by multiplying the mass in kilograms by a factor of 9.81. This will give you the weight in newtons. So what exactly is the factor of 9.81? Where does it come from? First, let's summarise some of the facts we already know:

- Weight is a force. It is the effect of the force of gravity acting on a mass.
- One of the effects of a force is to change the speed and/or direction of a body in motion. When a force acts on a mass, the speed of the mass changes or tries to change.
- A change in speed is an acceleration.

With the aid of Fig. C5.1 we can put these facts together as follows.

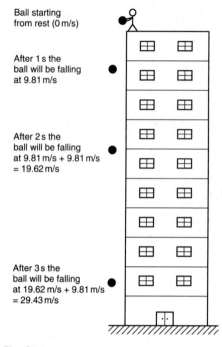

Ball starting
from rest (0 m/s)

After 1 s the
ball will be falling
at 9.81 m/s

After 2 s the
ball will be falling
at 9.81 m/s + 9.81 m/s
= 19.62 m/s

After 3 s the
ball will be falling
at 19.62 m/s + 9.81 m/s
= 29.43 m/s

Fig. C5.1

If we let a ball fall from a tall building, the force of gravity will pull the ball to the ground. Gravity is the force acting on the ball. A force acting on a mass (the ball) produces a change of speed. A change in speed is an acceleration. If the ball were falling in a vacuum, there would be no air resistance to slow it down, so it would accelerate at 9.81 m/s² as shown in Fig. C5.1. We call the acceleration due to gravity g. It has an average value, on planet Earth, of 9.81 m/s². The general equation connecting force, mass and acceleration is:

$$\text{force } (F) = \text{mass } (m) \times \text{acceleration } (a) \qquad (F = ma)$$

When the acceleration is due to the force of gravity we rewrite the equation as:

$$\text{force } (F) = \text{mass } (m) \times \text{gravitational acceleration } (g) \qquad (F = mg)$$

Therefore weight is just a special case of force where the gravitational attraction on planet Earth is accelerating, or trying to accelerate, a mass at 9.81 m/s². Because weight is a force acting downwards on a body, the base unit for both force and weight is the newton. We can now define the newton as follows.

If a body having a mass of one kilogram is accelerated from rest so that its speed increases by one metre per second every second, the force acting on that mass is one newton.

That was all a bit complicated but most of the time you can simply think of 9.81 as being a conversion factor between mass and weight. A useful formula for connecting speed, acceleration and time is:

$$v = u + at$$

where: v = final speed in m/s after t time in seconds
t = time in seconds during which the body is accelerating
u = is the starting speed in m/s
a = is the acceleration in m/s^2

Activity C5.1

Assuming the building in Fig. C5.1 is so tall that, after being dropped, the ball continues to fall for 5 seconds before it hits the ground, calculate:

$(g = 9.81$ m/s$^2)$

(a) the speed of the ball after 3 seconds
(b) the speed of the ball after 4 seconds
(c) the speed of the ball after 5 seconds (moment of impact with the ground).

Now check your response

That concludes Module C. Before proceeding, complete the following assignment and hand it to your tutor for assessment. Don't forget to put your name and assignment code on all your answer sheets.

Assignment for Module C

1 The mass of a body on the Moon is
 (a) the same as when the body is on Earth
 (b) one-sixth the mass of that body when it is on Earth
 (c) six times the mass of that body when it is onEarth
 (d) unrelated to its mass when on Earth

2 The volume of 5 kg of pure water is
 (a) 1/5 litre
 (b) 5 litres
 (c) 50 litres
 (d) 500 litres

3 The mass of 7×10^3 dm^3 of pure water is
 (a) 7 kg
 (b) 700 kg
 (c) 7 tonnes
 (d) 700 tonnes

4 To bend a thin metal stripin a vice you have to apply
 (a) a weight
 (b) a mass
 (c) a force
 (d) heat to soften the metal

5 A vector quantity has
   (a) magnitude
   (b) direction
   (c) magnitude and velocity
   (d) magnitude and direction

6 An example of a scalar quantity is
   (a) speed
   (b) velocity
   (c) an acceleration in a given direction
   (d) a force acting in a given direction

7 Weight is
   (a) mass alone
   (b) the force of gravity acting on the mass of
       a body
   (c) 1 tonne
   (d) 1/6 tonne

8 The mass of a body depends upon
   (a) the force of gravity acting on a body
   (b) gravitational acceleration
   (c) the total number of electrons in a body
   (d) the quantity of matter in a body

9 If a body has a mass of 6 tonnes on Earth, its
   mass on the Moon will be
   (a) 36 tonnes
   (b) 6 tonnes
   (c) 1 tonne
   (d) 1/6 tonne

10 The weight on planet Earth of a body of
    mass 100 kg is
    (a) 981 kN
    (b) 98.1 kN
    (c) 981 N
    (d) 9.81 N

11 Ignoring the effect of wind resistance, the
    speed of a stone dropped from a tall building
    will be
    (a) 0.981 m/s after 10 seconds
    (b) 9.81 m/s after 10 seconds
    (c) 19.81 m/s after 10 seconds
    (d) 98.1 m/s after 10 seconds

12 The speed of a vehicle increases from 6 km/h
    to 60 km/h in 10 seconds. Its acceleration is
    (a) 1.5 m/s
    (b) 15 m/s
    (c) 1.5 m/s^2
    (d) 15 m/s^2

Mass and weight per unit volume

 ## Mass per unit volume

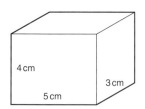

Fig. D1.1

The volume of the solid shown in Fig. D1.1 is 4 cm × 5 cm × 3 cm = **60 cm³**.
   If the mass of this solid is 600 grams, it is not too difficult to work out the mass of 1 cm³ of the same substance by proportion.

   60 cm³ has a mass of 600 g, therefore

   6 cm³ has a mass of 60 g, and

   1 cm³ has a mass of 10 g; we call 1 cm³ **unit volume**

Therefore 10 grams per cubic centimetre (10 g/cm³) is the mass per unit volume for this substance.

 Activity D1.1

Calculate the mass per unit volume, expressed in g/cm³, for the solid shown in Fig. D1.1 if its dimensions and mass are now:

(a)   4 m, 5 m and 3 m, and its mass is 600 tonnes
(b)   4 mm, 5 mm and 3 mm, and its mass is 0.6 gram

Now check your response

We give mass per unit volume a special name. We call it **density**. The symbol for density is the Greek letter rho (ρ). Mass per unit volume or density can be expressed mathematically as:

$$\rho = \frac{m}{V}$$

where: ρ = density
   m = mass
   V = volume

In our first example the mass is 600 g and the volume is 60 cm³. Applying this data to our new formula we get:

$$\rho = \frac{m}{V} = \frac{600 \text{ g}}{60 \text{ cm}^3} = 10 \text{ g/cm}^3$$

The same answer as before. We shall see later that the formula for density also applies to liquids and gases.

 Activity D1.2

Copy out and complete the following statement in your notebook using some of the words listed below:

> Density is the name given to the _____ per unit _____ of a substance.
> That is, _____ _____ by the _____ of a solid made from that
> substance.

Weight, mass, volume, grams, multiplied, divided.

Now check your response

 Activity D1.3

Copy out and complete the following table in your notebook. To give you a start, I have completed the first line for you.

Table D1.3A

Mass (*m*)	Volume (*V*)	Density (*ρ*)
500 g	50 mm³	$\rho = \dfrac{m}{V} = \dfrac{500 \text{ g}}{50 \text{ mm}^3} = 10 \text{ g/mm}^3$
20 kg	10 m³	–
–	35.5 cm³	15 g/cm³
13 kg	–	6.5 kg/m³
800 g	–	40 g/cm³
–	70 m³	1.5 kg/cm³
250 g	50 mm³	–

Now check your response

Table D1.1 lists the densities for some common substances. These are average values and may be affected by temperature, purity, etc.

Table D1.1

Substance	Density		Substance	Density	
	kg/m^3	g/cm^3		kg/m^3	g/cm^3
aluminium	2 720	2.72	alcohol	800	0.80
brass	8 480	8.48	mercury	13 590	13.59
copper	8 790	8.79	paraffin	800	0.80
cast iron	7 200	7.20	petrol	720	0.72
lead	11 350	11.35	water (pure)	1 000	1.00
nylon	1 120	1.12			
PVC	1 360	1.36	acetylene	1.17	0.0017
rubber	960	0.96	air	1.30	0.0013
steel	7 820	7.82	carbon dioxide	1.98	0.00198
tin	7 280	7.28	hydrogen	0.09	0.00009
zinc	7 120	7.12	nitrogen	1.25	0.00125
			oxygen	1.43	0.00143

 Activity D1.4

Using the values for density given in Table D1.1, calculate:

(a) the mass of a block of cast iron of volume 300 cm^3
(b) the volume of a brass casting of mass 2.12 t
(c) the volume of 3.2 t of paraffin
(d) the mass of 20 m^3 of nitrogen
(e) the mass of 50 litres of petrol

Now check your response

To calculate density we have to know the mass and volume of solids, liquids and gases. We can obtain this information by a combination of measurement and calculation. Some techniques will now be described.

D2 Measuring mass

Mass is measured using a beam balance. An example of a beam balance is shown in Fig. A6.4. The object of a beam balance is to compare a solid of unknown mass with standard masses of known value. The solid whose mass is to be determined is placed on the left-hand pan of the balance (if you are right-handed). Standard masses of known value are placed in the right-hand pan. These standard masses are often referred to – wrongly – as 'weights'.

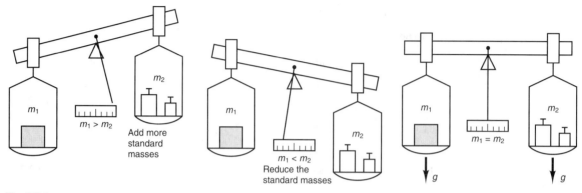

Fig. D2.1

Figure D2.1 shows the procedure for finding the mass of a solid object. Various combinations of standard masses are tried on the right-hand pan until the beam is balanced and the pointer hangs vertically and reads centre zero on the scale. Before using a sensitive laboratory balance check that:

- The balance has been levelled (a spirit level is built into the base and adjusting feet are provided).
- The calibration screws on the beam have been adjusted so that the pointer hangs vertically over the zero mark with both pans empty.

For the pointer to give a zero reading, the Earth's gravitational pull must be acting equally on the mass of the object being measured m_1 and the standard masses m_2. Therefore $m_1 = m_2$. Since we know the value of the standard masses (m_2), we now know the mass of the solid being measured (m_1).

A spring balance measures weight not mass. It measures the force acting on the spring. This force is the mass of the solid being measured multiplied by the gravitational acceleration of the Earth. Therefore a spring balance should not be used for measuring mass.

D3   # Measuring volume: regular solids

The volumes of solids can easily be calculated once accurate measurements of their side lengths have been taken using vernier or micrometer calipers. Here are some examples for practice.

 Activity D3.1

(a)   Calculate the volume of a rectangular solid of length 8 cm, breadth 4 cm and height 6 cm.

(b)   Calculate the volume (V) of a sphere, radius 10 cm, given that:

$$V = \frac{4}{3} \times \pi R^3$$

where: R = radius

(c)   Calculate the density of a triangular prism of base 50 mm, vertical height 60 mm and length 80 mm, given that its mass is 0.24 t. Express your answer in g/mm^3.

Now check your response

D4   Measuring volume: irregular solids

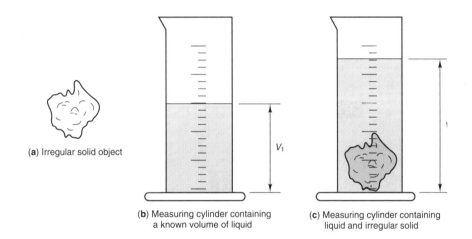

(a) Irregular solid object

(b) Measuring cylinder containing a known volume of liquid

(c) Measuring cylinder containing liquid and irregular solid

Fig. D4.1

Figure D4.1(a) shows an irregularly shaped solid object. This time we cannot take measurements and calculate its volume. So we find its volume as follows:

- Obtain a measuring cylinder like the one shown in Fig. D4.1(b). Make sure it is big enough for the solid to fit into it. Pour some water into the cylinder until it comes up to a convenient graduation. This indicates the volume (V_1) of water present. There must be sufficient water to cover the solid, but not so much that the cylinder overflows.
- The solid is gently lowered into the water in the measuring cylinder. Make sure that the solid is completely covered with water. The level of the water will now have risen to volume (V_2) as shown in Fig. D4.1(c).

- Since no water has been gained or lost during this experiment, the apparent increase in volume indicated must be the volume of the solid:

  volume of solid $= V_2 - V_1$

Activity D4.1

(a) Calculate the density of an irregular solid object given the following information:

volume of water in cylinder $= 0.5$ litre
volume of water plus solid $\;= 0.75$ litre
mass of solid $\qquad\qquad\;\; = 680$ g

(b) The density of water is 1 g/cm^3. If paraffin (density 0.8 g/cm^3) had been used instead of water, would this have affected the result? Explain your answer.

Now check your response

D5   Measuring volume: liquids

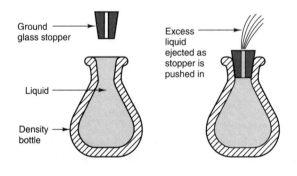

Fig. D5.1

A density bottle is used to measure the volume of a liquid as shown in Fig. D5.1. First fill the bottle completely with the liquid to be measured. Then insert the stopper slowly but firmly. The excess liquid escapes through the hole in the stopper. Sometimes there is a groove up the side of the stopper instead. With the stopper properly seated there is a known volume of liquid in the bottle. This will be engraved on the side of the bottle. Usually it is 50 cm^3 (50 millilitres). The mass of the liquid in the bottle is determined as follows:

- Let m_1 equal the mass of the **empty** bottle and stopper.
- Let m_2 equal the mass of the **full** bottle and stopper.
- Let m_3 equal the mass of the liquid.
- Then the mass of the liquid is calculated using the expression
  $$m_3 = m_2 - m_1$$
- A beam balance is used to determine the masses m_1 and m_2.

Since we now know the volume and the mass of the liquid we can calculate the density:

$$\text{density of the liquid} = \frac{\text{mass } m_3 \text{ as determined above}}{\text{volume of the density bottle}}$$

 Activity D5.1

Calculate the density of a liquid, given the following data:

    volume of density bottle   = 50 cm^3
    mass of empty bottle and stopper = 150 g
    mass of bottle, stopper and liquid = 190 g

Now check your response

D6   Measuring volume: gases

This time we use a small, lightweight pressure vessel of known volume. First we pump out all the air from the vessel using a vacuum pump and determine the mass of the empty vessel using a beam balance. Then we let the gas we are measuring flow into the empty vessel until it reaches atmospheric pressure. Since a gas fills any vessel in which it is stored, we have a known volume of gas. We use a beam balance to determine the mass of the refilled pressure vessel. The mass of the gas is the difference between the mass of the full vessel and the mass of the empty vessel. Again, the density is the mass of the gas divided by the volume of the gas (volume of the pressure vessel).

However, there is a snag. Unlike solids and liquids, gases are compressible. The more gas we pump into the vessel, the greater will be the pressure and the mass. Because the volume remains the same (the volume of the pressure vessel), the density appears to increase. Also the gas will expand if the temperature rises and contract if the temperature falls. So if we carry out the experiment on a hot day, the gas will have a lower density than if we carry out the experiment on a cold day.

Therefore all gas densities are stated assuming that the experiments were carried out under conditions of **standard temperature and pressure (STP)**. This is 0°C and a barometric (atmospheric) pressure of 760 mm of mercury. In practice the temperature and atmospheric pressure in the laboratory is noted at the time of carrying out the experiment and the results are converted to STP by calculation.

Activity D6.1

The following data refer to an experiment to find the apparent density of a gas ignoring STP:

volume of pressure vessel $= 125$ cm^3

mass of empty pressure vessel $= 150$ g

mass of pressure vessel plus gas $= 150.25$ g

Calculate the apparent density of the gas.

In the response I will show you how to obtain the true density at STP given that, at the time of the experiment, the temperature was 15°C and the barometric pressure was 755 mm of mercury.

Now check your response

D7 Weight per unit volume

There are two ways in which we can find weight per unit volume:

- By calculation from the density of the substance.
- In the same way as finding mass per unit volume (density) but using a spring balance to find weight in newtons instead of a beam balance to find mass.

$$\textbf{weight per unit volume} = \frac{\textbf{weight (N)}}{\textbf{volume (cm}^3\textbf{)}}$$

D8 Weight per unit volume by conversion calculation

$$\text{weight per unit volume} = \frac{W}{V} \tag{1}$$

Remember that the relationship between mass and weight is $W = m \times g$

From this formula we can find that 1 kg = 9.81 N

Remember that the relationship between density, mass and volume is:

$$\rho = \frac{m}{V} \qquad\qquad (2)$$

Combining formulae (1) and (2) we get:

$$\text{weight per unit volume} = \frac{W}{V} = \frac{m \times g}{V}$$

but $m/V = \rho$

Therefore, weight per unit volume is given by:

$$\frac{W}{V} = \rho \times g$$

where $g = 9.81$ m/s^2

Summarising:

weight per unit volume = density $\times$ 9.81

Note

- This conversion only applies to planet Earth. Anywhere else in space the local value of g must be used.
- Density must be in kilograms per unit volume.

 Activity D8.1

Copy out and complete the following table in your notebook. Take $g = 9.81$ m/s^2.

Table D8.1A

	Density	Weight per unit volume
(a)	2.72 g/cm^3	–
(b)	7820 kg/m^3	–
(c)	–	0.076 N/cm^3
(d)	–	83.2 kN/m^3

Now check your response

D9 Weight per unit volume by measurement

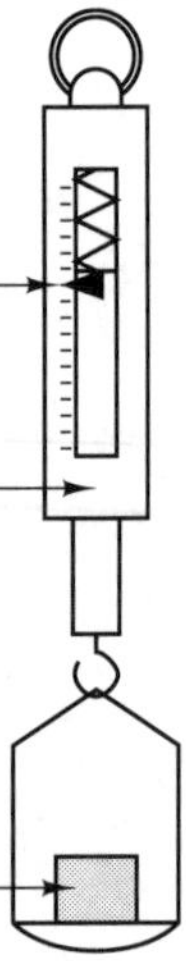

Reading in newtons

Spring balance

Sample

Fig. D9.1

A sample of the substance, whose weight per unit volume is to be found, is weighed on a spring balance as shown in Fig. D9.1. This indicates the gravitational force in newtons (N) acting on the sample. Any of the previous techniques discussed in this module can be used to determine the volume of the sample.

$$\text{weight per unit volume} = \frac{\text{weight in newtons}}{\text{volume}}$$

Example

Calculate the weight per unit volume for a substance if the sample is a cube of side length 2 cm and it weighs 64 N.

Solution

$$\text{weight per unit volume} = \frac{\text{weight as indicated on the spring balance}}{\text{volume}}$$

$$= \frac{64 \text{ N}}{2 \text{ cm} \times 2 \text{ cm} \times 2 \text{ cm}}$$

$$= \frac{64 \text{ N}}{8 \text{ cm}^3}$$

$$= \mathbf{8 \text{ N/cm}^3}$$

Activity D9.1

A cylindrical sample of a substance measures 20 mm diameter by 25 mm long. If its weight is 0.85 N, calculate its weight per unit volume in N/cm^3.

Now check your response

That concludes Module D. Before proceeding, complete the following assignment and hand it in to your tutor for assessment. Don't forget to put your name and assignment code on all your answer sheets.

Assignment for Module D

1 Mass per unit volume is called
 (a) weight
 (b) weight per unit volume
 (c) density
 (d) density per unit volume

2 Using the symbols ρ = density, m = mass, and V = volume, the formula for calculating density is
 (a) $\rho = m \times V$
 (b) $\rho = m/V$
 (c) $\rho = V/m$
 (d) $\rho = mV^2$

3 The density of a solid cube of side length 10 m and mass 5 kg is
 (a) 5 g/cm^3
 (b) 5 kg/cm^3
 (c) 50 g/cm^3
 (d) 50 kg/cm^3

4 The mass of 5 m^3 of lead (density = 11 360 kg/m^3) is
 (a) 2.27 t
 (b) 22.7 kg
 (c) 56.75 t
 (d) 567.5 kg

5 Given that the density of paraffin is 0.8 g/cm^3, the volume of 240 kg of paraffin is
 (a) 0.03 m^3
 (b) 0.3 m^3
 (c) 3.3 m^3
 (d) 19.2 m^3

6 Given that the density of petrol is 720 kg/m^3, the volume of 2 tonnes of petrol is
 (a) 278 litres
 (b) 2780 litres
 (c) 3600 litres
 (d) 36 000 litres

7 A beam balance is used to compare
 (a) masses
 (b) weights
 (c) densities
 (d) forces

8 The volume of liquid in a measuring cylinder is 200 millilitres. The volume appears to increase to 240 millilitres after a solid is totally immersed in the water. The volume of the solid is
 (a) 2.4 cm^3
 (b) 4.0 cm^3
 (c) 24 cm^3
 (d) 40 cm^3

9 A 50 ml density bottle has a mass of 150 g when empty and 201 g when filled. The density of the liquid it contains is
 (a) 1.02 g/cm^3
 (b) 10.2 g/cm^3
 (c) 51 g/cm^3
 (d) 20.1 g/cm^3

10 The density of gases must be corrected to standard temperature and pressure (STP) This is
 (a) 20°C and 760 mm of mercury
 (b) 0°C and 76 mm of mercury
 (c) 0°C and 760 mm of mercury
 (d) 68°F and 750 mm of mercury

11 Given that the density of pure water is 1000 kg/m^3 and g m/s^2, the weight per unit volume of the water is
 (a) 101.94 N/m^3
 (b) 9810 N/m^3
 (c) 101.94 kg/m^3
 (d) 9810 kg/m^3

12 A triangular prism is made from a material whose density is 1.12 g/cm^3. Given that g = 9.81 m/s^2, the weight per unit volume of the solid is
 (a) 10.98 N/cm^3
 (b) 10.98 kN/cm^3
 (c) 8.76 kN/cm^3
 (d) 8.76 kN/cm^3

E1 The effects of forces

In Module C you found that although forces cannot be seen, we can see their effects. Let's summarise what we already know about forces so that we have a foundation to build on:

- A force may change or try to change the shape of an object.
- A force may move or try to move a body that is at rest (stationary).
- A force may change or try to change the motion of a body that is already moving.

E2 The use of vectors to represent a force

We cannot see forces, so we cannot draw them. However, we can represent forces on paper by using vectors. Vectors were introduced in Section C3. To represent a force by means of a vector we need to know:

- The point of application of the force.
- The magnitude (size) of the force.
- The direction in which the force is acting.

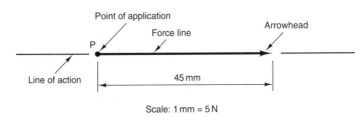

Scale: 1 mm = 5 N

Fig. E2.1

The vector drawn in Fig. E2.1 shows that the force is acting on the point P in an easterly direction. The magnitude of the force can be found by multiplying the length of the vector by the scale of the vector diagram: 45 mm × 5 N/mm = **225 N**.

Note that the **force line** of the vector is drawn along the **line of action**. The **arrowhead** is added to show in which direction the force is acting. The arrowhead may be at the end of the force line or in the middle of the force line, whichever is the more convenient. In the next activity I will draw the line of action and give you the point of application. You will then add the force line and arrowhead to complete the vector.

Example

Draw a vector along the line of action given in Fig. E2.2(a) to represent a force of 50 N acting on the point P in a leftward direction. Scale: 1 cm = 10 N.

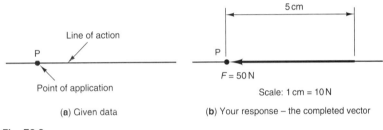

(a) Given data
(b) Your response – the completed vector

Fig. E2.2

Solution

Figure E2.2(b) shows the completed vector:

- Since the scale is 1 cm = 10 N, the force of 50 N $= \dfrac{50\ \text{N}}{10\ \text{N/cm}} =$ **5 cm**.
- The force line is superimposed on the line of action starting at P and drawn 5 m long.
- You add the arrowhead to show that the direction of action of the force is leftward as specified.
- The vector is now complete.

Activity E2.1

Copy the lines of action and the points of application into your notebook and draw vectors to represent the forces required. Use a scale of 1 cm = 10 N.

(a) Complete the diagram to show a force of 40 N acting at 30° to the horizontal and acting towards the point of application P.

(b) Complete the diagram to show a force of 30 N acting at 30° to the horizontal and a force of 45 N acting at 60° to the horizontal. Both forces act away from the point of application P.

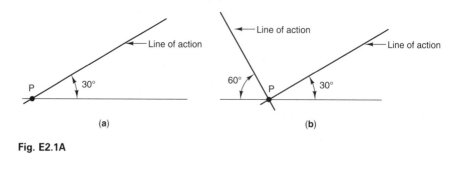

(a) (b)

Fig. E2.1A

Now check your response

In the next activity you will have to remember that weight is a force. It is the result of gravitational acceleration acting on the mass of a body. It acts towards the centre of planet Earth. Therefore we assume it is acting vertically downwards.

Activity E2.2

Copy the figure into your notebook. Draw the lines of action through P_1 and P_2 and add the force vectors to a scale of 1 cm = 10 kN. The loads on P_1 and P_2 are in the ratio of 3:4. Take $g = 10$ m/s^2.

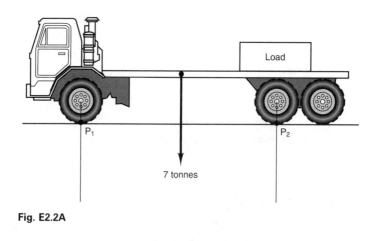

Fig. E2.2A

Now check your response

E3 Resultant forces

We call a force that can replace two or more other forces and produce the same effect a **resultant force**.

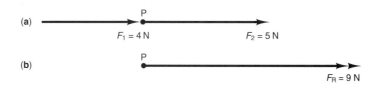

Fig. E3.1

For example, the forces F_1 and F_2 in Fig. E3.1(a) act in the same direction through the same point of application P and along the same line of action. Therefore to find the single force that will replace F_1 and F_2 and produce the same effect, we merely add their vectors together. The single vector that is the sum of F_1 and F_2 is the vector of the resultant force F_R.

Drawn to a scale of 1 cm = 1 N, vector F_1 will be 4 cm long, vector F_2 will be 5 cm long and the resultant force vector F_2 will be 9 cm long (4 cm + 5 cm = 9 cm). This is shown in Fig. E3.1(b). Note how the vector for the resultant force has a **double arrowhead** for easy identification. If the forces had acted in **opposite** directions we would have **subtracted** the vectors to obtain the resultant force.

 Activity E3.1

Copy these vector diagrams into your notebook then draw their corresponding resultant force vectors. Scale 5 N = 1 cm.

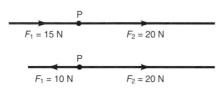

Fig. E3.1A

Now check your response

E4   # Parallelogram of forces

When forces act at an angle to each other, you cannot find the resultant force by simply adding or subtracting the individual forces. If only two forces are acting on the point P, we can find their resultant force by using a **parallelogram of forces** as shown in Fig. E4.1

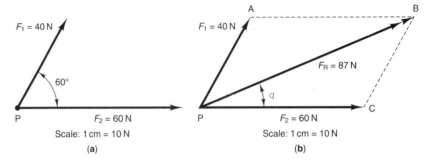

(a)   **(b)**

Fig. E4.1

Figure E4.1(a) shows the vectors for two forces acting on the point P at an angle of 60° to each other. Figure E4.1(b) shows how these vectors form two sides of a parallelogram PABC. That is, BC is drawn parallel to PA, where PA is the vector F_1. Similarly, AB is drawn parallel to PC, where PC is the vector F_2. The **resultant force** vector (F_R) is the **diagonal PB** of the parallelogram. The magnitude of the resultant force can be determined by measuring the length of the vector and multiplying by the scale. The angle θ can be measured with a protractor. In my example the values are as follows:

$F_R = \mathbf{87\ N}$ and $\theta = \mathbf{23°}$ (to the nearest whole numbers).

 ## Activity E4.1

Copy these diagrams into your notebook. In each instance complete the parallelogram of forces in order to find the magnitude and direction of the **resultant force**. Measure the angle of the line of action of the resultant force to the horizontal using a protractor. Use a scale of 1 cm = 10 N.

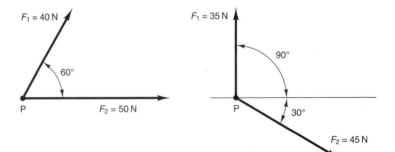

Fig. E4.1A

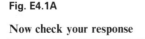

E5 Equilibrant forces

A force which cancels out the effect of all the other forces in a system is called the **equilibrant force** (F_E).

- It has the same magnitude as the resultant force.
- It has the same line of action as the resultant force.
- It acts in the **opposite** direction to the resultant force as shown in Fig. E5.1.

In Fig. E5.1 the equilibrant force (F_E) is equal in magnitude to the resultant

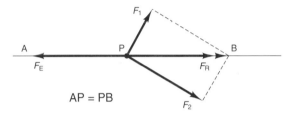

Fig. E5.1

force (F_R) but it acts in the opposite direction and cancels out the effect on the point P of the forces F_1 and F_2.

 Activity E5.1

Repeat Activity E4.1 but this time:

(a) Add the equilibrant force vector.
(b) State the magnitude of the equilibrant force.
(c) State the angle of action of the equilibrant force relative to the horizontal.

Now check your response

 ## E6 Three forces in equilibrium (triangle of forces)

- Three forces acting in the same plane on a body can have their vectors drawn on a flat sheet of paper.

- Forces which act in the same plane are said to be coplanar.
- If the three forces acting in the same plane on a body are in equilibrium, any one force balances the other two forces. Also the three forces may be represented by a **triangle** whose sides are the vectors of those forces.
- The three forces are said to be **concurrent** if their lines of action pass through the same point.

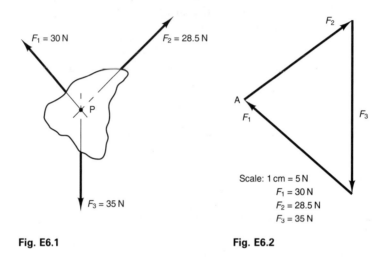

Fig. E6.1   Fig. E6.2

Figure E6.1 shows three coplanar forces acting on a body. The lines of action of the forces are extended backwards to meet at the point P. The point P is called the **point of concurrency**. If the three forces acting on a body, as shown in Fig. E6.1, are in equilibrium:

- Their effects will balance out.
- The body will remain stationary.
- Their vectors will form a closed triangle.

Let's now draw a triangle of forces. Figure E6.2 shows the force triangle for the forces acting on the body in Fig. E6.1.

- The force vectors form a complete and closed triangle so the forces are in equilibrium.
- Note how the directions of the vectors follow each other in a closed loop.

I drew the vector for F_3 first because I knew its scale length and I knew it was acting vertically downwards. It was the easiest to draw as a starting point. I then used my compasses to strike arcs of radii equal to the scale lengths of the F_1 and F_2 vectors. These arcs cut each other at the point A. I was then able to draw the vectors for the forces F_1 and F_2. Here's one for you to try.

Activity E6.1

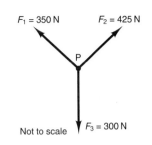

$F_1 = 350$ N $F_2 = 425$ N

P

Not to scale $F_3 = 300$ N

(a) Copy the system of forces shown in the figure into your notebook and draw a triangle of forces for the system to a scale of 1 mm = 5 N.

(b) Find the angles between the forces using a protractor.

Now check your response

Fig. E6.1A

 Activity E6.2

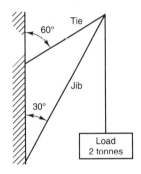

Tie   60°   Jib   30°   Load 2 tonnes

(a) Draw a triangle of forces for the jib-crane shown in the figure using a scale of 1 cm = 5 kN. Let $g = 10$ m/s^2.

(b) State the magnitude of the force in the jib and the magnitude of the force in the tie.

Now check your response

Fig. E6.2A

E7 # Polygon of forces

So far we have only found the resultant and equilibrant for two forces acting on a point P. Even the triangle of forces can be considered as two forces plus an equilibrant acting on the same point if the triangle is closed. Now we have to consider systems involving any number of concurrent, coplanar forces acting on a point P.

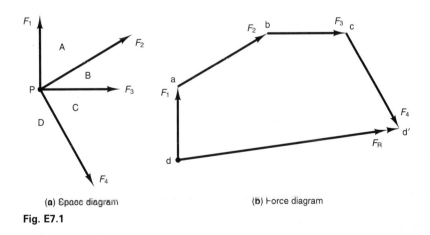

(a) Space diagram   (b) Force diagram

Fig. E7.1

Figure E7.1(a) shows a **space diagram** with the spaces between the forces designated by capital letters. The corresponding **force diagram** is shown in Fig. E7.1(b). I will now explain how to draw the force diagram.

- The forces acting on the point P are shown in the space diagram. This should be drawn with the correct angles between the force vectors.
- The spaces between the force vectors should be labelled using capital letters as shown. It does not matter where you start, providing the letters run sequentially. You normally letter in a clockwise direction.
- You can start your force diagram with any vector you like. I am going to start with the vector for the force F_1 because, being vertical, it is easy to position. Since this vector is positioned between the letters D and A in the space diagram, I will call it vector da in the force diagram (Fig. E7.1(b)). Note that lower case letters are used in the force diagram, corresponding to the capital letters in the space diagram.
- The force F_2 lies between A and B in the space diagram, so I draw the corresponding vector in the force diagram parallel to F_2 and to scale length. Note how vector ab follows on from vector da.
- Similarly the forces F_3 and F_4 in the space diagrams become the force vectors bc and cd′ in the force diagram. Again the vectors are drawn to scale length and parallel to the corresponding forces in the space diagram.
- Finally I can find the magnitude and direction of the resultant force (F_R) by joining the start and finish points of the force diagram (d and d′). Note how the direction of the resultant vector opposes the general 'flow' of the other vectors.

Note

The equilibrant force is drawn equal in magnitude to the resultant force but opposite in direction. The equilibrant vector would close the diagram with all the arrowheads following each other in the same direction. The force diagram is called a **polygon of forces** because the diagram has many sides. Any polygon is a many-sided figure.

Activity E7.1

(a)   Copy this space diagram accurately into your notebook.
(b)   Draw the corresponding force diagram (polygon of forces) using a scale of 1 cm = 10 N.
(c)   State the magnitude and direction of the resultant force.

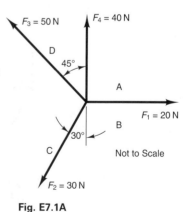

Fig. E7.1A

Now check your response

Before we move on, we have one more situation to consider – when the forces have lines of action which intersect at some point but do not have the same point of application. This is shown in Fig. E7.2 where two forces act on the same body. However, unlike the previous examples, the forces do not act at the same point. In this example the force F_1 acts at the point P_1 and the force F_2 acts at the point P_2. Their lines of action are concurrent because they intersect at some point C. Let's now see how we can find the vector of the resultant force (F_R) and its point of application.

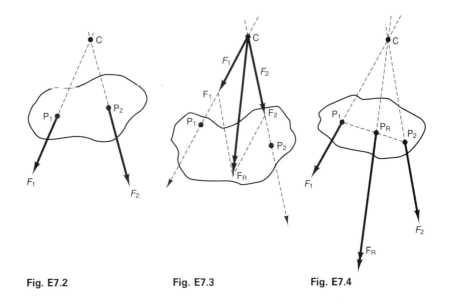

Fig. E7.2   **Fig. E7.3**   **Fig. E7.4**

The following notes refer to Fig. E7.3:

• Extend the lines of action of the forces backwards until they cross at the point of concurrency C.
• Draw the force vectors for F_1 and F_2 to scale from the point C. You can imagine that the force vectors have been slid up their lines of action until they start at the point C.
• Then complete the parallelogram of forces as shown in Fig. E7.3. This is done by drawing the line $F_2 F_R$ parallel to CF_1 and the line $F_1 F_R$ parallel to CF_2. The diagonal of the parallelogram (CF_R) is the vector of the resultant force.
• By measuring and scaling the drawing, we now have the magnitude, direction and line of action of the resultant force (F_R) but not its point of application. To find the point of application we must refer to Fig. E7.4.
• First join P_1 and P_2 with a straight line as shown.
• Then slide the resultant force vector (F_R) down its line of action.
• The point of application of the resultant force vector (F_R) is where its line of action cuts the line joining P_1 and P_2. This is the point P_R in Fig. E7.4.

Sometimes the lines of action of the force vectors will not pass through the same point. They will not intersect. They are said to be **non-concurrent**. It is still possible to find the resultant and equilibrant of such a system of forces by graphical methods but the process is rather complex and beyond the scope of this book.

Activity E7.2

Copy the figure into your notebook accurately, leaving room to construct the force diagram. Draw the force diagram as has just been described and so find the magnitude of the resultant force together with its line of action and its point of application. Use a scale of 1 cm = 10 N.

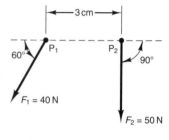

Fig. E7.2A

Now check your response

E8 Resolution of forces

Resolution is the reverse of the operations we have considered so far. We can define the resolution of forces as follows:

> **The resolution of a force is the replacement of that single force by two or more forces acting in specified directions.**

We will limit ourselves to two forces. The process of resolving forces is best explained by considering an actual example as shown in Fig. E8.1.

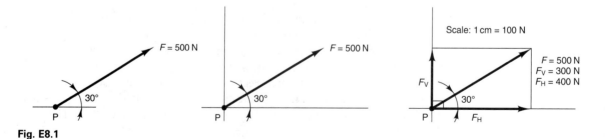

Fig. E8.1

- Figure E.8.1(a) shows the force that is to be resolved into its vertical and horizontal component forces.
- First draw the lines of action of the vertical force and the horizontal force at right angles to each other from the point P as shown in Fig. E8.1(b).
- Now complete the parallelogram of forces by drawing lines from the point F parallel to the lines of action of the vertical force and the horizontal force as shown in Fig. E8.1(c).
- Finally draw in the vectors for the vertical force F_V and the horizontal force F_H as shown in Fig. E8.1(c). The magnitude of these component forces can be obtained by measuring and scaling their vectors.

 Activity E8.1

Copy these diagrams accurately into your notebook leaving room to complete the construction. Resolve the forces shown in the figures into their vertical and horizontal component forces. State the magnitude of these components.

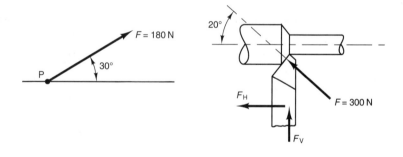

Fig. E8.1A

Now check your response

That concludes Module E. Before proceeding, complete the following assignment and hand it to your tutor for assessment. Don't forget to put your name and assignment code on all your answer sheets.

Assignment for Module E

Use a scale of 1 cm = 100 N throughout.

1   Draw a vector on the line of action given in Fig. EA.1 to represent a force of 400 N acting at 60° to the horizontal

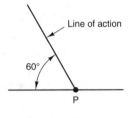

Fig. EA.1

2   Complete the parallelogram of forces for the vectors shown in Fig. EA.2 and determine the magnitude and direction of : (a) the resultant force; (b) the equilibrant force.

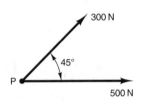

Fig. EA.2

3   Draw a triangle of forces for the jib-crane shown in Fig. EA.3 and determine the magnitude and direction of the forces in the jib and the tie. Let $g = 10$ m/s².

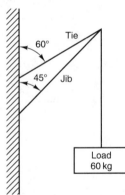

Fig. EA.3

4   Draw a polygon of forces for the system of forces shown in Fig. EA.4 and determine the magnitude and direction of (a) the resultant force; (b) the equilibrant force.

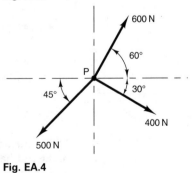

Fig. EA.4

5 Find the magnitude of the resultant force and the point of application for the system of forces shown in Fig. EA.5.

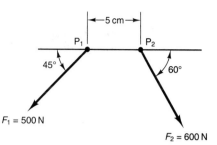

Fig. EA.5

6 Resolve the force shown in Fig. EA.6 into component forces along the lines of action given.

Fig. EA.6

F1 Turning moments

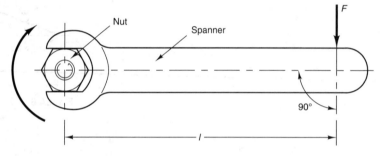

Fig. F1.1

When we use a spanner to turn a nut we have to apply a force (F) to the handle of the spanner at some distance (l) from the centre of the nut, as shown in Fig. F1.1. The turning effect of the force (F) is called the **moment of the force**.

- Any increase in the force (F) increases the moment of the force.
- Any increase in the **moment arm**, the length (l), also increases the moment of the force.

Note that the moment arm is sometimes called the leverage distance.

The moment (M) of the force (F) is found by multiplying the force (F) by the moment arm (l). The moment arm is the distance from the point of application of the force to the axis of rotation. This distance is measured at right angles (perpendicular) to the line of application of the force. All this can be expressed mathematically as:

$$M = F \times l$$

where: M = moment of the force (N m)
F = the applied force (N)
l = the moment arm (m)

Example

With reference to Fig. F1.1, calculate the turning moment of a force of 25 N applied to the handle of the spanner at a point 200 mm from the axis of the nut.

Solution

Remember that the distance (l) is in metres so we must first convert 200 mm to 0.2 m before inserting it in the formula.

$$\text{Therefore} \quad M = F \times l$$
$$= 25 \text{ N} \times 0.2 \text{ m}$$
$$= \textbf{5 N m}$$

where: M = moment of the force
$$F = 25 \text{ N}$$
$$l = 0.2 \ m$$

That wasn't too bad, was it? Now it's your turn.

 ## Activity F1.1

With reference to Fig. F1.1, copy out and complete the following table in your notebook. Work in units of newtons and metres. I have done the first one for you to give you a start.

Table F1.1A

	Force (F)	Length (l)	Turning moment (M)
(a)	30 N	0.5 m	$M = F \times l = 30 \text{ N} \times 0.5 \text{ m} = \textbf{15 N m}$
(b)	20 N	0.4 m	–
(c)	50 N	750 mm	–
(d)	100 N	2.4 m	–
(e)	–	0.5 M	32 N m
(f)	50 N	–	10 N m

Now check your response

Let's now see what happens when the line of action of the force is not perpendicular (not at right angles) to the spanner handle.

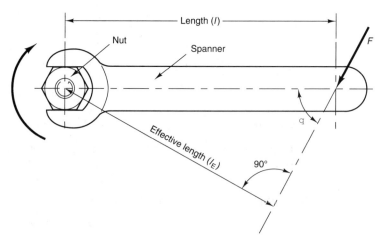

Fig. F1.2

Figure F1.2 shows the line of action of the force (F) inclined at some angle θ to the spanner handle. This time we do **not** use the length (l). Remember that the moment of a force is the magnitude of the force multiplied by the distance from the point of application of the force to the pivot point **measured at right angles (perpendicular) to the line of action** of the force. This effective distance or length (l_E) in Fig. F1.2 can be determined by measurement of a scale drawing or by calculation using trigonometry. For the time being we will use measurement from a scale drawing.

 Activity F1.2

With reference to Fig. F1.2, copy out and complete the following table in your notebook. Work in newtons and metres.

Table F1.2A

	Force (F)	Length (l)	Angle θ	Effective length (l_E)	Turning moment (M)
(a)	30 N	0.5 m	60°	—	—
(b)	10 N	120 mm	45°	—	—
(c)	120 N	250 mm	30°	—	—

Now check your response

F2 # Theorem (principle) of moments

Before I define the theorem and show you how to apply it, I am going to summarise the terms that I will be using. Hopefully this will avoid any misunderstanding later on.

Fulcrum This is the pivot point or axis about which rotation takes place or tends to take place, for example, the axis of the nut. Another example is the pivot that supports a see-saw.

Moment arm This is also called the leverage distance. It is the distance between the line of action of the force and the fulcrum point, measured at right angles to the line of action of the force.

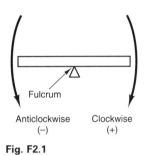

Fulcrum

Anticlockwise   Clockwise
    (−)   (+)

Fig. F2.1

Clockwise moment Any moment of a force that rotates or tends to rotate a body about its fulcrum in a clockwise direction. Clockwise means the direction in which the hands of a clock move. Clockwise moments are given a positive (+) sign as shown in Fig. F2.1.

Anticlockwise moment Any moment of a force that rotates or tends to rotate a body about its fulcrum in an anticlockwise direction. Anticlockwise means movement in the **opposite** direction to the direction in which the hands of a clock move. Anticlockwise moments are given a negative (−) sign as shown in Fig. F2.1.

Resultant moment This is the difference in magnitude between the total clockwise moments and the total anticlockwise moments.

Now that we are talking the same language, I can define the theorem (principle) of moments for you.

> **The algebraic sum of the moments of a number of forces about any point is equal to the resultant moment of force about the same point.**

We can express this mathematically as:

$$M_R = M_1 + M_2 + (-M_3) + \ldots + M_n$$

where: M_R = the resultant moment of force
M_1 to M_n = any number of moments acting about the same fulcrum point

The positive moments will be acting in a clockwise direction, whereas the negative moments (such as $-M_3$) will be acting in an anticlockwise direction.

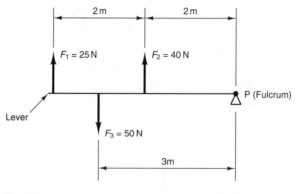

Fig. F2.2

Example

With reference to Fig. F2.2, calculate:

(a)   the magnitude of the resultant force
(b)   the magnitude of the resultant moment
(c)   the position of the line of action of the resultant force

Solution

(a)   To find the magnitude of the resultant force. Since the lines of action of
      the forces shown in Fig. F2.2 are parallel to each other, we can obtain
      the resultant force by simple addition and subtraction.

- Forces F_1 and F_2 tend to move the lever upwards. They are acting in the
  same direction, so they can be added together.
- Force F_3 acts in the opposite direction, so it is subtracted from the sum
  of F_1 and F_2.

Therefore:

$$F_R = F_1 + F_2 - F_3$$
$$= 25 \text{ N} + 40 \text{ N} - 50 \text{ N}$$
$$= \textbf{15 N}$$

(b) Now to find the magnitude of the resultant moment.

Clockwise moments $(+)$

$$M_1 = F_1 \times (2 \text{ m} + 2 \text{ m}) = 25 \text{ N} \times 4 \text{ m} = 100 \text{ N m}$$
$$M_2 = F_2 \times 2 \text{ m} \qquad = 40 \text{ N} \times 2 \text{ m} = 80 \text{ N m}$$

Anticlockwise moments $(-)$

$$M_3 = F_3 \times 3 \text{ m} \qquad = 50 \text{ N} \times 3 \text{ m} = 150 \text{ N m}$$

Resultant moment

$$M_R = M_1 + M_2 - M_3 \quad = 100 \text{ N m} + 80 \text{ N m} - 150 \text{ N m} = \textbf{30 N m}$$

(c)   We can now use the results for (a) and for (b) to find the position of the line of action of the resultant force.

Since $M_R = F_R \times x$

then $30 \text{ N m} = 15 \text{ N} \times x$

$$x = \frac{30 \text{ N m}}{15 \text{ N}}$$

$$x = \textbf{2 m}$$

where: x = the distance from the fulcrum point to the line of action of the resultant force.

We can replace the forces F_1, F_2 and F_3 by a single, resultant force F_R of 15 N acting at a position 2 m from the fulcrum as shown in Fig. F2.3.
    Since M_R is positive, we know that M_R and therefore F_R will move or tend to move the lever in a clockwise direction. This is why I have shown the force F_R pulling upwards in Fig. F2.3.
    Had M_R been negative then it would have tended to move the lever in an anticlockwise direction. I would then have shown F_R pulling downwards. If I had shown the forces to the right of the fulcrum, their directions would have needed reversing to give the correct movement.

Fig. F2.3

 Activity F2.1

Copy the figure into your notebook and calculate:

(a)   the magnitude of the resultant force
(b)   the magnitude of the resultant moment
(c)   the distance of the line of action of the resultant force from the fulcrum

Add a sketch to show the position of the resultant force and the direction in which it is acting.
    Note that you should get a negative answer for the resultant moment, therefore any movement it causes, or tends to cause, should be anticlockwise.

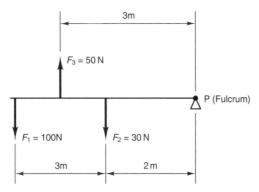

Fig. F2.1A

Now check your response

So far we have only considered cases where all the forces act on the same side of the fulcrum. Figure F2.4 show an example where there are forces acting on both sides of the fulcrum. Note that by lying on opposite sides of the fulcrum, the forces F_2 and F_3 both tend to cause a clockwise rotation despite the fact they are acting in opposite directions.

As in the previous example, we will commence by finding the resultant force:

$$F_R = F_2 + F_3 - F_1$$

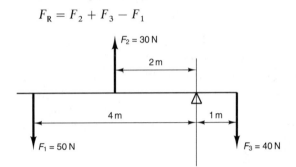

Fig. F2.4

$$= 30 \text{ N} + 40 \text{ N} - 50 \text{ N}$$
$$= \textbf{20 N}$$

Since you cannot have a negative force, only a negative moment, I have arranged the forces to give a positive answer.
    As in the previous example, we will now find the resultant moment:

$$M_R = M_2 + M_3 - M_1 \qquad \text{(M_1 is negative because it tends to}$$
$$\text{cause anticlockwise motion)}$$
$$= (30 \text{ N} \times 2 \text{ m}) + (40 \text{ N} \times 1 \text{ m}) - (50 \text{ N} \times 4 \text{ m})$$
$$= 60 \text{ N m} + 40 \text{ N m} - 200 \text{ N m}$$
$$= \textbf{--100 N m}$$

We can now find the distance of the line of action of the resultant force from the fulcrum:

$$M_R = F_R \times x$$
$$100 \text{ N m} = 20 \text{ N} \times x$$
$$x = \frac{100 \text{ N m}}{20 \text{ N}}$$
$$= \textbf{5 m}$$

where: $x =$ distance from the line of action of F_R to the fulcrum

Since M_R is negative we must position F_R at 5 m from the fulcrum in such a position to cause or tend to cause anticlockwise rotation as shown in Fig. F2.5(a). In theory there are two possible positions for F_R that will cause anticlockwise rotation. The second position is shown in Fig. F2.5(b). In practice this position cannot be used because it is beyond the end of the lever.

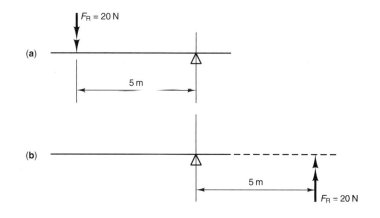

Fig. F2.5

Activity F2.2

Copy the following figures into your notebook and find the magnitude, direction and position of the resultant force (F_R) in each case.

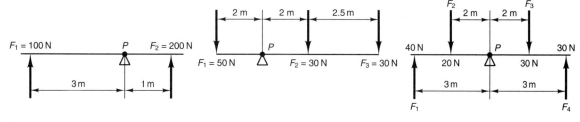

Fig. F2.2A

Now check your response

F3   Equilibrium

In all the examples and activities considered in Section F2, the moments
have not acted in equal and opposite directions. We have always been left
with a resultant force which causes or tends to cause rotation about the
fulcrum. Let's now see what happens when the moments do act in equal and
opposite directions as in the scales shown in Fig. F3.1.

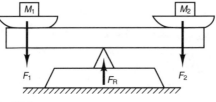

Fig. F3.1

In Fig. F3.1 the masses M_1 and M_2 in the scale-pans are equal so the scales
balance. The beam is horizontal. Since the force of gravity acts equally on
M_1 and M_2, the forces F_1 and F_2 are also equal. The reaction force (F_R)
equals the sum of the downward forces.

The forces are equidistant from the fulcrum, so the turning moments are
also equal. Since the turning moments act in opposite directions, these
moments are also in equilibrium. They balance each other and there is no
tendency for the scale-beam to rotate. We can summarise all the foregoing in
the following statement:

> **When a body is in a state of equilibrium (balance) under the action of a
> number of forces, the sum of the clockwise moments about any point is
> equal to the sum of the anticlockwise moments about the same point.**

For a body to be in a state of equilibrium the following conditions must
exist:

* The sum of the horizontal forces acting on the body must equal zero,
  $\Sigma F_H = 0$.
* The sum of the vertical forces acting on the body must equal zero,
  $\Sigma F_V = 0$.
* The sum of all the moments acting on the body must equal zero,
  $\Sigma M = 0$.

Note

Σ is the Greek capital sigma. Mathematically it stands for 'the sum of'.

Let's put some figures around our scales as shown in Fig. F3.2 and see
what happens:

* There are no horizontal forces so $\Sigma F_H = 0$
* The vertical forces acting downwards balance the vertical reaction force
  acting upwards at the fulcrum so $\Sigma F_V = 0$

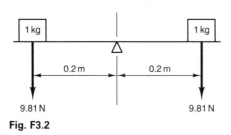

Fig. F3.2

- The moment of the left-hand force is acting anticlockwise so it is $-(9.81 \text{ N} \times 0.2 \text{ m}) = -1.962 \text{ N m}$
- The moment of the right-hand force is acting clockwise so it is $+(9.81 \text{ N} \times 0.2 \text{ m}) = +1.962 \text{ N m}$
- Therefore the sum of the moments is $+1.962 \text{ N m} - 1.962 \text{ N m} = 0$ $(\Sigma M = 0)$

Therefore with the sum of the horizontal forces equal to zero, the sum of the vertical forces equal to zero and the sum of the moments equal to zero; the scales are in equilibrium. They balance and the beam is horizontal.

Example

For the scales shown in Fig. F3.3, calculate the distance between the force F_2 and the fulcrum required to balance the load F_1

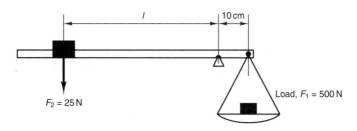

Fig. F3.3

Solution
First let's consider the units. We normally work in newtons, metres, and newton-metres for these types of calculation. However, it is permissible to work in centimetres and newton-centimetres, or in millimetres and newton-millimetres, providing we **do not mix our units**.

Taking moments about the fulcrum, for equilibrium:

$$\text{clockwise moments} = \text{anticlockwise moments}$$
$$500 \text{ N} \times 10 \text{ cm} = 25 \text{ N} \times l \text{ cm}$$
$$5000 \text{ N cm} = 25 \text{ N} \times l \text{ cm}$$
$$l = \frac{5000 \text{ N cm}}{25 \text{ N}}$$

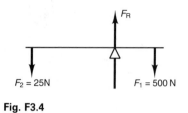

Fig. F3.4

$$l = 200 \text{ cm}$$

Sometimes we have to find the reaction force at the fulcrum as shown in Fig. F3.4. The reaction force must equal the forces acting on the fulcrum. Therefore:

$$F_R = F_1 + F_2 = 500 \text{ N} + 25 \text{ N} = \textbf{525 N}$$

You may find the use of F_R for both resultant force and for reaction force a bit confusing. Unfortunately symbols do have multiple uses from time to time. You have to interpret their meaning according to the context in which you find them.

Activity F3.1

(a) Calculate the distance (l) from the force (F_1) to the fulcrum to balance the load (F_2). Also calculate the magnitude of the reaction force (F_R) at the fulcrum.

(b) Calculate the magnitude of the force (F_1) to balance the load (F_2). Also calculate the magnitude of the reaction force at the fulcrum.

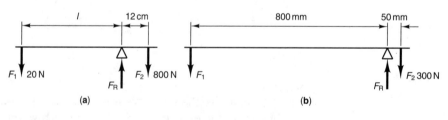

(a)   (b)

Fig. F3.1A

Now check your response

Here is another activity with some more examples. Practice makes perfect! Theyre a bit more difficult, but don't panic, just remember:

• The sum of all the clockwise moments equals the sum of all the anticlockwise moments.

- Clockwise moments are sometimes abbreviated CM or CWM.
- Anticlockwise moments are sometimes abbreviated ACM or ACWM.
- The reaction force at the fulcrum equals the sum of all the forces acting downwards on the beam.

Activity F3.2

(a) Calculate the force F_E that is required to create a state of equilibrium (balance) in the system. Also calculate the reaction force at the fulcrum.
(b) Calculate the force F_E that is required to create a state of equilibrium (balance) in the system. Also calculate the reaction force at the fulcrum.
(c) Calculate the force F_E required to balance the 100 N force acting on the bell-crank.

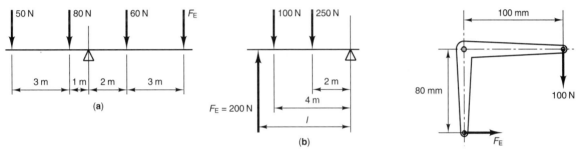

Fig. F3.2A

Now check your response

Having seen how we can produce equilibrium in a system of forces acting on a lever, it is now time to apply the same principles to a body supported at two points, such as a beam. Let's consider the system shown in Fig. F3.5.

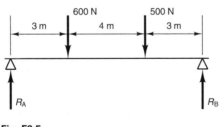

Fig. F3.5

To balance the forces acting downwards on the beam we have to provide reaction forces (R_A and R_B) at the points of support. For a beam I prefer the term *points of support* rather than fulcra since a fulcrum is, strictly, a pivot point. The last thing we want is for our beam to rotate about its supports!

To find the magnitude of R_A we take moments about R_B in order to eliminate it from the calculation for the time being. We can only deal with one unknown quantity at a time.

$$\text{clockwise moments} = \text{anticlockwise moments}$$
$$R_A \times 10 \text{ m} = (600 \text{ N} \times 7 \text{ m}) + (500 \text{ N} \times 3 \text{ m})$$
$$R_A \times 10 \text{ m} = 4200 \text{ N m} + 1500 \text{ N m}$$
$$R_A \times 10 \text{ m} = 5700 \text{ N m}$$

Therefore
$$R_A = \frac{5700 \text{ N m}}{10 \text{ m}}$$

$$R_A = \mathbf{570 \text{ N}}$$

To find the magnitude of R_B we reverse the procedure and take moments about R_A:

$$\text{clockwise moments} = \text{anticlockwise moments}$$
$$(600 \text{ N} \times 3 \text{ m}) + (500 \text{ N} \times 7 \text{ m}) = R_B \times 10 \text{ m}$$
$$1800 \text{ N m} + 3500 \text{ N m} = R_B \times 10 \text{ m}$$
$$5300 \text{ N m} = R_B \times 10 \text{ m}$$

Therefore
$$R_B = \frac{5300 \text{ N m}}{10 \text{ m}}$$

$$R_B = \mathbf{530 \text{ N}}$$

As a check, $R_A + R_B$ must equal the sum of the downward forces:

$$R_A + R_B = 600 \text{ N} + 500 \text{ N}$$
$$570 \text{ N} + 530 \text{ N} = 600 \text{ N} + 500 \text{ N}$$
$$1100 \text{ N} = 1100 \text{ N}$$

Which it does, so our calculations are correct. There is a temptation to take a short cut and find the second reaction force by subtracting the first reaction force from the total downward forces. This would work if you could be sure of getting your first reaction force calculation correct every time. If you make a mistake there is no cross-check.

Before moving on to your next activity, the last in this module, there is one more point I want to bring to your attention; this concerns the weight of the beam itself.

> **The weight of a uniform beam may be considered as a single concentrated force whose line of action is assumed to be at the centre of the length of the beam.**

For example, this additional force acting on a beam 10 metres long and weighing 5 kN per metre would be represented by a single force vector of 10 m × 5 kN/m = 50 kN acting downwards at 5 m from either end of the beam.

Sometimes you are given the mass per metre length of the beam. Mass has to be converted to weight (force) before it can be used.

Activity F3.3

Copy the following diagrams into your notebook and calculate the values for the reaction forces R_A and R_B in each instance.

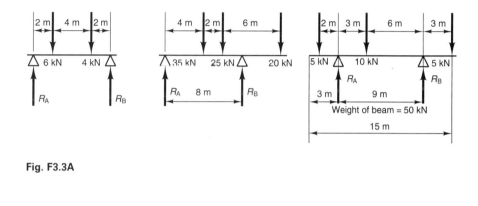

Fig. F3.3A

Now check your response

That concludes Module F. Before proceeding, complete the following assignment and hand it to your tutor for assessment. Don't forget to put your name and the assignment code on all your answer sheets

Assignment for Module F

1   The turning moment for the key shown in Fig. FA.1 is
(a) F
(b) $F \times l$
(c) F / l
(d) $F \times l^2$

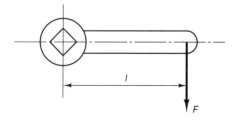

Fig. FA.1

2 **The unit for the moment of a force is**
   (a) N m
   (b) N/m
   (c) N
   (d) kg/m

3 **The turning moment for the key shown in Fig. FA.2 is**
   (a) 20 N/m
   (b) 25 N/m
   (c) 5 N m
   (d) 4 N m

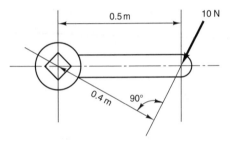

Fig. FA.2

4 **The pivot point about which rotation takes place or tends to take place is called**
   (a) a fulcrum
   (b) a moment arm
   (c) a resultant moment
   (d) a vector

5 **The magnitude of the resultant force for the system of forces shown in Fig. FA.3 is**
   (a) 3.5 N
   (b) 25 N
   (c) 30 N
   (d) 35 N

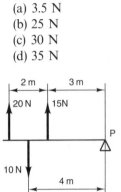

Fig. FA.3

6 **In Fig. FA.3, the distance between the fulcrum point (P) and the line of action of the resultant force is**
   (a) 4.2 m to the left of P acting upwards
   (b) 4.2 m to the right of P acting upwards
   (c) 9.2 m to the left of P acting upwards
   (d) 9.2 m to the right of P acting upwards

7 **For equilibrium**
   (a) the clockwise moments about a point must equal the anticlockwise moments
   (b) the clockwise moments about a point divided by the anticlockwise moments must equal zero
   (c) the clockwise moments about a point multiplied by the anticlockwise moments must equal unity
   (d) the clockwise moments about a point minus the anticlockwise moments must equal unity

8 The theorem of moments can be expressed mathematically as
(a) $M_R = M_1 + M_2 + \ldots M_n$
(b) $M_R = M_1 - M_2 - \ldots M_n$
(c) $M_R = M_1 \times M_2 \times \ldots M_n$
(d) $M = M + M - M + \ldots M_n$

9 For a body in equilibrium
(a) only $\Sigma F_H = 0$
(b) only $\Sigma F_V = 0$
(c) only $\Sigma F_M = 0$
(d) all the above apply

10 The length (*l*) for equilibrium in Fig. FA.4 is
(a) 1 m
(b) 5 m
(c) 10 m
(d) 20 m

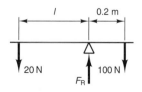

Fig. FA.4

11 The magnitude of the reaction force (F_R) in Fig. FA.4 is
(a) 5 N
(b) 80 N
(c) 120 N
(d) 2 kN

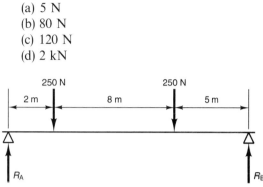

Fig. FA.5

12 In Fig. FA.5 the magnitudes for the reaction forces R_A and R_B are
(a) $R_A = R_B = 250$ N
(b) $R_A = R_B = 500$ N
(c) $R_A = 200$ N and $R_B = 300$ N
(d) $R_A = 300$ N and $R_B = 200$ N

13 Given that the beam in Fig. FA.5 has a **mass of 50 kg** and taking $g = 10$ m/s^2 the values of R_A and R_B become
(a) $R_A = R_B = 600$ N
(b) $R_A = R_B = 500$ N
(c) $R_A = 600$ N and $R_B = 500$ N
(d) $R_A = 500$ N and $R_B = 600$ N

Fig. FA.6

**14 For equilibrium, the length (l) in Fig. FA.6 has
a magnitude of**

(a) 450 mm
(b) 1125 mm
(c) 450 m
(d) 1125 m

Centre of gravity, equilibrium and stability

Centre of gravity

We have already found that:

- The mass of a body is the sum total of the masses of all the individual particles making up that body.
- The weight of a body is the force of gravity acting on all the individual particles making up that body.

We assume that the lines of action of all the forces acting on the particles are parallel. We also assume that all these individual particle forces can be replaced by a single **resultant force**. Finally we assume that the line of action of the resultant force is parallel to the lines of action of the particle forces as shown in Fig. G1.1.

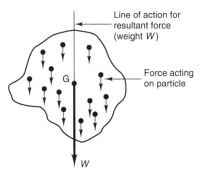

Fig. G1.1

We call this resultant force the weight of the body and we call the point at which it acts (G) the centre of gravity of the body. This is defined as follows:

> **The centre of gravity of a body is the point through which its resultant weight acts.**

Activity G1.1

Copy out and complete the following statement in your notebook using some of the words from the list below:

A body contains a large number of _____ each of which has _____. The weight of each _____ is the force of gravity acting on its _____. The lines of action of the _____ acting on these particles can be considered to be _____ with each other. They can be replaced by a single resultant _____ called the _____ of the body. The weight of the body acts through a point called the _____ of _____ of the body.

Force(s), particle(s), weight, mass, parallel, inclined, resultant, gravity, divergent, centre.

Now check your response

G2   Neutral equilibrium

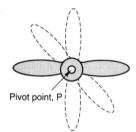

Pivot point, P

Fig. G2.1

Figure G2.1 shows a model aeroplane propeller. The propeller is pivoted at the point (P) at the centre of its boss and is free to turn to any position.

To prevent vibration the propeller is carefully balanced. Therefore it should stay in any position to which it is turned. Since it is symmetrical, its centre of gravity lies at the centre of the boss on the propeller's axis of rotation. The centre of gravity stays in this position and neither rises nor falls as the propeller rotates. The propeller is said to be in a state of **neutral equilibrium**.

G3   Unstable equilibrium

During an accident, one of the propeller blades was broken off as shown in Fig. G3.1. The centre of gravity (G) is no longer at the pivot point (P) but lies to one side of the axis of rotation.

With the remaining blade upright as shown in Fig. G3.1, the force of gravity acts through the pivot point and there is no turning moment. The slightest rotational movement of the blade will cause the centre of gravity to be displaced to one side of the vertical. This will cause the propeller to continue to rotate until its centre of gravity (G) is directly below the pivot point (P). There will then be no turning moment and the propeller will become stationary and will remain stationary.

With the centre of gravity (G) above the pivot point (P), as it is at the start, the centre of gravity can only move downwards. Therefore when its centre of gravity is above the pivot point, the propeller is said to be in a state of **unstable equilibrium**. That is, with the centre of gravity above the pivot point, the propeller will only remain stationary as long as it is not disturbed. Any disturbance will cause it to rotate until its centre of gravity is vertically below the pivot point.

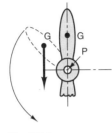

Fig. G3.1

G4   Stable equilibrium

We finished the previous section with the concept that any disturbance of the propeller would cause it to rotate until its centre of gravity lay vertically below the pivot point. This is shown in Fig. G4.1. If the propeller is now disturbed, it will always tend to return to rest with the blade hanging vertically downwards. This is because any movement of the propeller will tend to raise the position of the centre of gravity and produce a turning moment that will rotate the propeller until the centre of gravity again lies at its lowest position vertically below the pivot point. When displacement can only raise the centre of gravity, the propeller is said to be in a state of **stable equilibrium**.

Note

When disturbed, a body will always move or tend to move from a state of unstable equilibrium to a state of stable equilibrium.

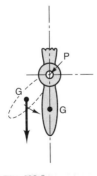

Fig. G4.1

Activity G4.1

State whether the plumb bob shown in the figure is in unstable equilibrium or in stable equilibrium. Give the reason for your answer.

Now check your response

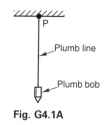

Fig. G4.1A

G5   Stability

When a body is placed on a horizontal surface or on an inclined plane, it will be **stable** providing a vertical line drawn through its centre of gravity (G) passes through the base of the body as shown in Fig. G5.1(a) and G5.1(b).

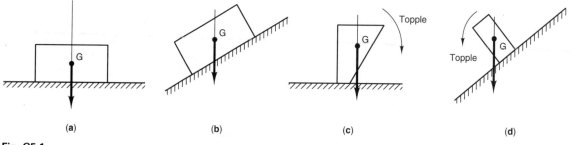

(a)   (b)   (c)   (d)

Fig. G5.1

If the line of action of the force of gravity does not pass through the base of a body, it will topple over. Figure G5.1(c) shows a body that is inherently unstable; as drawn, it will topple over without any disturbance. The body in Fig. G5.1(d) is inherently stable if placed on a horizontal plane, or inclined through a small angle so that the line of action of the force of gravity acts through the base of the body. But the plane on which the body is standing has been inclined until the line of action of the force of gravity lies outside the base of the body; it will now topple over.

Note

A body will always topple, or try to topple, from an **unstable** condition to a **stable** condition.

The general rules for stability are:

- The line of action of the force of gravity, acting through the centre of gravity of a body, must pass through the base of that body.
- The base of a body should be as large as possible so that the line of action of the force of gravity will continue to pass through the base even if the the body is displaced (tilted at an angle).

- The body should be designed so that the centre of gravity is as low as possible within that body.
- The body should be as heavy as possible.

 Activity G5.1

State which of the examples shown are stable and which are unstable and give reasons for your answers.

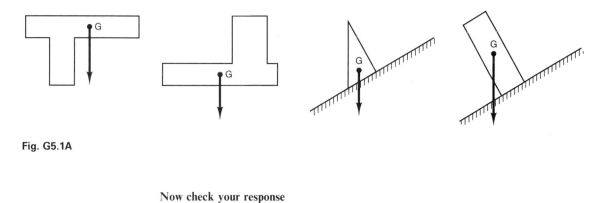

Fig. G5.1A

Now check your response

___

G6 Finding centres of area (graphical method)

Figure G6.1 shows the position of the centre of gravity for a cube. As you might expect in such a symmetrical figure, the centre of gravity lies at the geometrical centre of the body.

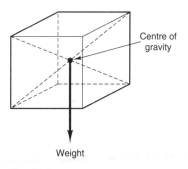

Fig. G6.1

Activity G6.1

Copy the symmetrical solids shown into your notebook and mark the position where you would expect to find their centres of gravity.

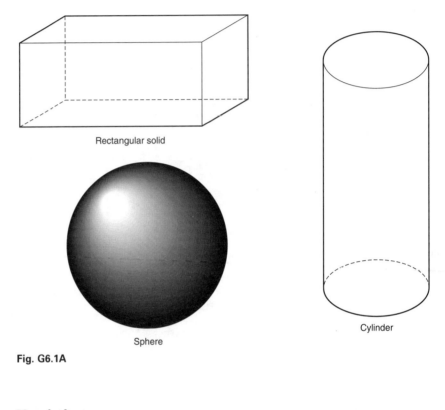

Rectangular solid

Sphere

Cylinder

Fig. G6.1A

Now check your response

Figure G6.2 shows a side view of our original cube. I have marked the position where the centre of gravity (G) would appear in this view.

Fig. G6.2

Let's now cut the cube in half and see what happens to the point G. We now have two solids each of which is only half as thick as our original cube. Each solid has its own centre of gravity positioned at the geometrical centre of the solid. I have indicated these positions in the side views of the solids shown in Fig. G6.3 Note how the centres of gravity (G) have become nearer to the surface of the solids.

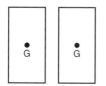

Fig. G6.3

If we could keep slicing up our solid, the slices would get thinner and thinner and the mass and the weight of each slice would get less and less. However, the centre of gravity (G) for each slice would still remain at the geometrical centre of each slice as shown in Fig. G6.4.

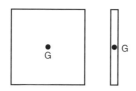

Fig. G6.4

As long as a solid has thickness, it has mass. As long as it has mass, it has weight and a centre of gravity. So finally we come to Fig. G6.5. It no longer has thickness, it is no longer a solid, it is an area. At the geometrical centre of this area I have placed a point C. Since the figure is no longer a solid and no longer has mass, it no longer has a centre of gravity. So we call the point C the **centre of area** or **centroid** of the figure. This is why we give it the letter C. We will now find out how we can determine the position for the centres of area for some common plane figures.

Fig. G6.5

G7 Triangles: method 1

The centre of area, or centroid, of a triangle can be found by joining the midpoint of each side to the opposite angle as shown in Fig. G7.1(a). Where these lines cross, at the point C, is the centre of area (centroid) of the triangle. The lines crossing at C are called medians.

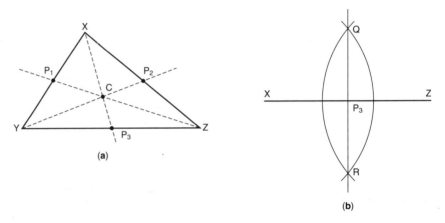

Fig. G7.1

To find the midpoint of a side we use the construction shown in Fig. G7.1(b). In this example I have used the side XZ.

- Set your compasses to just over half the distance between X and Z.
- Strike arcs with centres X and Z as shown. These arcs cut at Q and R.
- Join the points Q and R with a straight line.
- Where the line QR cuts the line XZ is the midpoint of XZ. This is the point P_3 in Fig. G7.1(a).

As a matter of interest, QR is at right angles to XZ. This is a useful construction for drawing lines at right angles to each other.

Activity G7.1

Copy the triangle shown in the figure into your notebook and find its centre of area by using the construction just described.

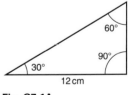

Fig. G7.1A

Now check your response

G8 # Triangles: method 2

The centre of area (centroid) of any triangle lies at a point measured one-third of the perpendicular distance from any side to the opposite angle. For the triangle shown in Fig. G8.1 these distances are measured as follows.

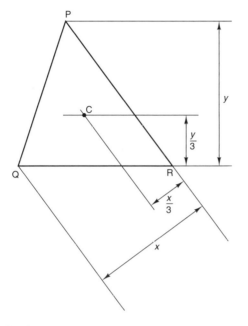

Fig. G8.1

Let's start with the side QR. Measure the distance y at right angles to QR. Now measure a distance that is one-third of the distance y, also perpendicular to QR. This is the distance $y/3$ in Fig. G8.1. Draw a line parallel to QR that is at a distance $y/3$ from QR as shown. This line will pass through the point C.

Repeat the process for the side PR by drawing a line parallel to PR at one-third the distance between PR and the opposite angle Q. This is the distance $x/3$ in Fig. G8.1, measured at right angles to the line PR. Where these lines cross at the point C is the centre of area (centroid) of the triangle.

 ## Activity G8.1

Copy the triangles shown into your notebook and find their centres of area using the method just described (method 2).

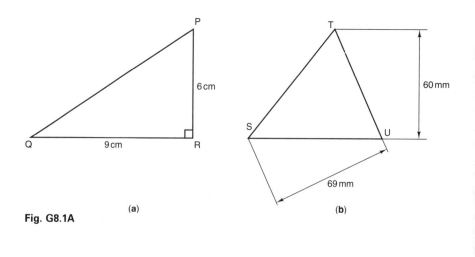

Fig. G8.1A

(a)

(b)

Now check your response

G9 Quadrilaterals

Any four-sided figure is a quadrilateral. Some examples are shown in Fig. G9.1. The centres of area of the first three figures can be found quite easily. In Fig. G9.1 (a), (b) and (c) we simply draw in the diagonals and the centres of area lie at the points (C) where the diagonals cross.

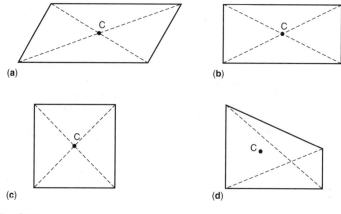

(a)

(b)

(c)

(d)

Fig. G9.1

In the case of Fig. G9.1(d), it can be seen that the centre of area (C) does not lie at the point of intersection of the diagonals. This is because, unlike the previous figures, Fig. G9.1(d) is not symmetrical. We can find the position of the centroid for Fig. G9.1(d), but we would have to calculate its position. We cannot use a simple geometrical construction. This brings us nicely to **lines of symmetry**.

G10   Lines of symmetry

A line of symmetry divides a figure into two parts which are mirror images of each other. This is shown in Fig. G10.1.

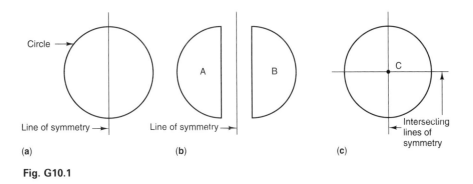

Circle

Line of symmetry →

(a)

A

Line of symmetry →

(b)

B

C

Intersecting lines of symmetry

(c)

Fig. G10.1

A symmetrical figure such as a square or a circle can be divided into two parts by a line of symmetry passing through its centre as shown in Fig. G10.1(a). This divides the circle into two parts, A and B, which are mirror images of each other as shown in Fig. G10.1(b). The centre of area will lie at some point along this line of symmetry. If two or more lines of symmetry can be drawn for the same figure, as shown in Fig. G10.1(c), then their point of intersection is the centre of area (C) for the figure. A symmetrical quadrilateral can be treated in the same way as shown in Fig. G10.2. The point of intersection (C) of the lines of symmetry is again the centre of area.

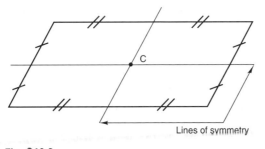

C

Lines of symmetry

Fig. G10.2

Activity G10.1

Copy the symmetrical plane figures shown into your notebook. Add as many lines of symmetry as you can find and, thus, determine the centre of area (centroid) for each figure.

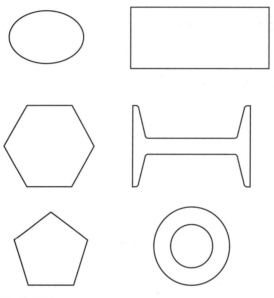

Fig. G10.1A

Now check your response

G11 Centre of gravity of a composite solid

Before we finish this module, we have to return to the centre of gravity of a solid. To find the centre of gravity of a composite solid, such as the one shown in Fig. G11.1, we have to use the principle of moments.

For the stepped shaft shown in Fig. G11.1 we know a number of facts:

- The weight of that part of the shaft with the larger diameter is 5 kN.
- The larger end of the shaft is a cylinder, so its centre of gravity will lie at the midpoint of its axis (G_1).
- The weight of that part of the shaft with the smaller diameter is 2 kN.
- The smaller end of the shaft is also a cylinder, so its centre of gravity will also lie at the midpoint of its axis (G_2).
- The overall weight of the shaft will be the sum of the weights of its larger and smaller parts, that is, 5 kN + 2 kN = 7 kN.

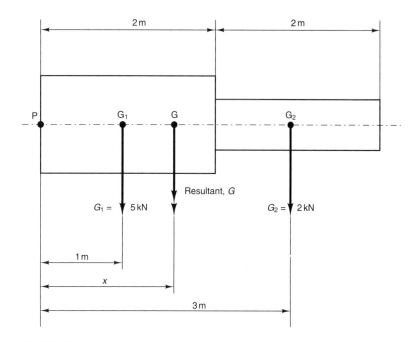

Fig. G11.1

- The total weight of 7 kN will act through the centre of gravity (G) of the shaft as a whole. The point G will lie on the axis of the shaft at some distance (x) from the point P at the end of the shaft. We can find the distance (x) by taking moments about P:

clockwise moments = anticlockwise moments

$$(G_1 \times 1 \text{ m}) + (G_2 \times 3 \text{ m}) = (G \times x \text{ m})$$

Wait a minute, I here you protest, the moment of G, acting at x metres from point P, is also tending to produce a clockwise rotation. So it is, strictly speaking, but at this point you have to accept a mathematical wangle. When using moments to find the position of a centre of gravity, we always assume that the resultant force (G) is acting to produce a moment in opposition to the moments produced by the weights of the constituent parts of the solid. Thus:

$$(5 \text{ kN} \times 1 \text{ m}) + (2 \text{ kN} \times 3 \text{ m}) = (7 \text{ kN} \times x \text{ m})$$

$$5 \text{ kN} \qquad + 6 \text{ kN} \qquad = 7x \text{ kN m}$$

$$11 \text{ kN} \qquad\qquad\qquad = 7x \text{ kN m}$$

Therefore $\qquad\qquad x = \dfrac{11 \text{ kN m}}{7 \text{ kN m}}$

$$x = \mathbf{1.57 \text{ m}} \text{ (2 d.p.)}$$

Therefore the centre of gravity (G) for the shaft lies 1.57 m from the left-hand end of the shaft. This answer is correct to two decimal places.

Activity G11.1

Copy the following figure into your notebook. Taking moments about the point P, find the distance x and, therefore, the position of the centre of gravity for the shaft.

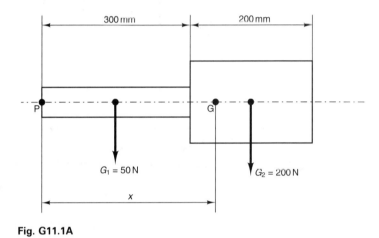

Fig. G11.1A

Now check your response

That concludes Module G. Before proceeding, complete the following assignment and hand it to your tutor for assessment. Don't forget to put your name and assignment code on all your answer sheets.

Assignment for Module G

1 **A perfectly balanced wheel is free to rotate on its axle. It will be in a state of**
   (a) stable equilibrium
   (b) unstable equilibrium
   (c) neutral equilibrium
   (d) negative equilibrium

2 **If a heavy body has a wide base and the line of action of the force of gravity acts through the base, the body will be**
   (a) stable
   (b) not very stable
   (c) slightly unstable
   (d) unstable

3   Which of the solids shown in Fig. GA.1 has the position of its centre of gravity correctly marked?

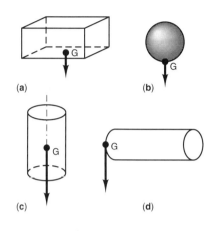

(a)   (b)

(c)   (d)

Fig. GA.1

4   For the equilateral triangle of height (h) shown in Fig. GA.2, the distance x from the base of its centre of gravity is
(a) $h/4$
(b) $h/3$
(c) $h/2$
(d) $2h/3$

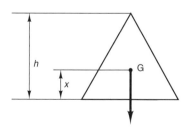

Fig. GA.2

5   In which of the quadrilaterals shown in Fig. GA.3 does the centre of gravity lie at the intersection of its diagonals?

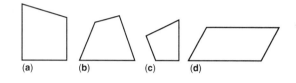

(a)   (b)   (c)   (d)

Fig. GA.3

6   A line that divides a figure into two parts that are mirror images of each other is called
(a) a line of action
(b) an axis
(c) a line of symmetry
(d) a construction line

7   Copy out the shapes shown in Fig. GA.4 and find the position of the centres of area in each case by adding the lines of symmetry.

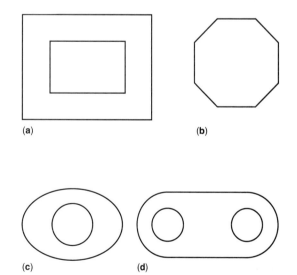

(a)   (b)

(c)   (d)

Fig. GA.4

8   **A cube of brass is attached to a cube of steel by a thin film of adhesive which can be ignored. Each cube has a side length of 100 mm.**

The density of brass is 8.5 g/cm^3

The density of steel is 7.8 g/cm^3

Take $g = 10$ m/s^2

Calculate the position of the centre of gravity from the brass end of the composite body.

Hint: Draw a dimensioned sketch of the composite body as a guide to your calculations.

H1 Sliding friction

Friction can be defined as the resistance which opposes the motion of one surface across another. When examined under a microscope, a finely machined surface consists of a very large number of ridges and valleys. Figure H1.1 shows just a few such high spots forming points of support between the two surfaces.

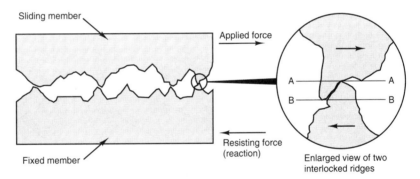

Fig. H1.1

This enlarged view of bearing surfaces shows how all the weight of the upper member is supported at the tips of the ridges and how they bite into each other and become interlocked. Before movement can take place, the interlocked ridges have to shear along the plane AA, along the plane BB or along both. Since this happens at all the points of interaction between the surfaces, the resisting (frictional) force is the sum of all these shear forces. The continual interlocking and shearing away of the ridges results in the wear that occurs between unlubricated (dry) mating surfaces. Friction in a bearing not only results in premature wear but it also wastes energy. The mechanical energy required to constantly shear the high spots from the surfaces is turned into heat energy and sound energy (squeaking). Energy has to be paid for, so this is very wasteful. In extreme cases the heating can become so excessive that either the bearing metal melts or the bearing surfaces weld together. This latter condition is called seizure of the bearing. In either case the bearing is destroyed.

The dust you find in the brake drums of your car or motor cycle consist of fine particles of brake-lining and brake-drum material. The dust particles are the high spots of the linings and drum that have sheared away at the points of interaction. So far we have only considered friction as a cause of wear. In fact, friction has both advantages and disadvantages. Some examples are shown in Fig. H1.2.

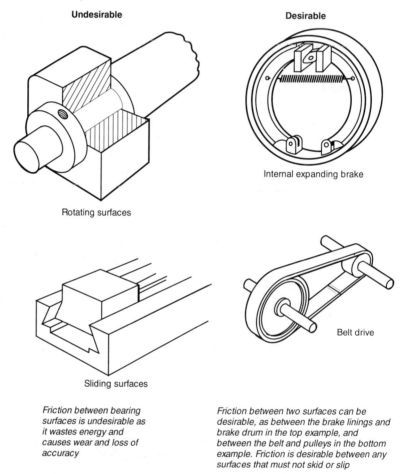

Undesirable

Rotating surfaces

Desirable

Internal expanding brake

Sliding surfaces

Belt drive

Friction between bearing surfaces is undesirable as it wastes energy and causes wear and loss of accuracy

Friction between two surfaces can be desirable, as between the brake linings and brake drum in the top example, and between the belt and pulleys in the bottom example. Friction is desirable between any surfaces that must not skid or slip

Fig. H1.2

Activity H1.1

(a)   List **three** more situations where friction is desirable.
(b)   List **three** more situations where friction is undesirable.

Now check your response

Figure H1.3 shows a body at rest on a surface and the forces acting upon it:
- Weight is the force of gravity acting on the mass of the body.
- The normal reaction force is the upward force exerted by the surface material on which the body is resting in order to prevent it moving downwards. Normal, in this instance, means 'acting at right angles to'. The reaction is acting at right angles to the surface.
- The applied force that is trying to move the body across the surface.
- The frictional force, caused by the interaction of the surface ridges, that is resisting the applied force.

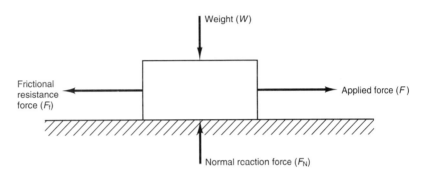

Fig. H1.3

Movement of the body in Fig. H1.3 requires the application of a force (F) to overcome the friction. In this example the applied force (F) is shown as a traction or pulling force. It could equally as well be a pushing force without any change of effect.

Since the frictional resistance force (F_F) and the normal force (F_N) are reaction forces, they can be less than, equal to, but never greater than the forces against which they are reacting. Expressed mathematically:

$$F_F \leqslant F \quad \text{and} \quad F_N \leqslant W$$

Let's consider the relationship of the forces for **static friction**. That is, when the magnitude of F is just insufficient to overcome the friction between the surfaces and the body does not move. For static friction the relationships between the forces shown in Fig. H1.3 are:

$$\mu = \frac{F_F}{F_N}$$

where: $F_F = F$
$$F_N = W$$
$$\mu = \text{the coefficient of friction}$$

The coefficient of friction (μ) is the Greek letter mu. It is sometimes called the coefficient of limiting friction because it is limited to the static condition. Once the object starts to move, the value of the coefficient of friction becomes smaller.

Sliding friction is always less than static friction.

Table H1.1 lists some typical values for the coefficient of static or limiting friction.

Table H1.1

Materials in dry contact	μ
cast iron on brass	0.15
steel on brass	0.16
steel on cast iron	0.20
steel on steel	0.25
cast iron on leather	0.55
brake lining (Ferodo) on cast iron	0.60
rubber on asphalt	0.65
rubber on concrete	0.70

Example

Calculate the coefficient of friction between two surfaces if a force of 50 N just fails to move a load of 250 N.

Solution

$$\mu = \frac{F_F}{F_N}$$

$$= \frac{50 \ N}{250 \ N}$$

$$= 0.2$$

where: $F_F = F = 50 \ N$
$F_N = W = 250 \ N$

Note how the units cancel out. Coefficients do not have units, they are ratios.
   Up to now we have only considered static friction as being limited to the point where movement is just about to take place. It is virtually impossible to judge when this point has been reached, so for practical purposes the same conditions are assumed to apply if movement only just occurs. These conditions apply in the next activity.

 Activity H1.2

(a)   Calculate the coefficient of friction (μ) when a machine weighing 200 kN can just be moved on a concrete floor by a force of 120 kN.
(b)   A brass block can just be moved on a cast iron surface plate by a force of 30 N. Calculate the weight of the brass block. Find the appropriate value for the coefficient of friction from Table H1.1.

Now check your response

H2   Lubrication

The magnitude of the coefficient of friction (μ) between two surfaces depends upon the following factors:

- The surface finish of the bearing surfaces.
- The materials from which the bearing surfaces are made.
- Motion (the coefficient for sliding friction is less than that for static friction – all other conditions being equal).
- Whether or not there is a lubricant between the bearing surfaces.

Note

The area of the surfaces in contact does not affect the friction between them. It only affects the rate of wear when movement takes place.

Activity H2.1

(a)   Which do you think is going to require the greater force, dragging the boat over the rough shingle or rowing the boat on calm water?

(b)   Which do you think is going to cause the most wear to the bottom of the boat, dragging the boat over the rough shingle or rowing the boat on calm water?

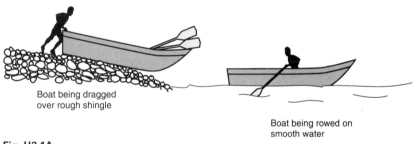

Boat being dragged over rough shingle

Boat being rowed on smooth water

Fig. H2.1A

Now check your response

The previous activity illustrates the benefits of using a lubricant. The lubricant must be capable of keeping the bearing surfaces apart. The lubricant must itself have a very low coefficient of friction. It must also be capable of adhering to the bearing surfaces so that a film of lubricant is always present. Figure H2.1 shows the difference between a dry bearing and a lubricated bearing.

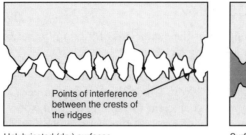
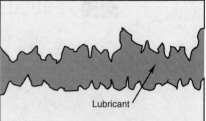

Points of interference
between the crests of
the ridges

Lubricant

Unlubricated (dry) surfaces

Surfaces separated by a lubricant

Fig. H2.1

Most bearing lubricants are based upon mineral oils produced by the petrochemical industry, but synthetic oils are now being developed for special purposes. Synthetic oils have the advantage that their properties can be tailored to suit a given application. Synthetic oils are also non-flammable. Some applications use oils derived from plant seeds or from animal fats. They are sometimes blended with mineral oils to produce heavy-duty cutting lubricants. Mineral oils alone are not suitable for cutting purposes. They cannot withstand the high temperatures and pressures that exist between the cutting tool and the chip of metal being removed. Apart from not giving adequate lubrication, mineral oils also give off noxious fumes when used for metal cutting.

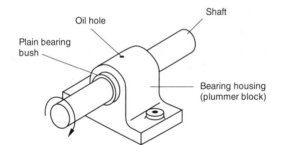

Oil hole

Shaft

Plain bearing
bush

Bearing housing
(plummer block)

As the shaft rotates in the bearing it pulls the oil round between itself and the bearing to prevent a metal to metal contact.

(a) Plain journal bearings (rotating-sliding)

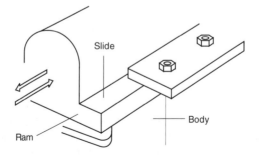

Slide

Body

Ram

In the example shown, a shaping machine ram is sliding back and forth in the body of the machine. Unlike example (a) there is no tendency for oil to be pulled into the bearing. The oil used in this situation must have properties that make it adhere to the metal surfaces

(b) Slide and slideway (reciprocating-sliding)

Fig. H2.2

Note

- Oils are liquid lubricants.
- Greases are a mixture of an oil and a soft soap.
- Most liquids can provide some degree of lubrication even when they are not oils. A car is more likely to skid on a wet road than on a dry one, water is the lubricant on the wet road.

Some examples of bearings that require lubrication are shown in Fig. H2.2.

 Activity H2.2

Indicate whether the following statements are correct or incorrect. If incorrect, explain why.

(a) A lubricant increases the friction between two bearing surfaces.
(b) A lubricant is used to prevent bearing surfaces coming into contact with each other.
(c) A thick oil is always better than a thin oil.
(d) A lubricant is used to reduce wear in a bearing.
(e) Mineral lubricating oils are not suitable for metal-cutting situations.

Now check your response

H3 Rolling bearings

Ideally a roller will be a pure cylinder and it will only have line contact with a plane surface. No distortion of the roller or the plane surface will occur. Sliding will not take place and there will be no friction. In practice this ideal cannot exist. Some distortion of the bearing surfaces will occur and some sliding will take place. Distortion occurs until the contact surfaces are sufficiently large to support the load on the bearing. This can be most easily visualised by considering the relationship between the wheels and the workshop floor in Fig. H3.1.

The load can be spread either by the hard wheel digging into the floor or by the soft, pneumatic tyre distorting until sufficient bearing surface has been achieved to support the load. The pneumatic tyre causes the least damage to the surface it is rolling over. The construction of a typical rolling bearing is shown in Fig. H3.2; this shows a ball-bearing. Both ball and roller bearings work on the same principle. Roller bearings can carry greater loads. The bearing shown in Fig. H3.2 consists of an inner race, an outer race, the balls and a cage to keep the balls equally spaced. In a ball or roller bearing both the races and the ball or rollers distort sufficiently to carry the load. Therefore, even with ball and roller bearing some sliding will occur, so a

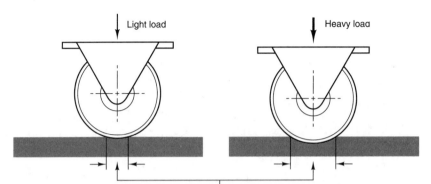

Hard, rigid, metal wheels bite into the floor until the area of contact will support the load

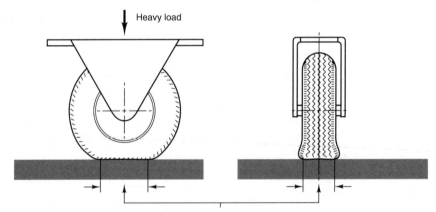

Rubber tyres distort under load until the area of contact will support the load

Fig. H3.1

lubricant is still required. However, the friction of such a bearing under load will be very much less than the friction of a plain bearing of corresponding load-carrying capacity.

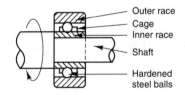

Ball journal bearing (rotating-rolling)

Unlike the bearing shown in Fig. H2.2, there should be no sliding taking place in a perfect ball-bearing. In practice some slip does occur and a lubricant is required. Because of the small area supporting the load, an extreme pressure lubricant is advisable

Fig. H3.2

For the calculation of the coefficient of limiting friction for a rolling bearing, as shown in Fig. H3.3, we again use the formula:

$$\mu = \frac{F_F}{F_N}$$

This time, however, the values for μ are very much less.

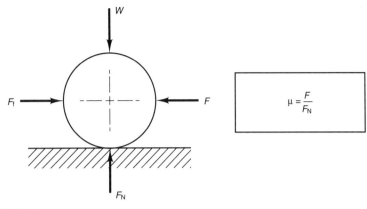

Fig. H3.3

The smaller the distortion of the balls or rollers and the races required to support the load, the smaller the amount of sliding that takes place. This in turn will reduce the coefficient of friction. To keep the distortion to a minimum the balls, rollers and races of antifriction bearings are made from very hard materials. They are ground to very high levels of accuracy and finish to minimise wear and friction.

That concludes Module H. Before proceeding, complete the following assignment and hand it to your tutor for assessment. Don't forget to put your name and the assignment code on all your answer sheets.

Assignment for Module H

1 The resistance that opposes the motion of one surface across another is called
(a) roughness
(b) the normal reaction force
(c) drag
(d) friction

2 The continual interlocking and shearing away of the ridges of unlubricated bearing surfaces results in
(a) wear
(b) a better fit
(c) a lubricant not being required
(d) a longer-lasting bearing

3 Friction is undesirable between
(a) the sole of your shoe and the pavement
(b) the wheel and axle of a bicycle
(c) the tyre of a bicycle and the road
(d) a belt and a pulley

4 A force of 12.5 N is required to just move a metal block of weight 50 N across a plane surface. The value of μ for these surfaces is
(a) 0.25
(b) 4.0
(c) 0.25 N
(d) 4.0 N

5 The force required to just move a machine of mass 1 tonne on a concrete floor is 5.886 kN. Taking $g = 9.81$ m/s^2, the coefficient of friction is
(a) 0.16
(b) 0.60
(c) 0.16 kN
(d) 0.60 kN

6 Compared with an applied force, the corresponding reaction force is
(a) always less
(b) always greater
(c) equal to or less than the applied force
(d) equal to or greater than the applied force

7 A lubricant is used to reduce the friction between two surfaces by
(a) separating the surfaces so that their irregularities do not interlock
(b) etching the surfaces to give them a better finish
(c) hardening the surfaces by a chemical reaction
(d) Burnishing the surfaces to give them a better finish

8 When a bearing warms up in use, the oil
(a) becomes thicker
(b) stays the same
(c) becomes thinner
(d) becomes a grease

9 In a perfect rolling bearing,
(a) some sliding occurs
(b) lubrication is always required
(c) there is appreciable distortion at the point of contact to support the load
(d) no sliding occurs

10 Rolling bearings are used because
(a) the friction is less than for plain bearings
(b) the friction is greater than for plain bearings
(c) the friction is the same as for plain bearings
(d) they cost less than plain bearings

Pressure

I1   Solid bodies

Pressure is defined as **force per unit area**. Referring to Fig. I1.1 we can see that:

$$\text{pressure } (p) = \frac{\text{force}}{\text{area}} = \frac{F}{A}$$

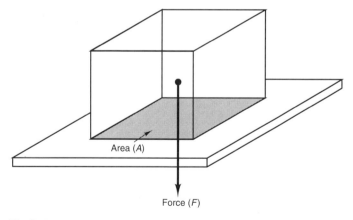

Area (A)

Force (F)

Fig. I1.1

Let's try calculating pressure for various combinations of force and area. In the first activity we will keep the area (A) constant but change the force (F).

Activity I1.1

Copy out and complete the table in your notebook. To give you a start I have completed the first calculation.

Table I1.1A

	Force (F)	Area (A)	Pressure (p)
(a)	300 N	2 m^2	$p = \dfrac{F}{A} = \dfrac{800\ \text{N}}{2\ \text{m}^2} = $ **150 N/m^2**
(b)	400 N	2 m^2	–
(c)	600 N	2 m^2	–
(d)	800 N	2 m^2	–
(e)	1 kN	2 m^2	–

Now check your response

In the next activity we will keep the force constant but change the area.

Activity I1.2

Copy out and complete the table in your notebook.

Table I1.2A

	Force (F)	Area (A)	Pressure (p)
(a)	300 N	2 m^2	–
(b)	300 N	4 m^2	–
(c)	300 N	6 m^2	–
(d)	300 N	1 m^2	–
(e)	300 N	0.5 m^2	–

Now check your response

If you turn back to Fig. H3.1, you will see how the load is spread by the wheels of the vehicle. Pneumatic rubber tyres are preferred because any increase in weight causes the tyre to flatten out even further. This increases the area of tyre in contact with the floor so that the pressure on the floor remains reasonably constant irrespective of the load. Therefore this type of wheel and tyre does the least damage to the floor over which it is rolling.

The unit for pressure is the **pascal (Pa)**; this is equal to a pressure of 1 newton per square metre:

$$1\ \text{Pa} = 1\ \text{N/m}^2$$

This would be a very small pressure indeed and a more practical multiple of the unit is the kilopascal:

$$1 \text{ kPa} = 1 \text{ kN/m}^2$$

Pressures may also be expressed in newtons per square centimetre (N/cm^2) or newtons per square millimetre (N/mm^2) where these are more convenient. Note that:

$$1 \text{ MPa} = 1 \text{ N/mm}^2$$

 Activity I1.3

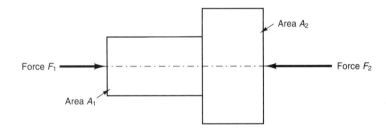

Fig. I1.3A

Given: force $F_1 = 250$ N

area $A_1 = 0.5 \text{ m}^2$

area $A_2 = 2.0 \text{ m}^2$

With reference to the figure and the given data, calculate:

(a)   the pressure on area A_1 in pascals
(b)   the pressure on area A_2 (in pascals) required to prevent axial movement of the component

Now check your response

From time to time you will have to transpose the pressure formula. Here are all the possible variations:

$$p = \frac{F}{A} \qquad A = \frac{F}{p} \qquad F = p \times A$$

where: p = pressure (Pa)
A — area (m^2)
F = force (N)

Sometimes you will be given the data to put into the formula in multiples and submultiples of the units I have given above. Always remember to convert the given data into pascals, square metres and newtons.

12 Hydrostatic pressure

The liquid in the container shown in Fig. I2.1 exerts pressure on the sides and bottom of the container. This is called **hydrostatic** pressure.

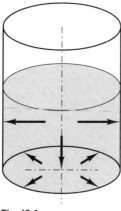

Fig. I2.1

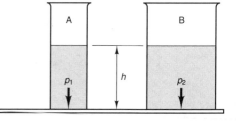

Fig. I2.2

When we considered solid bodies in Section I1, the pressure was dependent upon the force exerted by or on the body and the area over which it acted. The situation is rather different when dealing with liquids. In this case the pressure exerted by a liquid depends upon:

- The density of the liquid (ρ).
- The depth of the liquid at which it is acting on a body (h).
- The gravitational constant (g).

Note that the pressure exerted by a liquid is the same in all directions at any given level.

Figure I2.2 shows two containers A and B. The depth of the fluid (h) is the same in both containers. Therefore, providing both containers hold fluid of the same density, the pressures p_1 and p_2 will be equal. This is true despite the fact that the cross-sectional area of container B is greater than the cross-sectional area of container A.

Activity I2.1

Given that the liquid in each flask shown in the figure has the same density, state which of the two pressures (p_1 and p_2) is the greater and give the reason for your choice.

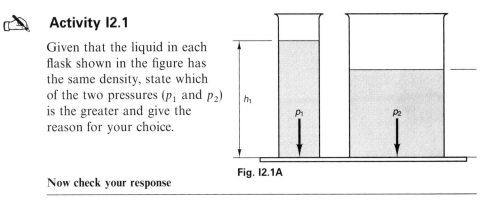

Fig. I2.1A

Now check your response

The depth of the liquid above a given point at which a pressure is being measured or calculated is also referred to as:

- The height of the column of liquid above the point
- The pressure head
- The head

Pressure in a liquid is calculated using the expression:

$$p = h \times \rho \times g$$

where: p = pressure (Pa)
h = depth at which the pressure is being measured (m)
ρ = density of the liquid (kg/m^3)
g = gravitational constant (9.81 m/s^2)

Remember that density is mass per unit volume. Therefore to convert mass to weight (force) we have to multiply density by the gravitational constant. We can then calculate the pressure in newtons per square metre, which is the same as the pressure in pascals.

Example

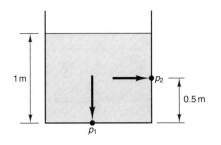

Fig. I2.3

Figure I2.3 shows a container filled with paraffin to a depth of 1 m. Calculate the pressures p_1 and p_2 given:

$$\text{the density of paraffin} = 800 \text{ kg/m}^3$$

$$g = 9.81 \text{ m/s}^2$$

Solution

$$p_1 = h \times \rho \times g$$

$$= 1 \text{ m} \times 800 \text{ kg/m}^3 \times 9.81 \text{ m/s}^2$$

$$= 7848 \text{ Pa}$$

$$= \textbf{7.848 kPa}$$

where: p_1 = pressure (Pa) at a depth of 1 m
   h = depth of 1 m
   ρ = density of 800 kg/m^3
   g = 9.81 m/s^2

Similarly, we can find the pressure p_2 at a depth of 0.5 m:

$$p_2 = h \times \rho \times g$$

$$= 0.5 \text{ m} \times 800 \text{ kg/m}^3 \times 9.81 \text{ m/s}^2$$

$$= 3924 \text{ Pa}$$

$$= \textbf{3.924 kPa}$$

where: p_2 = pressure (Pa) at a depth of 0.5 m
   h = depth of 0.5 m
   ρ = density of 800 kg/m^3
   g = 9.81 m/s^2

At half the depth we have half the pressure, therefore pressure is proportional to depth. At the surface $h = 0$, so with no depth there is no pressure. The pressure varies uniformly from zero at the surface to a maximum at the bottom of the container.

 Activity I2.2

Calculate the pressure in pascals acting on a diver at a depth of 15 m, given that the density of seawater is 1020 kg/m^3. ($g = 9.81$ m/s^2)

Now check your response

To reinforce what you have done so far, complete the following activity before moving on to the processes for calculating the forces acting on the sides and bottoms of containers.

Activity I2.3

Copy out and complete the table in your notebook. ($g = 10$ m/s^2)

Table I2.3A

	Depth (h)	**Density** (ρ)	**Pressure** (p)
(a)	10 m	1000 kg/m^3	–
(b)	2 m	0.8 g/cm^3	–
(c)	–	720 kg/m^3	144 kPa
(d)	80 m	–	8.16×10^5 Pa

Now check your response

When designing a container, we often need to know the forces acting on its sides and its bottom. Let's first consider the bottom of a container since this is the easier. Figure I2.4 represents a rectangular container filled with a liquid to a depth h. The base of the container measures 2 m × 2 m and the pressure (p) acting on the base is 500 Pa.

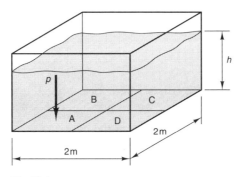

Fig. I2.4

First, let's consider area A of 1 m^2. It is subjected to a pressure of 500 Pa. However, 500 Pa is the same as saying 500 N/m^2. Since area A is 1 m^2 the force acting on it will be 500 N. The remaining areas B, C and D are all at the same depth as area A so they too will be subjected to a pressure of 500 Pa. The areas B, C and D are also 1 m^2 each. Thus, by the same arguments as for area A, the force acting on areas B, C and D will also be 500 N. Summarising:

- The force acting downwards on area A = 500 N.
- The force acting downwards on area B = 500 N.
- The force acting downwards on area C = 500 N.
- The force acting downwards on area D = 500 N.

Therefore, the total force acting on the bottom of the container is:

$$4 \times 500N = \mathbf{2000\ N}$$

This load will be spread uniformly over the whole of the bottom of the tank. However, if we represent this force (F) by a single vector, the line of action of this vector will pass through the centre of area (centroid) of the base as shown in Fig. 12.5.

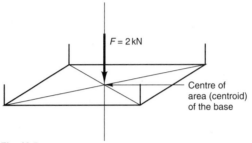

Fig. 12.5

If you refer back to Section G4.3, you will see that the centre of area for a rectangle lies at the point where its diagonals cross each other. The 2 kN vector in Fig 12.5 passes through this point.

Activity 12.4

A rectangular container has a base measuring 3 m × 4 m. If the liquid in the container acts on the base with a pressure of 600 Pa:

(a) Calculate the force acting on the base.
(b) Show by means of a sketch the position of the line of action of the force acting on the base.

Now check your response

Let's now consider the side of our container as shown in Fig. 12.6. Calculation of the forces acting on the sides of the container is slightly more

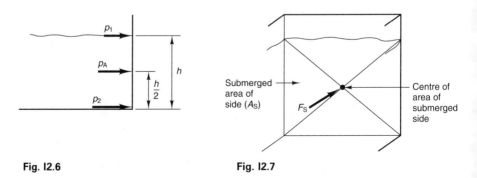

Fig. 12.6   Fig. 12.7

complicated because the pressure is not constant over the whole area of each side.

- The pressure (p_1) at the surface of the liquid will be zero because there is no depth. (We've come across this earlier in the section.)
- The pressure (p_2) at the point where the side joins the base will be the same as the pressure on the bottom of the container because they are both at the same depth (h).
- The pressure (p_A) is the average pressure of p_1 and p_2 because it is acting at the midpoint of the side at a depth of $(H)/(2)$.

Expressed mathematically:

$$p_A = \frac{p_1 + p_2}{2} = \frac{p_2}{2} \quad \text{(since } p_1 = 0)$$

This is the pressure at the depth $h/2$ in Fig. I2.6.

The force acting on the side of the container will be the **submerged area** of the side (A_S) multiplied by the average pressure (p_A). Expressed mathematically:

$$F_S = p_A \times A_S$$

where: F_S = the force acting on the side of the container
p_A = the average pressure
A_S = the submerged area

Again, the force will act at the centre of area. But now we do not use the full area of the side of the container, only that part of the side which is submerged below the liquid. This is shown in Fig. I2.7. The submerged area is again a rectangle, so the centre of area lies at the point of intersection of the diagonals.

Example

With reference back to Fig. I2.4, calculate the force acting on the side of the container given that the depth of the liquid is 1.5 m and the pressure at the bottom of the container is still 500 Pa.

Solution

First find the average pressure:

$$p_A = \frac{p_1 + p_2}{2}$$

$$= \frac{0 + 500 \text{ Pa}}{2}$$

$$= \textbf{250 Pa}$$

where: p_1 = the pressure at the surface
p_2 = the pressure at the bottom

Next, find the submerged area (A_S) of the side. This is the width of the container multiplied by the submerged depth of the side (h). Therefore:

$$A_S = 2 \text{ m} \times 1.5 \text{ m} = \mathbf{3 \text{ m}^2}$$

Finally, we find the force (F_S) acting on the side of the container:

$$F_S = p_A \times A_S$$
$$= 250 \text{ Pa} \times 3 \text{ m}^2$$
$$= \mathbf{750 \text{ N}} \qquad \text{(Remember that 1 Pa} = 1 \text{ N/m}^2\text{)}$$

The force F_S will act at the centre of area (centroid) of the submerged area of the side of the container as shown in Fig. I2.7.

Activity I2.5

With reference to the figure and given that $p_1 = 40$ kPa, calculate:

(a) the pressure at p_2
(b) the pressure at p_3
(c) the pressure at p_4
(d) the surface

Now check your response

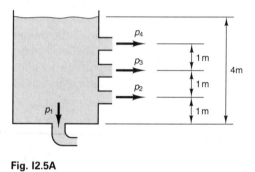

Fig. I2.5A

Activity I2.6

The figure shows a rectangular tank with a base of area 3 metres squared. It is filled to a depth of 2 m with a liquid whose density is 1000 kg/m³. Taking $g = 10$ m/s², calculate:

(a) the pressure acting on the bottom of the tank
(b) the force acting on the bottom of the tank
(c) the average pressure acting on the sides of the tank
(d) the force (F_S) acting on the side of the tank
(e) the height (h) at which the force (F_S) acts above the base of the tank

Now check your response

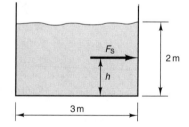

Fig. I2.6A

I3 Pressure exerted by gases

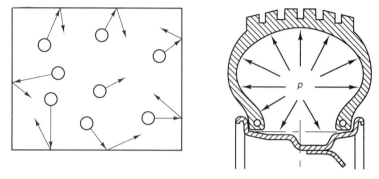

Fig. I3.1   **Fig. I3.2**

Figure I3.1 shows gas molecules in a closed container. Here are some facts about their behaviour:

- The gas molecules are constantly on the move.
- They travel very fast in straight lines.
- They are constantly colliding with each other and with the walls of the container.
- Each time a molecule collides with the wall of the container it exerts a force on it.
- The pressure the gas exerts on the walls of the container is the sum total of all the collision forces per unit area in unit time.

Figure I3.2 shows a section through a car wheel-rim and tyre. The pressure (p) acts uniformly in all directions.

If we pump more air into the tyre, the tyre does not get bigger but it contains more molecules. Therefore the number of collision forces per unit area becomes greater. Increasing the force per unit area increases the pressure. The more air we pump into a tyre of more or less constant volume, the greater will be the pressure in the tyre. The more air we pump into the tyre, the more the air becomes **compressed**. We call the air pump used to inflate the tyre a **compressor**. Unlike solids and liquids, gases can be compressed.

Activity I3.1

Indicate which of the following statements are **true** and which are **false**. If false, explain why they are false.

(a) Gases can exert a pressure.
(b) Gases cannot be compressed.

(c)   Liquids can be compressed.

(d)   Fluids can be compressed.

(e)   Gas pressure is the result of gas molecules colliding with the walls of the container into which the gas has been pumped.

(f)   The gas enclosed in a sealed container exerts a uniform pressure on the walls of the container.

Now check your response

I4   Atmospheric pressure

Planet Earth is surrounded by a layer of air (the atmosphere). The air is a mixture of gases which have mass and are acted upon by the Earth's gravitational field, therefore air has weight. Weight is a force, and the force exerted by the air bears down on the surface of the Earth and on us. Force exerted on an area is pressure, so the air exerts a pressure. Figure I4.1 shows a device for measuring atmospheric pressure.

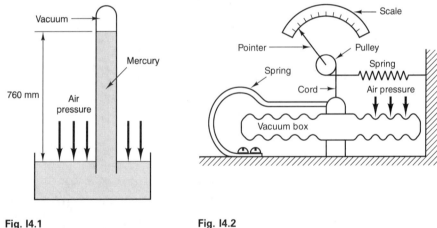

Fig. I4.1   **Fig. I4.2**

To measure air pressure we use a **barometer**. There are two types of barometer. The simplest is shown in Fig. I4.1. The air presses on the mercury in the trough and supports the mercury column in the tube, which is closed at the top. There is a vacuum above the mercury in the closed tube. Therefore there is no downward atmospheric pressure on the mercury in the closed tube. The standard atmospheric pressure can support a column of mercury 760 mm high in the tube. If the atmospheric pressure rises, it exerts greater pressure on the mercury in the trough and forces more mercury into the tube. The mercury in the tube **rises**. If the atmospheric pressure falls, it can no longer sustain the mercury column in the tube, so the height of the column **falls**. The column of mercury in the tube continues to fall until, once more, the atmospheric pressure on the mercury in the trough can balance the weight of the mercury in the tube. By placing a scale against the side of the tube we can measure the atmospheric pressure accurately.

The other type of barometer is called an **aneroid** barometer. Its principle of operation is shown in Fig. I4.2. If the air pressure increases, the vacuum box collapses slightly against the pull of the C-spring. The cord attached to the top of the vacuum is pulled and it rotates the pulley attached to the pointer. This causes the pointer to move across the scale. The smaller tension spring keeps the cord taut. If the air pressure falls, the C-spring is able to lift the top of the vacuum box slightly and the pointer moves in the opposite direction. This is only one means of magnifying the movement of the vacuum box. Systems of levers or even gear trains are sometimes used.

Atmospheric pressure is greatest at the surface of the Earth; it progressively reduces with height. This explains why it is difficult to breathe at the top of high mountains. In high-flying aircraft the cabin is pressurised to keep the passengers comfortable irrespective of the height of the aircraft.

 Activity I4.1

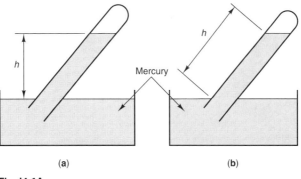

(a)   (b)

Fig. I4.1A

(a) State in which figure the height (h) of the mercury column is correctly dimensioned and give reasons for your answer.
(b) Explain why mercury is used instead of water, which is cheaper, more readily available and more environmentally acceptable.

Now check your response

Activity I4.2

(a) State **two** advantages and **two** disadvantages of the mercury barometer compared with the aneroid barometer.

(b) State **two** advantages and **two** disadvantages of the aneroid barometer compared with the mercury barometer.

Now check your response

I5   Measuring gas pressure

Manometer

A manometer consists of a U-tube that is open at one end to the atmosphere. The other end is connected to the gas supply whose pressure is to be measured. A coloured liquid or mercury is contained within the U-tube depending upon the magnitude of the pressure being measured. In Fig. I5.1(a) the gas is at atmospheric pressure. This is indicated by the liquid being at the same level in both limbs of the U-tube.

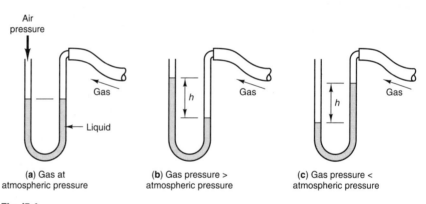

(a) Gas at atmospheric pressure

(b) Gas pressure > atmospheric pressure

(c) Gas pressure < atmospheric pressure

Fig. I5.1

If the gas pressure is greater than the atmospheric pressure, the liquid is forced up the open limb of the U-tube, that is, the limb open to the atmosphere. This is shown in Fig. I5.1(b).

If the gas pressure is less than the atmospheric pressure, the liquid is forced back into the other limb of the U-tube, that is, the limb connected to the gas supply. This is shown in Fig. I5.1(c)

Bourdon tube pressure gauge

Figure I5.2 shows the principle of a simple pressure gauge. The Bourdon tube is of oval section and it tries to straighten out when it is subjected to gas pressure. A system of levers is used to magnify the movement of the Bourdon tube and to move the pointer across the scale. This type of pressure gauge is used for measuring high pressure.

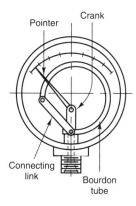

Fig. I5.2

Activity I5.1

(a) State **two** advantages and **two** disadvantages of the U-tube manometer compared with the Bourdon-tube pressure gauge.
(b) State **two** advantages and **two** disadvantages of the Bourdon-tube pressure gauge compared with the U-tube manometer.

Now check your response

I6 Absolute pressure

Both the pressure measuring devices described in Section I5 measure the pressure difference between a gas and the atmosphere. For many purposes in the design and testing of engines and pumps, we need to know the **absolute pressure**. This is the actual pressure of the gas compared with a perfect vacuum:

absolute pressure = gauge pressure + atmospheric pressure

Before we can perform the calculations to find absolute pressure, we need to consider the basic quantities and units used to measure gas pressure. Atmospheric pressure is usually expressed in **millibars** or in **millimetres of mercury**. Let's see how these are related and how they can be converted to pascals.

Millimetres of mercury

The following formula is used to convert the reading of a mercury barometer in millimetres into pascals. We will use it to convert an atmospheric pressure of 750 mm of mercury into a pressure in pascals.

$$p = h \times \rho \times g$$
$$= 0.75 \text{ m} \times 13\,600 \text{ kg/m}^3 \times 9.81 \text{ m/s}^2$$
$$= \mathbf{100\,062 \text{ Pa}}$$

where: p = pressure (Pa)
ρ = 13 600 kg/m^3
h = 750 mm = 0.75 m
g = 9.81 m/s^2

Note that I had to convert the barometric reading into metres before I could insert it into the formula.

Millibars

Weather forecasters often give atmospheric pressure in millibars. This is how the various units of pressure are related:

1 N/m^2 = 1 Pa
1 bar   = 1 × 10^5 Pa
1 mbar = 1 × 10^2 Pa   (mbar = millibar)

 ### Activity I6.1

Convert the following barometer readings into pressure in kilopascals (kPa):

(a)   760 mm of mercury
(b)   770 mm of mercury
(c)   950 millibars
(d)   State whether a weather forecaster would describe (b) and (c) as high or low pressure.

Now check your response

 ### Activity I6.2

Calculate the absolute pressure given that:

atmospheric pressure = 750 mm of mercury
gauge pressure = 400 kPa

Now check your response

17 Pascal's law

We have already met the unit of pressure called the pascal (Pa). This unit is named after the French physicist and mathematician Blaise Pascal. He also formulated **Pascal's law** which states:

> **If a pressure is exerted on a liquid in a container, the liquid will disperse the pressure uniformly in all directions.**

This is shown pictorially in Fig. I7.1. The pressure (p), which is exerted uniformly within the enclosed space, can be calculated as follows:

$$\text{pressure } (p) = \frac{\text{force } (F)}{\text{area } (A)}$$

$$= \frac{100 \text{ N}}{0.5 \text{ m}^2}$$

$$= 200 \text{ N/m}^2$$

$$= \textbf{200 Pa}$$

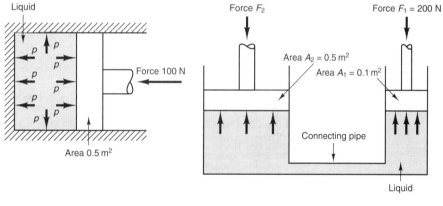

Fig. I7.1   **Fig. I7.2**

From Pascal's law we know that in Fig. I7.1 the pressure of 200 Pa is acting uniformly on every surface. It is acting on the piston, on the cylinder wall and on the cylinder head. Because the mass of the liquid is small, I have ignored any hydrostatic pressures and forces that may be present. Let's now see how we can apply Pascal's law to a simple piece of hydraulic equipment as shown in Fig. I7.2.

Figure I7.2 shows two cylinders of unequal areas connected into a single system and filled with water or hydraulic oil. The pressure in the system is calculated using the now familiar formula:

$$p = \frac{F}{A}$$

For the smaller cylinder this is:

$$p = \frac{F_1}{A_1} = \frac{200 \text{ N}}{0.1 \text{ m}} = 2000 \text{ n/m}^2 = \textbf{2000 Pa} \text{ or } \textbf{2 kPa}$$

But the two cylinders are connected together into a single system by a pipe, so we can consider them to be a single container. According to Pascal's law, there is a uniform pressure of 2 kPa acting throughout this system. It will act on the cylinders, on the pistons and on the connecting pipe. Let's now calculate the force acting on the larger piston:

$$F_2 = p \times A_2 = 2 \text{ kPa} \times 0.5 \text{ m}^2 = 2000 \text{ N/m}^2 \times 0.5 \text{ m}^2 = \textbf{1000 N} \text{ or } \textbf{1 kN}$$

So we find that force F_2 is five times as big as force F_1. This is because area A_2 is five times as big as area A_1. So have we got something for nothing? Unfortunately there are no free lunches in engineering. In practice we would find that, although force F_2 is five times bigger than force F_1, force F_2 would only move one-fifth the distance of force F_1.

Example

With reference to Fig. I7.2, calculate the distance moved by the larger piston if the smaller piston moves downwards by 10 cm.

Solution

From the previous notes we realise that F_2 only moves one-fifth the distance of F_1.
Therefore the larger piston will only move one-fifth the distance of the smaller piston.
The larger piston will move $(10 \text{ cm})/5 = \textbf{2 cm}$.

We can summarise all we have learnt about Pascal's law in the following general formula that we can use in a variety of situations:

$$\frac{F_1}{A_1} = \frac{F_2}{A_2} \tag{1}$$

so

$$F_2 = \frac{F_1 A_2}{A_1} \tag{2}$$

However, we are more likely to be given the piston diameters than their areas, so:

$$A_1 = \frac{\pi(D_1)^2}{4} \quad \text{and} \quad A_2 = \frac{\pi(D_2)^2}{4}$$

Substituting in formula (2) for the areas, we get:

$$F_2 = F_1 \frac{\pi(D_2)^2/4}{\pi(D_1)^2/4}$$

Since $\pi/4$ appears above and below the fraction bar, it cancels out and we are left with:

$$F_2 = \frac{F_1(D_2)^2}{(D_1)^2}$$

 Activity I7.1

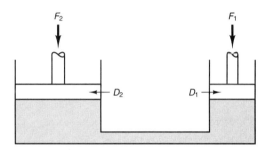

Fig. I7.1A

With reference to the figure and given the diameters $D_1 = 20$ cm, $D_2 = 80$ cm,

(a) Calculate:
   (i) the magnitude of the force F_2 when the force $F_1 = 50$ N
   (ii) The distance moved by the larger piston if the smaller piston moves through 10 cm
(b) the larger piston has to raise a load of 2 kN through a distance of 60 cm. Calculate the force that has to be exerted on the smaller piston and the distance through which it has to move.

Now check your response

Before we move on, let's see what happens when one master cylinder feeds several slave cylinders as shown in Fig. I7.3.

The pressure in the system is uniform no matter how many slave cylinders there are. Therefore we can still apply the formula:

$$F_2 = \frac{F_1(D_2)^2}{(D_1)^2}$$

For cylinder A:

$$F_A = \frac{F_M(D_A)^2}{(D_M)^2} = \frac{200 \text{ N} \times 2^2 \text{ cm}}{1^2 \text{ cm}} = \textbf{800 N}$$

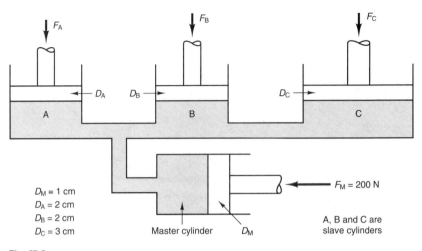

$D_M = 1$ cm
$D_A = 2$ cm
$D_B = 2$ cm
$D_C = 3$ cm

Master cylinder D_M

A, B and C are slave cylinders

Fig. I7.3

For cylinder B:

$$F_B = \frac{F_M (D_B)^2}{(D_M)^2} = \frac{200 \text{ N} \times 2^2 \text{ cm}}{1^2 \text{ cm}} = \mathbf{800 \text{ N}}$$

For cylinder C:

$$F_C = \frac{F_M (D_C)^2}{(D_M)^2} = \frac{200 \text{ N} \times 3^2 \text{ cm}}{1^2 \text{ cm}} = \mathbf{1800 \text{ N} \text{ or } 1.8 \text{ kN}}$$

Activity I7.2

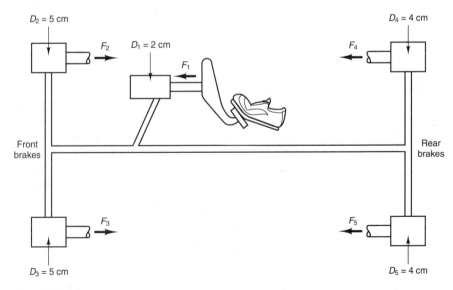

Fig. I7.2A

The figure shows a simple hydraulic braking system for a vehicle.
    If the force $F_1 = 400$ N, calculate:

(a)   the pressure in the system
(b)   the forces acting on the front brakes (F_2 and F_3)
(c)   the forces acting on the rear brakes (F_4 and F_5)

Now check your response

I8   Connected vessels

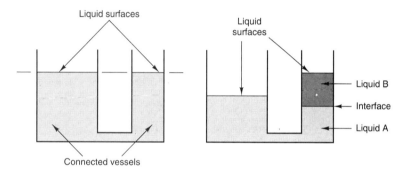

Fig. I8.1

Figure I8.1 shows open vessels connected at their bases; they are called
connected vessels. Here are some terms relating to connected vessels:

*   The interface between the liquid and the atmosphere above it is called
    the **liquid surface**. This atmosphere may be air or any other gas or
    mixture of gases.
*   The surface separating two dissimilar liquids in the same vessel is called
    an **interface**. It can also be the surface separating a liquid and a solid
    such as a piston.

Here are some general rules relating to connected vessels:

*   For connected vessels that are open to the atmosphere and are
    containing the same liquid, all the liquid surfaces will lie in the same
    horizontal plane, independent of the shape of the vessels or the angle at
    which they stand. This is shown in Fig. I8.2
*   Changes in atmospheric pressure will not result in any change in the
    height of the liquid levels in the vessels. This is because the atmospheric
    pressure acts equally on all the liquid surfaces and the liquid is
    incompressible.

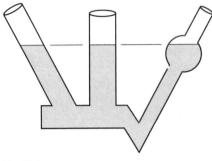

Fig. I8.2

 Activity I8.1

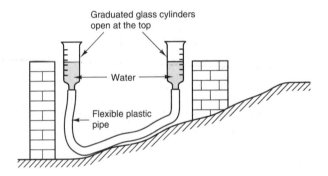

Fig. I8.1A

The figure shows a water level being used to check that the tops of the walls on a building site lie in the same plane. Explain briefly how a water level works and how it is used.

Now check your response

I have already explained how any change in atmospheric pressure has no effect on the levels in the vessels, providing that all the vessels are open-topped and the atmospheric pressure acts uniformly over all the liquid surfaces. However, any change in the pressure acting on the surface of the liquid in only **one** of the connected vessels will result in a compensating change of liquid level in the other connected vessels. This is the principle of the U-tube manometer described in Section I5. It also applies to the pressure change exerted by the plunger in Fig. I8.3

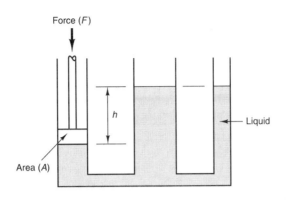

Fig. I8.3

In Fig. I8.3 the pressure increase in the system, caused by the force exerted downwards on the plunger, is balanced by the rise in the columns of liquid in the connected vessels. Therefore the following relationships hold true:

$$p = \frac{F}{A} = \rho \times g \times h$$

where: p = the pressure exerted by the plunger and also the pressure exerted by the columns of fluid in the connected vessels; it is the pressure in the system
F = force exerted on the plunger
A = area of the plunger
ρ = density of the liquid
g = gravitational constant (9.81 m/s^2)
h = height of liquid columns (pressure head)

 Activity I8.2

With reference to Fig. I8.3 and the above relationships, calculate the following from the given data:

(a)   The pressure (p) in the system in pascals (Pa)
(b)   The height (h) of the liquid in the connected vessels

Given: F = 50 N, A = 20 cm^2, ρ = 1 g/cm^3, g = 9.81 m/s^2

Hint: Convert the values given so that you work in kilograms and metres.

Now check your response

When the connected vessels are filled with different liquids which will not mix, there is an interface between the liquids as shown in Fig. I8.4. Providing the vessels are open topped, the pressure is the same on both sides of the interface.

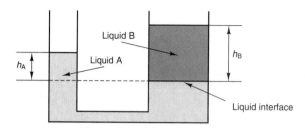

Fig. I8.4

For the conditons in Fig. I8.4, the following relationships hold true:

$$p_A = \rho_A \times g \times h_A \quad \text{and} \quad p_B = \rho_B \times g \times h_B$$

But $p_A = p_B$ because the pressure is the same on each side of the interface, so:

$$p = \rho_A \times g \times h_A = \rho_B \times g \times h_B$$

where: p = pressure at the interface
ρ_A = density of liquid A
h_A = height of column (pressure head) of liquid A
ρ_B = density of liquid B
h_B = height of column (pressure head) of liquid B
g = gravitational constant (9.81 m/s²)

Activity I8.3

With reference to Fig. I8.4 and the above relationships, solve the following calculations from the given data:

(a)   the pressure (p) at the interface
(b)   the height (h_B) of liquid B above the interface

Given: $\rho_A = 13\,590$ kg/m³, $h_A = 0.02$ m, $\rho_B = 800$ kg/m³, $g = 9.81$ m/s²

Now check your response

There are two exceptions to all the rules we have just been using:

Capillary effects   Capillary tubes are glass tubes with a very fine bore. The bores of the tubes shown in Fig. I8.5 are not to scale. They have been very much enlarged for clarity. If two clean capillary tubes are placed in coloured water, as shown in Fig. I8.5(a), the water will rise up the tubes. This is because the **adhesion** between the water molecules and the glass molecules is greater than the **cohesion** between the water molecules themselves. This is also why the **meniscus** at the top of the water column curves upwards at the edges. Note how the water rises higher in the tube with the finer bore.

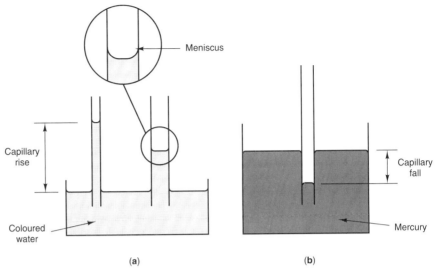

Fig. I8.5

In the case of mercury, as shown in Fig. I8.5(b), the reverse is true. This is because the adhesion between the mercury and the glass is less than the cohesion between the particles in the mercury. This is also the reason why the mercury meniscus curves downwards at the edges.

Liquids in motion   The rules for connected vessels do not apply to liquids in motion. We have only considered hydrostatics. Liquids in motion belong to the province of hydrodynamics. This is much more complex and beyond the scope of this book.

I9 Upthrust

Figure I9.1(a) shows a metal block being weighed by a spring balance in air. Figure I9.1(b) shows the same metal block being weighed by a spring balance with the block immersed in water. The dial appears to read lower when the block is immersed in water. When any body is wholly or partially immersed in a fluid (liquid or gas) there is a force acting upwards on the body. This force is called the **upthrust** and it explains the lower reading on the dial. The ancient Greek philosopher Archimedes recognised that there is a relationship between the upthrust and the weight of fluid displaced by a body immersed in a fluid.

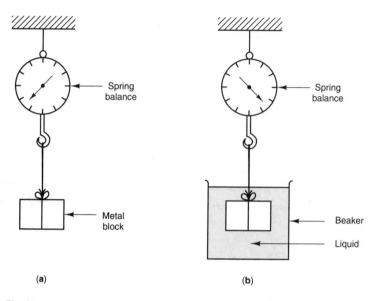

(a)   (b)

Fig. I9.1

Archimedes' principle states:

> **When a body is wholly or partly immersed in a fluid (liquid or gas), the upthrust on that body is equal to the weight of the fluid displaced by that body.**

Let's now try and calculate the apparent weight loss of a metal block when it is totally immersed in water as shown in Fig. I9.2.

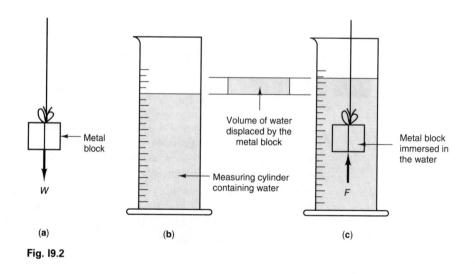

(a)   (b)   (c)

Fig. I9.2

Figure I9.2(a) shows a metal block suspended from a spring balance by a fine thread. It has a volume of 8 cm^3 and a weight of 0.89 N.

Figure I9.2(b) shows a measuring cylinder containing a measured volume of water.

Figure I9.2(c) shows the metal block immersed in the water. Note that the level of the water has risen. This is the water displaced by the metal block. The metal block is completely immersed in the water, so the volume of water displaced equals the volume of the metal block, therefore the water displaced also equals 8 cm^3. Now let's calculate the weight of 8 cm^3 of pure water.

From Table D1.1 we know that 1 cm^3 of pure water has a mass of 1 gram. So 8 cm^3 of pure water has a mass of 8 grams. We know that a mass of 1 kg has a weight of 9.81 N, so by proportion, 8 grams must have a mass of 0.0785 N.

Since the upthrust on a body equals the weight of fluid displaced, the upthrust (F) on the metal block must be 0.0785 N. This is the magnitude of the apparent weight loss when the metal block is totally immersed in pure water. Summarising what we have found:

- The metal block weighs 0.89 N in air.
- The metal block weighs only 0.89 N − 0.0785 N = **0.0811 5 N** in water

There are three conditions of buoyancy which can affect a body when it is lowered into a liquid. These conditions are shown in Fig. I9.3.

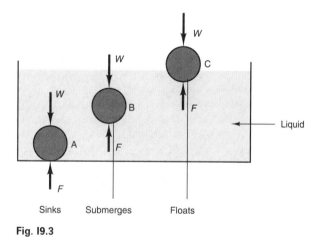

Fig. I9.3

Body A   sinks to the bottom of the container and only stops sinking when it reaches the bottom. This body has **negative** buoyancy, where $W > F$.

Body B   remains submerged and neither floats to the surface nor sinks to the bottom. It behaves like a submarine. This body has **neutral** buoyancy, where $W = F$.

Body C   floats at the surface of the liquid. It behaves like a ship. This body has positive buoyancy, where $W < F$.

In all these examples:

W = the weight of the body in air

F = the upthrust on the body

We can summarise all the previous arguments by a simple mathematical relationship. For a vessel to float:

$$W = F = V \times \rho \times g$$

where: W = the weight of the vessel in air (N)
F = the upthrust (N)
V = the volume of fluid displaced (m³); in the case of a ship, this is the volume of the ship's hull below the water level
ρ = the density of the fluid
g = the gravitational constant (9.81 m/s²)

 Activity I9.1

(a)   A ship weighs 5 MN. What is the weight of the seawater it must displace in order to float?
(b)   1 MN of cargo is loaded onto a ship:
   (i)   What will happen to the amount of water displaced by the ship?
   (ii)   Will the ship float higher or lower in the water?

Now check your response

Activity I9.2

A sheet metal box in the form of a cube has a side length of 2 m. The box weighs 20 kN and it is floating in pure water whose density is 1000 kg/m³. ($g = 10$ m/s²)

(a)   Calculate the height of the box above the surface of the water.
(b)   If 2000 litres of oil, density 800 kg/m³, is poured into the box, calculate the height of the box that will now be above the surface of the water.

Now check your response

That concludes Module I. Before proceeding, complete the following assignment and hand it to your tutor for assessment. Don't forget to put your name and the assignment code on all your answer sheets.

Assignment for Module I

1 Pressure is calculated using the formula
(a) $p = F/A$
(b) $p = F \times A$
(c) $p = F + A$
(d) $p = F - A$

2 For a pressure 20 N/cm², the force acting on an area of 2 cm² is
(a) 10 N
(b) 20 N
(c) 40 N
(d) 80 N

3 A force of 150 N is acting on a piston whose area is 3 m². The pressure in the cylinder is
(a) 50 Pa
(b) 150 Pa
(c) 450 Pa
(d) 150 kPa

4 In Fig. IA.1 the pressure p_1 is
(a) twice as great as pressure p_2
(b) three times as great as pressure p_2
(c) half as great as p_2
(d) one-third as great as p_2

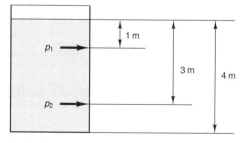

Fig. IA.1

5 Given that ρ for pure water is 1000 kg/m³ and $g = 10$ m/s², then the pressure p_2 in Fig. IA1 is
(a) 5 kPa
(b) 10 kPa
(c) 30 kPa
(d) 40 kPa

6 The water in in the container in Fig. IA.1 has been replaced with paraffin ($\rho = 800$ kg/m³). Given that the base area of the container is 4 m², the force acting on the base of the container is
(a) 16 kN
(b) 32 kN
(c) 96 kN
(d) 128 kN

7 The container shown in Fig. IA.1 is square in section (base = 2 m × 2 m) and has flat sides. When holding paraffin ($\rho = 800$ kg/m³) and taking $g = 10$ m/s², the force acting on each side is
(a) 16 kN
(b) 32 kN
(c) 128 kN
(d) 256 kN

8 Which of the following can be compressed under normal conditions
(a) gases
(b) liquids
(c) solids
(d) all fluids

9 If the height of the mercury column in a
   barometer is 780 mm, $\rho = 13\,600$ kg/m^3 and
   $g = 9.81$ m/s^2, the atmospheric pressure is
   (a) 10.4 Pa
   (b) 104 Pa
   (c) 104 kPa
   (d) 104 MPa

10 If 1 bar pressure $= 1 \times 10^5$ Pa, then 100 Pa
   expressed in millibars is
   (a) 100 mbar
   (b) 1000 mbar
   (c) 1×10^5 mbar
   (d) 1×10^6 mbar

11 Low gas pressures in a system can best be
   read accurately using
   (a) a U-tube manometer
   (b) an aneroid barometer
   (c) a Fortin (mercury) barometer
   (d) a Bourdon-tube pressure gauge

12 In Fig. IA.2 the force F_2 required to balance
   the force F_1 is
   (a) 20 N
   (b) 100 N
   (c) 250 N
   (d) 500 N

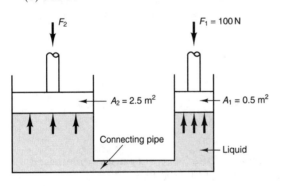

Fig. IA.2

13 Figure IA.3 shows four open-topped,
   connected vessels. If a liquid is poured into
   the vessels, its level will be
   (a) highest in vessel D
   (b) the same in all the vessels
   (c) highest in vessel A
   (d) lowest in vessel B

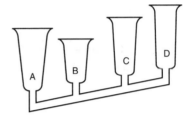

Fig. IA.3

14 Which diagram in Fig. IA.4 correctly shows a
   manometer measuring a gas pressure that is
   greater than atmospheric pressure?

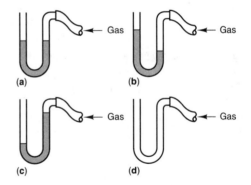

Fig. IA.4

15 In Fig. IA.5:

$h_A = 0.2$ m, $\rho_A = 1000$ kg/m³

$\rho_B = 800$ kg/m³, $g = 10$ m/s²,

The pressure at the liquid interface is
(a) 1600 Pa
(b) 1600 mbar
(c) 2000 Pa
(d) 2000 mbar

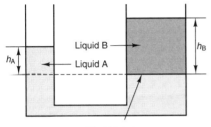

Fig. IA.5

16 **For the same conditions as Question 15, Fig. IA.5, the height h_B is**
(a) 0.25 m
(b) 2.5 m
(c) 25 m
(d) 50 m

17 **A garage mechanic inflates a tyre to a pressure of 180 kPa. This is**
(a) atmospheric pressure
(b) gauge pressure
(c) absolute pressure
(d) barometric pressure

18 **Given that the gauge pressure of a gas is 350 kPa, the atmospheric pressure is 780 mm of mercury, ρ for mercury is 13 600 kg/m³ and $g = 9.81$ m/s², to the nearest whole number, the absolute pressure is**
(a) 246 kPa
(b) 297 kPa
(c) 454 kPa
(d) 1130 kPa

19 **A solid metal sphere is totally immersed in a liquid. Its weight appears to**
(a) increase
(b) decrease
(c) stay the same
(d) become negligible

20 **A sheet metal box in the form of a cube has a side length of 3 m and it weighs 90 kN. When floating in pure water ($\rho = 1000$ kg/m³ and $g = 10$ m/s²) the height of the box above the surface of the water is**
(a) 1.0 m
(b) 1.5 m
(c) 2.0 m
(d) 2.5 m

Basic theory of electricity

Before we consider the basic theory of electricity, I would like you to revise Sections B1 and B4. These sections are concerned with the electronic structure of atoms. Remember that:

- Electrons are negatively charged particlcs.
- Electrons are held in their orbits by the attraction forces of the positively charged nucleus.
- Atoms that have gained or lost one or more electrons are called ions.

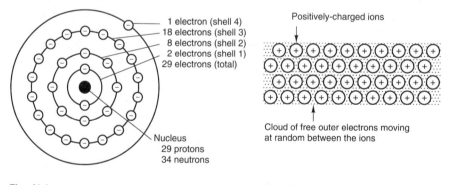

Fig. J1.1   Fig. J1.2

Figure J1.1 shows a Bohr model for a copper atom. Like all metals, most of the electrons are clustered in orbits around the nucleus to which they are strongly attracted; they are called **bonded** electrons. The orbit of the outermost electron is so far from the nucleus that it is only weakly attracted. It can easily become detached from the atom; it then becomes a **free** electron.

As explained in Section B4, metal atoms do not form molecules; they form lattices by the process of ionic metallic bonding. A simple example of such a bond is shown in Fig. J1.2. In reality such a lattice is three-dimensional. In our study of electricity we are only concerned with the **free** electrons.

Figure J1.3(a) shows a metal rod with some free electrons very highly magnified for clarity. All the free electrons are moving around in a random manner. Their movements cancel out. There is no flow of electrons (and therefore electricity) in any one direction. Figure J.3(b) shows the same metal rod connected to some source of electrical energy. The free electrons now line up and flow away from the negatively charged terminal of the energy source (supply) and towards the positively charged terminal. Remember that like charges repel each other and unlike charges attract each other.

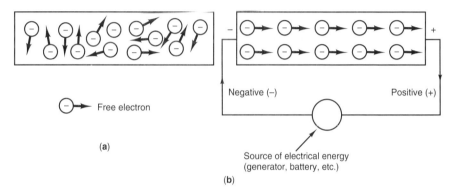

Fig. J1.3

The free electrons flow from the rod into the positive terminal of the energy source. At the same time, an equal number of electrons flow from the negative terminal of the energy source back into the rod. There is always a constant number of electrons circulating in the system. Electrons are neither made nor destroyed; electrons are neither gained nor lost. Think of a central-heating system. The pump uses energy to circulate the water round the system. It is always the same water and, unless the system is leaky, no water is gained or lost. Similarly an electrical energy source such as a battery uses chemical energy to 'pump' the electrons around an electrical circuit without gain or loss of electrons, providing the circuit is properly insulated to prevent any leakage currents.

The flow of electrons through a conductor is called an **electric current**. When a current of 1 ampere flows in a circuit, 6.24×10^{18} electrons flow past any given point in the circuit every second. This is a considerable number of electrons.

 Activity J1.1

Copy out and complete the following statement in your notebook using some of the words listed below:

As well as bonded _____, metal atoms also have one or more _____ attached electrons. They are easily detached and become _____ electrons. There is a constant, random movement of _____ _____ within any piece of metal. The movements of the individual _____ cancel out and there is no current flow. When the piece of metal is connected across the terminals of a _____ of electrical _____, all the free _____ flow in the _____ direction. We now have an _____ current.

Same, different, source, energy, electrons, atoms, ions, free, bonded, electric, loosely, closely.

Now check your response

 Activity J1.2

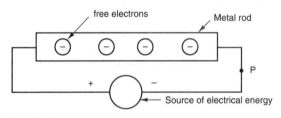

Fig. J1.2A

Copy the figure into your notebook and:

(a) Add arrows to the electron symbols in the figure in order to show in which direction they are flowing along the metal rod.

(b) State how many electrons per second will pass point P if a current of 5 amperes is flowing in the circuit.

Now check your response

Electromotive force (emf)

Back in Section E1 you learnt that a force is required to move a body. We also need a force to move electrons around a circuit and produce a flow of electric current. This force is called an **electromotive force (emf)**. This is voltage (potential) that can be measured across the terminals of a battery or a generator when no load is connected, as shown in Fig. J1.4. The quantity symbol for electromotive force (emf) is E and the unit of electromotive force is the volt (V).

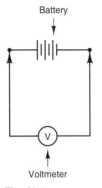

Battery

Voltmeter

Fig. J1.4

Potential difference (pd)

Potential difference is the difference in voltage or potential measured across any two points in a circuit when a current is flowing. It is also referred to as the voltage drop between two points in a circuit when a current is flowing.

- Potential difference can only exist when a current flows in a circuit. No current flow; no potential difference.
- The quantity symbol is V or U. I will use U to avoid confusion with the unit symbol for the volt (V).

Terminal potential difference

When we connect a voltmeter across some source of electrical energy under no-load conditions we measure the electromotive force (emf). If we now connect a load across the source of electrical energy with the voltmeter still connected, we shall see the reading of the voltmeter fall. The bigger the load the more the voltage drops back to a lower reading. This is because there is now a complete circuit and a current will be flowing. It will not only flow through the load but also through the source of energy. Figure J1.5 shows the potential being measured with a load connected across the battery. Some of the emf will be needed to drive the current through the source (internal circuit) and the rest of the emf will be available to drive the current through the load (external circuit). So not all the emf is available for measurement across the load. Hence the apparent fall in emf when a load is connected. This lower potential (voltage) is called the **terminal potential difference**.

- Terminal pd can only be measured under load conditions when a current is flowing in the circuit.
- The greater the load the lower will be the terminal pd.
- The terminal pd will always be lower than the emf measured under no-load conditions.
- The emf is often referred to as the **no-load volts** and the terminal pd as the **on-load volts**.

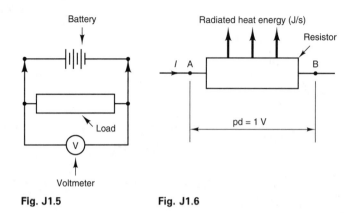

Fig. J1.5   Fig. J1.6

The volt

Heat energy is produced when an electric current flows through a resistor. If a current of one ampere (1 A) produces heat energy at the rate of one joule per second (1 J/s) a potential difference of one volt will exist across the resistor, that is, $U = 1$ V across the points A and B in Fig. J1.6.

Example

Calculate the potential difference across a resistor if a current of 5 A causes heat energy to be produced at the rate of 20 J/s.

Solution

$$\text{Heat energy} = \text{current} \times \text{pd}$$
$$20 \text{ J/s} \qquad = 5 \text{ A} \times U$$
$$\text{Therefore } U = \frac{20 \text{ J/s}}{5 \text{ A}}$$
$$= \mathbf{4 \text{ V}}$$

 ### Activity J1.3

(a) When you operate the starter motor of a car with the headlights turned on, they will become less bright. Explain why this happens.
(b) When you check the condition of a car battery with everything switched off, explain whether the voltmeter will be measuring the emf or the terminal pd of the battery.
(c) The rear window demister of a car produces heat energy at the rate of 60 J/s. If the pd across the demister is 12V, calculate the current flowing through it.

Now check your response

J2   Sources of electrical energy

Chemical

Figure J2.1 shows some typical sources of electrical energy that depend upon chemical reactions to produce electricity. In a primary cell (Fig. J2.1(a)) the chemical reaction is not reversible. When the cell ceases to function it is discarded. In a secondary cell or accumulator (Fig. J2.1(b)) the chemical reaction is reversible. When the emf falls to a predetermined value, the secondary cell can be connected to a battery charger and recharged. A battery consists of several cells connected together; they may be primary cells or secondary cells. The series and parallel connection of cells will be considered in Sections K4 and K5.

Primary cell
*Often called a dry cell.
Several primary cells
connected in series
form a battery*

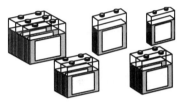

Secondary cells and batteries
*These are often called accumulators
or storage batteries as they are
a rechargeable source of electricity*

Fig. J2.1

Electromagnetic

Figure J2.2 shows a typical small generator. An emf is generated by the rotation of electrical conductors in a magnetic field. This will be described more fully in Section L3. If a load is connected across a generator so that a current flows, the load on the engine driving the generator will increase as it becomes harder to rotate the conductors. This is because the current flowing through the conductors produces a magnetic flux field around them; the magnetic field produced by the current reacts with the magnetic field of the generator in such a way as to oppose the motion of the conductors.

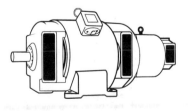

Fig. J2.2

Generators can be driven by internal combustion engines, gas turbines, steam turbines, wind turbines and water turbines. They convert mechanical energy into electrical energy. Generators which produce alternating currents (ac) are called alternators. Generators that produce direct current (dc) are called dynamos. Very large alternators are used in the power stations supplying the national grid system.

Thermal

A very small emf is generated by heating the junction of two wires made from dissimilar metals, such as iron and copper. If a sensitive galvanometer is connected across the dissimilar wires to complete the circuit, it will detect a very small electric current flow. This circuit is shown in Fig. J2.3. The use of heat energy to generate electrical energy directly in this manner is called the **thermocouple** effect. It is the principle of the pyrometers used to measure the temperatures of furnaces. The higher the temperature, the larger the current generated. The dial of the galvanometer is marked in degrees of temperature when·used in a pyrometer. A pyrometer is a thermometer for use at high temperatures.

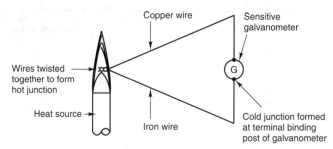

Fig. J2.3

 Activity J2.1

Copy out and complete the following statements in your notebook using some of the words listed below:

There are _____ main sources of electrical energy. They are:
(a) The _____ reaction that takes place in a _____ .
(b) The _____ effect that takes place in a _____ when it is heated.
(c) The _____ effect that takes place in a _____ when its conductors are rotated by an engine.

Thermal, chemical, electromagnetic, cell, motor, generator, three, four, thermocouple.

Now check your response

J3 Effects of an electric current

The law of conservation of energy states that energy cannot be created or destroyed. Energy can only be converted from one form to another. The appliances shown in Fig. J3.1 are used to convert electrical energy into other forms of energy.

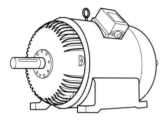

(a) Motor
This converts electrical energy into mechanical energy

(b) Loudspeaker
This converts electrical energy into sound energy

(c) Secondary cell
This converts electrical energy into chemical energy

(d) Heater
This converts electrical energy into heat energy

Fig. J3.1

Electromagnetic effect

Figure J3.1(a) shows an electric motor. This operates in the reverse manner to a generator and uses the electromagnetic effect to convert electrical energy into mechanical energy. The electromagnetic effect produced by the electric current causes an armature or a rotor to rotate. Figure J3.1(b) shows a loudspeaker from a radio receiver. This also makes use of the electromagnetic effect to cause motion. In this example electrical energy is converted into sound energy by using the electromagnetic effect to vibrate a diaphragm.

Electrochemical effect

Figure J3.1(c) shows a secondary cell. Secondary cells are also called storage cells and accumulators. We have already learnt that the chemical effect in such a cell can produce an electric current. The reverse is also true. The cell can be recharged by passing a controlled electric current through it. This reverses the chemical reaction, so the electrical energy used in recharging the cell is stored as chemical energy. Other chemical effects of an electric current are to be found in electroplating processes such as nickel plating and chrome plating. Electrochemical reactions are also used in the extraction and refining of chemical substances.

Heating effect

We have already seen how heat energy can be converted directly into electrical energy in the thermocouple pyrometer. This process is not reversible, but electrical energy can be used to produce heat energy in a variety of ways. Figure J3.1(d) shows a typical electric heater. The electric current is passed through a nickel–chromium alloy wire wound on a ceramic former. The work done by the electric current in overcoming the resistance of the wire converts electrical energy into heat energy. The nickel–chromium alloy resists oxidation at high temperatures and prevents the wire being burnt away.

Activity J3.1

(a)   Describe another device that converts electrical energy into mechanical energy.
(b)   Describe another device that converts electrical energy into heat energy.
(c)   Describe, briefly, what is meant by the process of electroplating. (You may have to refer to a book on metal finishing.)

Now check your response

J4 Conductors and insulators

We have already seen that conductive materials (metals) have free electrons which can be moved easily through the lattice structure of metal ions by an electromotive force (emf). The opposite is also true. Non-metallic elements and compounds have their electrons much more firmly bonded together so that free electrons are vitually non-existent. This makes the passage of an electric current almost impossible. Such materials are called **insulators**.

Notes

- The exception is the non-metal carbon which is conductive. It has a high resistance compared with metals.
- There is no such thing as a perfect conductor. All normally available conductors offer some resistance to the flow of an electric current. (Superconductors operate at very low temperatures and are still in the research stage of development)
- There is no such thing as a perfect insulator, only materials with a very high resistance to the passage of an electric current. All insulators are leaky to some extent. However, for most practical purposes, leakage currents through insulating materials can be ignored.

Tables J4.1 and J4.2 list some typical conductors and insulators.

Table J4.1

Conductor material	Properties	Typical applications
Platinum, gold, silver	Very good conductors Too costly to use in bulk Do not oxidise appreciably	Plating plug and socket contacts and switch-blades in electronic devices to reduce surface resistance Facings in air-break power contactors
Copper, aluminium	Very good conductors Relatively low cost and high strength	Commercial conductors in cables, busbar systems, switchgear, machine windings, etc.
Tin	Good conductor but costly	Coating copper conductors to prevent corrosion and facilitate soldering
Lead	Good conductor and very malleable	Moisture-proof sheath around some types of armoured cable Earth continuity conductor in armoured cables
Brass (copper–tin alloy)	Good conductor and easily machined	Terminals and switchgear components
Soft solder (tin–lead alloy)	Good conductor with low melting point	Improving electrical conductivity and reliability of cable joints and terminations
Tungsten	Good conductor Very high melting temperature	Incandescent lamp filaments – operates continuously at white heat
Nichrome (nickel–chromium alloy)	Relatively poor conductor Does not oxidise appreciably at red heat	Electric fire and furnace elements – operates continuously at red heat in air
Manganin (nickel–copper–manganese alloy)	Relatively poor conductor Its resistance does not vary much with changes in temperature	Wire-wound instrument resistors
Carbon	Very poor conductor (non-metal) Self-lubricating properties	Brushes of rotating machines – reduces wear due to friction and arcing at commutators and slip-rings Resistors in electronic devices

Table J4.2

Insulating material	Properties	Typical applications
PVC (polyvinyl chloride) rubber	Good insulation Relatively high mechanical strength Flexible	Widely used for insulating and sheathing flexible cables and cords
Magnesia (mineral)	A powder insulating material Withstands high temperatures continuously	Mineral-insulated, copper-sheathed cables Mineral insulated, sheathed heating elements in domestic appliances and furnaces

Table J4.2 (*continued*)

Insulating material	Properties	Typical applications
Ceramics (glazed)	Rigid after firing, but easily moulded during manufacture very smooth surface can withstand weathering	High voltage insulators for overhead wiring systems – hard, smooth surface keeps clean and prevents leakage paths Switchgear and fuse bodies
Ceramics (unglazed)	As glazed ceramics but with a rough, porous surface Can operate continusly at high temperatures without developing surface cracks Unsuitable for exterior insulators	Formers for electric fire elements and wire-bound resistor elements Insulator beads for conductors operating at high temperatures Porous pots for Leclanché cells
Glass	Good insulator Unaffected by damp Becomes a conductor at dull red heat	Envelope and base insulation of lamps and thermionic valves Special insulators for high power transmitting aerials Used in resin-bonded, glass-fibre circuit boards
Perspex (acrylic resin)	Good insulator Easily formed and machined Transparent	Demonstration instrument bodies exploit its transparency
Tufnol (resin-bonded linen boards)	High strength Easily machined Good insulating properties	Experimental circuit mounting boards Printed circuit boards at low and medium frequencies
Bonded glass fibre	As Tufnol but more difficult to machine More environmentally stable than Tufnol	Printed circuit boards for computer, radio and television equipment

 Activity J4.1

The figure shows two cables joined by a connector block which has been cut away to expose its construction. Choose suitable materials for the following items giving reasons for your choice:

(a) Cable: (i)   the metal conductor
            (ii)   the plastic insulation
(b) Connector block: (i)   the metal connectors
                      (ii)   the metal clamp screws
                      (iii)   the moulded insulation
(c) Select suitable materials for the following applications, giving reasons for your answers:
    (i)   vacuum cleaner motor brushes
    (ii)   electric light-bulb filament
    (iii)   insulators for national grid system pylons

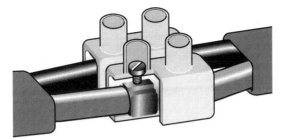

Fig. J4.1A

Now check your response

<table><tr><td>**J5**</td><td># Resistance</td></tr></table>

As I have previously stated, every material resists the passage of an electric current to a greater or lesser degree. The resistance of a conductor depends upon four things:

- The length of the conductor.
- The cross-sectional area (thickness) of the conductor.
- The material from which the conductor is made.
- The temperature of the conductor. The resistance of metals (conductors) increases as the temperature rises. The resistance of non-metals (insulators) decreases as the temperature rises.

The effects of these factors are shown diagrammatically in Fig. J5.1

Note

The calculation of the effect of temperature on the resistance of a conductor is beyond the scope of this book. However, we do need to be able to calculate the effects of length, cross-sectional area and resistivity of the material on the resistance of a conductor, so here goes.

The formula for calculating the resistance of a conductor is:

$$R = \frac{\rho \times l}{A}$$

where: R = resistance in ohms (Ω)
ρ = resistivity for a given material (Ω m)
l = length of the conductor (m)
A = cross-sectional area of the conductor (m^2)

Length

Long conductor
High resistance

Short conductor
Low resistance

Load   Source   Load

*The resistance of a conductor increases in
proportion to the length of the conductor*

Cross-sectional area

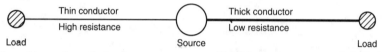

Thin conductor
High resistance

Thick conductor
Low resistance

Load   Source   Load

*The resistance of a conductor decreases
when the cross-sectional area increases*

*The resistance is inversely proportional to
the cross-sectional area of the conductor*

Material

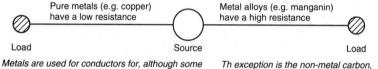

Pure metals (e.g. copper)
have a low resistance

Metal alloys (e.g. manganin)
have a high resistance

Load   Source   Load

*Metals are used for conductors for, although some
metals have a higher resistance than others, their
resistance is always very much lower than most
non-metals, which are used for insulators*

*Th exception is the non-metal carbon,
which is used to make resistors
requiring a high value of resistance*

Temperature

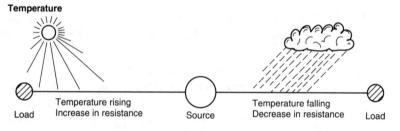

Temperature rising
Increase in resistance

Temperature falling
Decrease in resistance

Load   Source   Load

*The resistance of most metals increases when
the temperature increases and decreases when
the temperature decreases*

*Non-metals used as insulators decrease in
resistance when their temperature increases.
Glass is a good insulator at room temperature
but becomes a conductor at red heat*

Fig. J5.1

Resistivity is defined as the resistance of a unit cube of the material measured
between **opposite faces** as shown in Fig. J5.2. Some typical values of
resistivity for a range of commonly used metals and alloys are listed in Table
J5.1. Carbon is included because it is considered as a conductor even though
it is a non-metal.

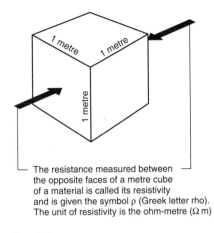

The resistance measured between
the opposite faces of a metre cube
of a material is called its resistivity
and is given the symbol ρ (Greek letter rho).
The unit of resistivity is the ohm-metre (Ω m)

Fig. J5.2

Table J5.1

Conductor material	Resistivity (Ω m at $0\,^\circ$C)
aluminium	2.7×10^{-8}
brass	7.2×10^{-8}
carbon	4400×10^{-8} to 8600×10^{-8}
constantan (Eureka)	49×10^{-8}
copper	1.59×10^{-8}
iron	9.1×10^{-8}
manganin	42×10^{-8}
mercury	94×10^{-8}
nickel	12.3×10^{-8} (typical value)
tin	13.3×10^{-8}
tungsten	5.35×10^{-8}
zinc	5.57×10^{-8}

Example

Calculate the resistance of a coil that has been wound from 15 m of copper wire having a cross-sectional area of 1 mm^2.

Solution

From Table J5.1 we know that resistivity (ρ) for copper is 1.59×10^{-8} Ω m. The units for resistivity are the ohm and the metre, so the wire dimensions must also be converted into metres:

$$R = \frac{\rho l}{A}$$

$$= \frac{1.59 \times 10^{-8}\ \Omega\ \text{m} \times 15\ \text{m}}{1 \times 10^{-6}\ \text{m}^2}$$

$$= 1.59 \times 10^{-2} \times 15$$
$$= \mathbf{0.2385 \ \Omega}$$

where: $R =$ resistance (Ω)
   $\rho = 1.59 \times 10^{-8} \ \Omega \ \text{m}$
   $l = 15 \ \text{m}$
   $A = 1 \ \text{mm}^2 = 1 \times 10^{-6} \ \text{m}^2$

 Activity J5.1

Calculate the resistance of the coil in the above example using manganin resistance wire instead of copper wire.

Now check your response

The formula $R = \dfrac{\rho l}{A}$ can also be written:

$$A = \frac{\rho l}{R} \qquad \rho = \frac{AR}{l} \qquad l = \frac{AR}{l}$$

Use these alternatives in the next activity

 Activity J5.2

Copy out and complete the table in your notebook.

Table J5.2A

Area (A)	Length (l)	Resistivity (ρ)	Resistance (R)
1.5 mm^2	1 km	$2.7 \times 10^{-8} \ \Omega \ \text{m}$	–
0.5 mm^2	12 m	–	0.384 Ω
0.2 mm^2	–	$4400 \times 10^{-8} \ \Omega \ \text{m}$	22 Ω
–	1 m	$42 \times 10^{-8} \ \Omega \ \text{m}$	42 Ω

Now check your response

 Activity J5.3

Calculate the resistance of a 2 km copper cable whose conductor has a diameter of 10 mm.

Now check your response

J6 Ohm's law

Georg Simon Ohm was the German scientist who discovered a definite relationship between the potential difference (pd) across the ends of a conductor and the magnitude of the current flowing through that conductor. The relationship holds for any given material, providing the temperature is kept constant. Ohm published his findings in 1827 and they can be expressed mathematically as:

$$R = \frac{U}{I}$$

where: R = resistance of the conductor (Ω)
U = potential difference across the ends of the conductor (V)
I = current flowing through the conductor (A)

You may also see this relationship written as $R = V/I$ and $R = E/I$; they all mean the same thing.

Figure J6.1 shows a simple circuit in which an ammeter is being used to measure the current flowing through a resistor and a voltmeter is being used to measure the potential difference across the resistor. You will learn more about circuits in Module K.

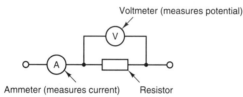

Voltmeter (measures potential)

Ammeter (measures current)   Resistor

Fig. J6.1

Example

Calculate the resistance of a resistor if a potential difference of 15 V causes a current of 5 A to flow through it.

Solution

$$R = \frac{U}{I}$$

$$= \frac{15 \text{ V}}{5 \text{ A}}$$

$$= 3\Omega$$

where: $U = 15$ V
$I = 5$ A
R = resistance (Ω)

In the next activity you will need to transpose the basic formula as follows. If $R = U/I$ then $I = U/R$ and $U = I \times R$

 Activity J6.1

Copy out and complete the table in your notebook.

Table J6.1A

Current (I)	Potential (U)	Resistance (R)
2 A	240 V	–
–	80 V	160 Ω
15 A	–	100 Ω

Now check your response

 Activity J6.2

Using a similar circuit to that shown in Fig. J6.1, various values of potential difference and related current were obtained for a given resistor; they are listed in Table J6.2A.

Table J6.2A

Potential (V)	0	2	4	6	8	10	12
Current (A)	0	0.25	0.5	0.75	1.0	1.25	1.5

(a)   Plot the graph for the values of potential difference and current given in the table. Values of potential difference should be assigned to the vertical axis and values of current to the horizontal axis.

(b)   Use the graph to find:
(i)   the current when the potential difference is 5 V
(ii)   the potential difference when the current is 0.875 A

(c)   Calculate the value of the resistance used to obtain these readings. Is it constant over the whole range of readings?

Now check your response

J7   Energy

We found in Section J1 that when a current flows through a conductor it has to overcome the resistance of that conductor by doing work and producing

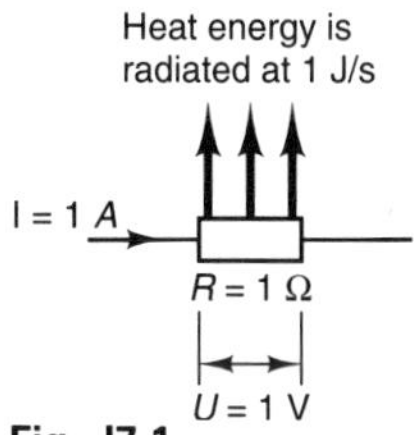

Heat energy is radiated at 1 J/s

I = 1 A

R = 1 Ω

U = 1 V

Fig. J7.1

heat. Figure J7.1 shows that when a current of 1 ampere flows through a resistor of 1 ohm for 1 second the amount of work done is 1 joule. Also the potential difference across the resistor will be 1 volt (see Ohm's law, previous section).

We can express all this mathematically as follows:

$$Q = U \times I \times t \tag{1}$$

where: Q = the quantity of heat energy (J)
U = the potential difference across the resistor (V)
I = the current flowing through the resistor (A)
t = time (s)

But from Ohm's law:

$$U = I \times R$$

Substitiuting this expression for U in formula (1) we get:

$$Q = IR \times I \times t$$
$$Q = I^2 \times R \times t \tag{2}$$

where: R = resistance of the resistor (Ω)

Example

Calculate the heat energy produced if a potential of 240 V causes a current of 5 A to flow through a resistor for 1 minute

Solution

Using formula (1):

$$Q = U \times I \times t$$
$$= 240 \text{ V} \times 5 \text{ A} \times 60 \text{ s}$$
$$= 72\,000 \text{ J}$$
$$= \textbf{72 kJ}$$

where: Q = heat energy produced (J)
U = 240 V
I = 5 A
t = 1 min = 60 s

Example

Calculate the energy produced when a current of 3 A flows through a 10 Ω resistor for 10 s.

Solution

Using formula (2):

$$Q = I^2 \times R \times t$$
$$= 3 \text{ A} \times 3 \text{ A} \times 10 \text{ }\Omega \times 10 \text{ s}$$
$$= \textbf{900 J}$$

where: Q = heat energy produced (J)
$\qquad I = 3$ A
$\qquad R = 10$ Ω
$\qquad t = 10$ s

 Activity J7.1

Copy out and complete the table in your notebook.

Table J7.1A

	Potential (U)	Current (I)	Time (t)	Resistance (R)	Energy (Q)
(a)	100 V	3 A	120 s		–
(b)	12 V	–	15 s		900 J
(c)	–	30 A	25 s		18 MJ
(d)	50 V	5 A	–		2 kJ
(e)		0.5 A	60 s	500 Ω	–

Now check your response

J8 Power

Power is the rate of doing work or using up energy. Therefore:

$$\text{power } (P) = \frac{Q}{t} \text{ J/s}$$

We give power in joules per second (J/s) a special unit, the **watt** (W), where:

1 watt (W) = 1 joule per second (J/s)

Since we have two formulae for finding energy Q, we have two formulae for finding power P.

$$P = \frac{Q}{t} = \frac{U \times I \times t}{t} = U \text{ (volts)} \times I \text{ (amps)} \qquad (1)$$

$$P = \frac{Q}{t} = \frac{I^2 \times R \times t}{t} = I^2 \text{ (amps)} \times R \text{ (ohms)} \qquad (2)$$

Example

Calculate the power in watts expended by an electric radiator, connected to a 240 V supply, if it draws a current of 10 A.

Solution

Using formula (1):

$$P = U \times I$$
$$= 240 \text{ V} \times 10 \text{ A}$$
$$= 2400 \text{ W}$$
$$= \textbf{2.4 kW}$$

where: P = power (W)
$\quad\quad U = 240$ V
$\quad\quad I = 10$ A

Example

Calculate the power in watts dissipated by a 14.7 kΩ resistor when a current of 20 mA flows through it.

Solution

Using formula (2):

$$P = I^2 R$$
$$= 0.02 \text{ A} \times 0.02 \text{ A} \times 14\,700 \text{ }\Omega$$
$$= \textbf{5.88 W}$$

where: P = power (W)
$\quad\quad I = 20$ mA $= 0.02$ A
$\quad\quad R = 14.7$ kΩ $= 14\,700$ Ω

Note how I had to convert milliamperes into amperes and kilohms into ohms before I could substitute them in the formula. In all formulae, remember to use the fundamental units, never the multiples or submultiples.

 ## Activity J8.1

Copy out and complete the table in your notebook.

Table J8.1A

	Potential (*U*)	Current (*I*)	Resistance (*R*)	Power (*P*)
(a)	200 V	5 A	–	–
(b)	–	0.2 A	1500 Ω	–
(c)	–	2 A	–	480 W
(d)	1.5 kV	2 mA	–	–
(e)	–	10 mA	14.7 kΩ	–
(f)	–	5 µA	–	10 mW

Now check your response

The joule is the quantity of energy (Q) required to drive a current of 1 ampere through a conductor of resistance 1 ohm so that a potential difference of 1 volt is produced across the ends of the conductor for 1 second. This is not a lot of energy and the joule would be an inconveniently small unit for stating the amount of energy used on the average domestic electricity bill, let alone an industrial electricity bill. For example, a 1 kilowatt radiator operating for 4 hours would require 14 400 000 J (14.4 MJ).

Therefore we use a larger unit called the kilowatt-hour (kWh) also known as the 'unit' on electricity bills. Since 1 watt equals 1 joule per second (and there are $60 \times 60 = 3600$ seconds in 1 hour), 1 kilowatt-hour equals 3 600 000 J. Therefore our 1 kW radiator operating for 4 hours would require:

$$4 \times 3\,600\,000 \text{ J} = \textbf{14 400 000 J}$$

It is much more convenient to use the kilowatt-hour (kWh) as follows:

$$1 \text{ kW} \times 4 \text{ h} = \textbf{4 kWh}$$

 Activity J8.2

(a) Calculate the energy required by a household in one day if they used:

cooker	5 kW for 2 hours
hob	1.5 kW for 3 hours
radiator	2 kW for 6 hours
immersion heater	3 kW for 2 hours
lights	0.5 kW for 8 hours

(b) Calculate the total cost of using the appliances listed in part (a) if the electricity company charges 7.2 pence per unit of electricity. Correct your answer to the nearest whole number of pence.

Now check your response

J9 Efficiency

Efficiency is the ratio between the amount of energy or power we get out of a system compared with the amount of energy or power that has to be put into the same system. This applies in all cases and not just to electrical systems. The symbol for efficiency is the Greek letter eta (η).

Expressed as a fraction:

$$\eta = \frac{Q_{out}}{Q_{in}} \quad or \quad \eta = \frac{P_{out}}{P_{in}}$$

Expressed as a percentage:

$$\eta = \frac{Q_{out} \times 100}{Q_{in}} \quad or \quad \eta = \frac{P_{out} \times 100}{P_{in}}$$

Example

An electric motor delivers 5 kW of mechanical power and is 80% efficient. Calculate the electrical power input to the motor.

Solution

$$\eta = \frac{P_{out} \times 100}{P_{in}}$$

$$P_{in} = \frac{P_{out} \times 100}{\eta}$$

$$= \frac{5 \ kW \times 100}{80}$$

$$= \textbf{6.25 kW}$$

No need to work in fundamental units this time since efficiency is only a ratio and ratios do not have units.

 ### Activity J9.1

Copy out and complete the table in your notebook.

Table J9.1A

	Power input	Power output	Efficiency
(a)	120 W	100 W	– %
(b)	2 kW	–	75%
(c)	–	6 kW	80%
(d)	8.1 kW	–	0.9
(e)	–	36 W	0.7

Now check your response

That concludes Module J. Before proceeding, complete the following assignment and hand it to your tutor for assessment. Don't forget to put your name and the assignment code on all your answer sheets.

Assignment for Module J

1 An electric current in a conductor is a directed flow of
(a) protons
(b) free electrons
(c) neutrons
(d) bonded electrons

2 The electromotive force (emf) of a battery can be measured by a voltmeter connected across its terminals when
(a) no load is connected across the battery
(b) a small load is connected across the battery
(c) an average load is connected across the battery
(d) a very heavy load is connected across the battery

3 Potential difference (pd) is measured across two points in a circuit when
(a) no current is flowing
(b) a current is flowing
(c) the circuit is open
(d) the supply is disconnected.

4 The number of electrons passing a point in a circuit in 1 s when a current of 100 A is flowing is
(a) 6.24×10^9
(b) 6.24×10^{16}
(c) 6.24×10^{18}
(d) 6.24×10^{20}

5 The heat energy given out by the resistor in Fig. JA.1 when the current flow is 5 A and the potential difference is 10 V is
(a) 2 J/s
(b) 5 J/s
(c) 15 J/s
(d) 50 J/s

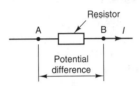

Fig. JA.1

6 If the current is 1 A and the potential difference across AB is 12 V, the total heat energy given out by the resistor in Fig. JA.1 in 5 minutes is
(a) 25 J
(b) 60 J
(c) 600 J
(d) 3600 J

7 A material with very high resistance to the flow of an electric current would make
(a) a good insulator
(b) a good conductor
(c) a good thermocouple
(d) a good magnet

8 A conductor 1 km long has a cross-sectional area of 10 mm^2 and a resistivity of 1.6×10^{-18} Ω m. Its resistance is
(a) 0.16 Ω
(b) 0.256 Ω
(c) 1.6 Ω
(d) 2.56 Ω

9 With reference to Fig. JA.2, if the current is 2 A and the pd is 12 V, the resistance (R) of the resistor will be
(a) 6 Ω
(b) 10 Ω
(c) 14 Ω
(d) 24 Ω

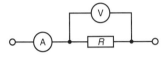

Fig. JA.2

10 With reference to Fig. JA.2, if the current is 50 mA and the resistance of the resistor is 10 kΩ, the pd across the resistor is
(a) 200 V
(b) 500 V
(c) 200 kV
(d) 500 kV

11 With reference to Fig. JA.2, if the pd is 100 V, and the resistance of the resistor is 50 Ω, the current flowing in the circuit is
(a) 0.5 A
(b) 2.0 A
(c) 150 A
(d) 5000 A

12 With reference to Fig. JA.2, if the current is 5 A and the pd is 100 V, the power dissipated by the resistor is
(a) 20 W
(b) 20 J
(c) 500 W
(d) 500 J

13 With reference to Fig. JA.2, if the current is 5 A and the resistance of the resistor is 10 Ω, the power dissipated by the resistor is
(a) 2 W
(b) 2.5 W
(c) 50 W
(d) 250 W

14 A 3 kW electric heater is left switched on for 9 hours. The quantity of energy used is
(a) 3 KWh
(b) 27 kWh
(c) 3 kJ
(d) 27 kJ

15 A 2 kW electric heater is left switched on for 4 hours. The quantity of energy used is
(a) 0.288 MJ
(b) 0.5 MJ
(c) 8.0 MJ
(d) 28.8 MJ

16 A machine has an efficiency of 80%. If the input power is 400 W, the output power is
(a) 120 W
(b) 320 W
(c) 480 W
(d) 720 W

17 A chemical reaction produces electrical energy in
(a) a primary cell
(b) an electroplating vat
(c) an alternator
(d) solar cell

18 Electrical energy is converted into mechanical energy by means of
(a) a chemical reaction
(b) electromagnetism
(c) the thermocouple principle
(d) electrolysis

K1 Circuit symbols

Figure K1.1 shows a simple electrical circuit. This circuit has all the basic requirements of every electrical circuit, namely:

- A source of supply (battery).
- A load or appliance to convert electrical energy into useful work (bulb).
- A means of control (switch).
- Connecting leads to complete the circuit. An electric current can only flow in a complete, closed circuit.

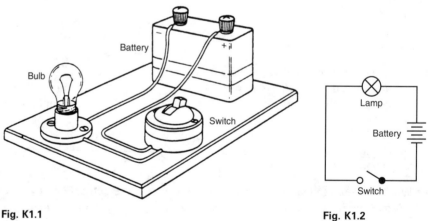

Fig. K1.1   Fig. K1.2

To draw a circuit pictorially, as I have done in Fig. K1.1, is difficult and time-consuming. Therefore we have to find a simpler and quicker way of drawing a circuit. Figure K1.2 shows the same circuit drawn using standard symbols. We will be using standard circuit symbols throughout this Module and throughout Module L. In fact you have already met some in Module J. The switch symbol shown in Fig. K1.2 is shown in the open or safe position so that the current cannot flow. This is normal drawing practice.

The circuit symbols that we are going to use are shown in Fig. K1.3. This is not a comprehensive list of symbols, just those that apply in Modules J, K and L. You should consult BS 3939 for the full list of symbols and how to use them correctly when drawing circuit diagrams.

Note

Except for simple circuits powered by primary cells, it is usual and good practice to include an overcurrent protection device such as a fuse or a miniature circuit-breaker. This should be wired in series with the source of supply. If the current rises to an unsafe value due to an accident or a component failure, the protective device breaks the circuit and the current ceases to flow.

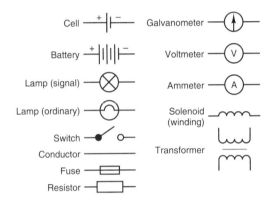

Fig. K1.3

 Activity K1.1

Copy out and complete the following statement in your notebook using some of the words from the list provided:

An electric _____ consists of a source of electrical _____, an _____ to convert the flow of current into useful work, a _____ to control the _____ of _____, and _____ leads. Most circuits are also fitted with an overcurrent protection device such as a _____ or a miniature circuit-breaker (MCB).

Fuse, resistor, current, potential, energy, appliance, flow, connecting, switch, ammeter, voltmeter, circuit, cell, battery.

Now check your response

K2   Series circuits

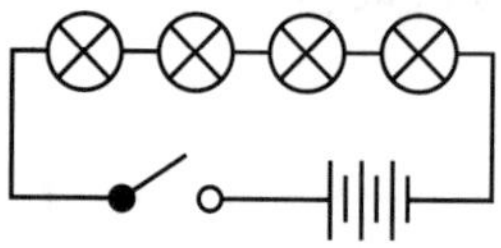

Fig. K2.1

Figure K2.1 shows four electric bulbs connected in **series**, that is, they are connected so the same current will flow through each bulb in turn when the switch is closed and the circuit is completed. The cells in the battery are also connected in series.

Figure K2.2 shows a rather more complicated circuit. It consists of:

- Three resistors connected in series.
- An ammeter (A) connected in series with the resistors to measure the current flowing in the circuit.
- A voltmeter connected across each resistor (V_1, V_2, V_3) to measure the potential difference across each resistor.
- A voltmeter (V_4) connected across the battery. This will read the emf when the circuit is open or the terminal pd when the switch is closed and a current is flowing.
- A switch to open or close the circuit and control the flow of electric current.

Note

I have used an alternative battery symbol that is used when many cells are connected in series.

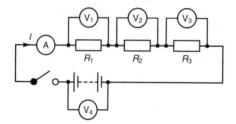

Fig. K2.2

Let's now see what is happening in our circuit:

- With the switch open, no current will flow in the circuit. Voltmeter V_4 will read the open circuit voltage or emf. None of the other meters will register.
- With the switch closed, a current will flow in the circuit. Ammeter A will indicate the size of this current. In a series circuit the current is constant at every point around the circuit. The voltage measured by voltmeter V_4 will be seen to be less than when the circuit was open. This is because voltmeter V_4 is now reading the terminal pd of the battery, not its emf. The greater the load on the battery, the lower the pd indicated by

voltmeter V_4. Voltmeters V_1, V_2 and V_3 will also be showing readings; they will depend upon the size of the resistors and the size of the current flowing through them (see Ohm's law, Section J6).

For any **series circuit** the following facts hold true:

- The current (I) is constant at all points around the circuit.
- $U_4 = U_1 + U_2 + U_3$

where: U_1 = the potential difference indicated by voltmeter V_1
U_2 = the potential difference indicated by voltmeter V_2
U_3 = the potential difference indicated by voltmeter V_3
U_4 = the terminal potential difference indicated by voltmeter V_4

- $R_{total} = R_1 + R_2 + R_3$

Let's now put some values around the circuit shown in Fig. K2.2 and see what we can calculate.

Example

Given: $I = 5$ A, $R_1 = 8\ \Omega$, $R_2 = 10\ \Omega$, $U_3 = 10$ V

Calculate: (a) the resistance R_3
(b) the total resistance for the circuit
(c) the readings for the voltmeters V_1 and V_2
(d) the terminal pd across the battery as indicated by voltmeter V_4

Solution

(a) From Ohm's law, $R_3 = U_3/I = (10\text{ V})/(5\text{ A}) = \textbf{2}\ \boldsymbol{\Omega}$
(b) $R_{total} = R_1 + R_2 + R_3 = 8\ \Omega + 10\ \Omega + 2\ \Omega = \textbf{20}\ \boldsymbol{\Omega}$
(c) U_1 as indicated by voltmeter $V_1 = I \times R_1 = 5$ A $\times$ 8 $\Omega = \textbf{40 V}$
U_2 as indicated by voltmeter $V_2 = I \times R_2 = 5$ A $\times$ 10 $\Omega = \textbf{50 V}$
(d) Terminal pd as indicated by voltmeter V_4.

$U_4 = U_1 + U_2 + U_3$

$= 40$ V $+ 50$ V $+ 10$ V $= \textbf{100 V}$

Alternatively:

terminal pd $= I \times R_{total}$

$= 5$ A $\times$ 20 $\Omega = \textbf{100 V}$

which proves our calculations are correct.

Activity K2.1

With reference to the circuit shown in Fig. K2.2, the following data holds true:

$I = 2$ A, $R_1 = 10\ \Omega$, $U_2 = 8$ V, $U_3 = 12$ V

Calculate:

(a) the resistance R_2
(b) the resistance R_3
(c) the total resistance for the circuit
(d) the terminal pd across the battery
(e) the power dissipated by resistance R_1
(f) the total energy dissipated by the whole circuit in joules over a period of 10 seconds

Now check your response

K3   Parallel circuits

Figure K3.1 shows three resistors connected in parallel; we have a **parallel**

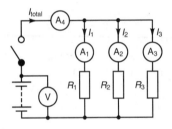

Fig. K3.1

circuit. In the series circuits of the previous section the current flowed through the components one after the other. In a parallel circuit the current flows through all the component simultaneously (at the same time).
Let's see what happens in this parallel circuit:

• With the switch open as drawn, no current will flow in the circuit. Voltmeter V will indicate the no-load voltage across the battery; this is the emf. None of the ammeters will register because no current is flowing in any part of the circuit.
• With the switch closed, the battery will be under load and the reading of voltmeter V will become less; it is now reading the terminal pd. A current will flow in the circuit and all the ammeters will register.

For any parallel circuit the following facts hold true:

• The potential difference (U) as indicated by voltmeter V is not only the terminal pd for the battery, it is also the pd across each limb of the circuit (each resistor represents a limb). Thus, when a current is flowing in the circuit, U is the pd (voltage) across the battery, the pd across R_1, the pd across R_2 and the pd across R_3.

- The total current (I_{total}) as indicated by ammeter A_4 is the sum of the currents in the limbs of the circuit. Therefore:

$$I_{total} = I_1 + I_2 + I_3$$

- The total resistance (R_{total}) is found by the formula:

$$\frac{1}{R_{total}} = \frac{1}{R_1} + \frac{1}{R_2} + \frac{1}{R_3}$$

Let's now put some values around the circuit shown in Fig. K3.1 and see what we can calculate.

Example

Given: $U = 60$ V, $R_1 = 20 \ \Omega$, $R_2 = 15 \ \Omega$, $R_3 = 12 \ \Omega$

Calculate: (a)   the total resistance for the circuit
              (b)   the currents: I_1, I_2 and I_3
              (c)   the total current flowing from the battery as indicated by ammeter A_4
              (d)   the power dissipated by the circuit

Solution

(a) $\dfrac{1}{R_{total}} = \dfrac{1}{R_1} + \dfrac{1}{R_2} + \dfrac{1}{R_3}$

$$= \frac{1}{20} + \frac{1}{15} + \frac{1}{12}$$

$$= \frac{3 + 4 + 5}{60}$$

$$= \frac{12}{60}$$

To find R_{total} you have to turn this fraction upside down:

$$R_{total} = \frac{60}{12}$$

$$= 5 \ \Omega$$

(b)   From Ohm's law, $I = (U)/(R)$, therefore:

$$I_1 = \frac{60 \text{ V}}{20 \ \Omega} = 3 \text{ A}$$

$$I_2 = \frac{60 \text{ V}}{15 \ \Omega} = 4 \text{ A}$$

$$I_3 = \frac{60 \text{ V}}{12 \ \Omega} = 5 \text{ A}$$

(c) $I_{\text{total}} = I_1 + I_2 + I_3$

$\qquad = 3\text{ A} + 4\text{ A} + 5\text{ A}$

$\qquad = \mathbf{12\ A}$

(d) Power dissipated by the circuit can be calculated by use of the formula:

$P = U \times I_{\text{total}}$

$\qquad = 60\text{ V} \times 12\text{ A}$

$\qquad = \mathbf{720\ W}$

Now it's your turn.

Activity K3.1

With reference to the circuit shown in Fig. K3.1, the following data holds true:

$$R_1 = 8\ \Omega,\ R_2 = 12\ \Omega,\ R_3 = 24\ \Omega,\ U = 36\text{ V}$$

Calculate:

(a) the total resistance for the circuit
(b) the currents I_1, I_2 and I_3
(c) the total current flowing from the battery
(d) the power dissipated by resistance R_3

Now check your response

Sometimes series and parallel circuits are combined so that the network of resistors looks quite complicated. The secret is to calculate the value of that single resistor which will replace each parallel group of resistors. You are then left with a simple series circuit. Just add up the resistor values for the equivalent series circuit and you have the value of the single resistor that will replace the original network.

Example

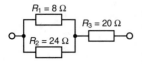

Fig. K3.2

Calculate the resistance of the network shown in Fig. K3.2 and thus obtain the value of the single resistor that can replace the network.

Solution

Solve the parallel group of resistors first:

$$\frac{1}{R_P} = \frac{1}{R_1} + \frac{1}{R_2}$$

$$= \frac{1}{8} + \frac{1}{24}$$

$$= \frac{3+1}{24}$$

$$= \frac{4}{24}$$

$$\text{Therefore } R_P = \frac{24}{4}$$

$$= \textbf{6 } \Omega$$

So we can now replace resistors R_1 and R_2 by a single 6 Ω resistor. This gives us a simple circuit with a 6 Ω resistor in series with a 20 Ω resistor:

$$R_S = R_P + R_3$$
$$= 6 \text{ } \Omega + 20 \text{ } \Omega$$
$$= \textbf{26 } \Omega$$

This is the resistance of the network shown in Fig. K3.2 and the value of the single resistor that can replace the network and produce the same effect.

 Activity K3.2

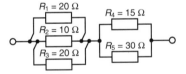

Fig. K3.2A

Calculate the resistance of the network shown and thus find the value of the single resistor that can replace it.

Now check your response

Here are some points concerning electric circuits that you need to remember:

- The total resistance of series-connected resistors is always **greater** than any single resistor in the circuit.
- The total resistance of parallel-connected resistors is always **less** than any single resistor in the circuit
- Ammeters are always connected in **series** with the circuit so that the circuit current can flow through them.

- Voltmeters are always connected in **parallel** across the circuit where a potential difference is being measured.
- Potential difference can only be measured when a current is flowing.
- The terminal potential difference of a source of electrical energy is always **less** than the open-circuit (no-load) electromotive force (emf) for the battery.

K4 Cells in series

Fig. K4.1

The overall emf of a number of cells connected in series to make up a battery is the sum of the emf's of the individual cells. Figure K4.1 shows three cells connected in series.

For the example shown in Fig. K4.1:

$$E = E_1 + E_2 + E_3$$

The current-handling capacity of this arrangement is the same as that for any individual cell, providing they all have similar characteristics. If the individual cells do not have similar characteristics, the current-handling capacity of the battery is equivalent to that of the weakest cell.

 Activity K4.1

Calculate the emf of a battery made up of 12 series-connected cells each of emf 2 V.

Now check your response

K5 Cells in parallel

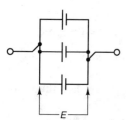

Fig. K5.1

When cells are connected in parallel, as shown in Fig. K5.1, there is no increase in emf. The overall emf (E) is the same as the emf for any individual cell in the battery. All the cells **must** have the same emf. The current-handling capacity of this arrangement equals the sum of the current-handling capacities of the individual cells. In this case the cells do not have to have the same current-handling characteristics.

Activity K5.1

(a) Three cells are connected in parallel. Their current-handling capacities are 20 A, 25 A and 35 A respectively. Calculate the overall current-handling capacity of this parallel arrangement of cells.
(b) If each of the above cells has an emf of 2 V, calculate the overall emf.

Now check your response

K6 # Lamps in series

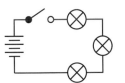

Fig. K6.1

Figure K6.1 shows three lamps connected in series. Some decorative (Christmas tree) lights are connected like this. It enables low voltage bulbs to be connected across a high voltage mains supply.

Since current is constant in a series circuit all the lamps must have the same current rating. The disadvantages of this circuit are that:

- The lamps cannot be individually switched off.
- If one lamp fails all the lamps go out since the circuit has been broken.
- The system is dangerous. While a current is flowing, the pd across the terminals of any lamp-holder is equal to the low voltage of the lamp. If a lamp fails, no current flows so there is no pd across the lamp-holder terminals. The full mains emf of 240 V now appears across the terminals of all the lamp-holders.

Example

(a) Calculate the minimum number of 16 V lamps which can be operated from a 240 V supply when the lamps are series connected.
(b) Calculate the current flowing in the circuit if each individual lamp is rated at 5 W.

Solution

(a) number of lamps $= \dfrac{\text{supply emf}}{\text{pd across each lamp}}$

$= \dfrac{240 \text{ V}}{16 \text{ V}}$

$= \textbf{15 lamps}$

(b) $P = \dfrac{I}{U}$ so $I = \dfrac{P}{U} = \dfrac{5 \text{ W}}{16 \text{ V}} = \textbf{0.3125 A}$

Alternatively we could have used the total load and the supply potential:

total load = 15 lamps × 5 W each = 75 W

$$I = \frac{P}{U} = \frac{75 \text{ W}}{240 \text{ V}} = \mathbf{0.3125 \text{ A}}$$

 ### Activity K6.1

Ten lamps are connected in series. Each lamp has a current rating of 0.2 A and a power rating of 5 W. Can these series-connected lamps be connected safely across a 240 V supply?

Hint: If the 'ideal' series-connected supply voltage is greater than 240 V, the lamps can be operated safely from the mains supply.

Now check your response

 ## K7 Lamps in parallel

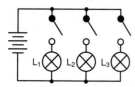

Fig. K7.1

Figure K7.1 shows three lamps connected in parallel. The advantages of this (normal) method of connection are:

- The lamps can be switched on or off individually.
- If one lamp fails the other lamps are not affected.
- The lamps can have different power ratings. However, all the lamps must have the same voltage rating and this must equal the supply emf.

Example

With reference to Fig. K7.1, calculate the maximum current flowing from the battery when all the lamps are switched on, given:

$P_1 = 4$ W

$P_2 = 6$ W

$P_3 = 10$ W

$U = 6$ V

where: P_1 = power of lamp L_1
P_2 = power of lamp L_2
P_3 = power of lamp L_3
U = terminal pd of the battery

Solution

$$\text{total load} = 4 \text{ W} + 6 \text{ W} + 10 \text{ W} = 20 \text{ W}$$

$$P = I \times U \text{ so } I = \frac{P}{U} = \frac{20 \text{ W}}{6 \text{ V}} = 3\tfrac{1}{3} \text{ A}$$

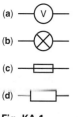 **Activity K7.1**

With reference to Fig. K7.1 and the previous example, calculate the current being drawn from the battery if lamp L_1 is switched off. Ignore any change in terminal pd.

Now check your response

That concludes Module K. Before proceeding, complete the following assignment and hand it to your tutor for assessment. Don't forget to put your name and assignment code on each of your answer sheets.

Assignment for Module K

1 The instrument used to measure electrical potential is
(a) an ammeter
(b) a wattmeter
(c) an ohmmeter
(d) a voltmeter

2 Which of the circuit symbols shown in Fig. KA.1 represents a fuse?

(a) ─(V)─

(b) ─⊗─

(c) ─▭─

(d) ─▭─

Fig. KA.1

3 An ammeter is connected
(a) either in series or in parallel
(b) only in parallel
(c) only in series
(d) neither in series nor in parallel

4 Figure KA.2 shows three lamps connected in
(a) series
(b) parallel
(c) a combined series and parallel network
(d) neither series nor parallel

L_1 L_2 L_3

─⊗──⊗──⊗─

○ U ○

Fig. KA.2

5 Given that each lamp in Fig. KA.2 is rated at
   12 V and 6 W, the current flowing in the
   circuit is
   (a) 0.5 A
   (b) 1.5 A
   (c) 2.0 A
   (d) 6.0 A

6 Given that each lamp in Fig. KA.2 is rated at
   12 V and 6 W, the supply potential U should
   be
   (a) 4 V
   (b) 12 V
   (c) 15 V
   (d) 36 V

7 The total resistance of the circuit shown in
   Fig. KA.3 is
   (a) 3.75 Ω
   (b) 32 Ω
   (c) 40 Ω
   (d) 72 Ω

Fig. KA.3

8 With reference to Fig. KA.3, if a current of 2 A
   is flowing in the circuit, the pd across R_4 is
   (a) 7.5 V
   (b) 15 V
   (c) 60 V
   (d) 120 V

9 With reference to Fig. KA.3, the power
   dissipated by R_2 when a current of 1 A is
   flowing is
   (a) 2.5 W
   (b) 5 W
   (c) 20 W
   (d) 40 W

10 The lamps shown in Fig. KA.4 are connected
   in
   (a) series
   (b) parallel
   (c) a combination of series and parallel
   (d) neither series nor parallel

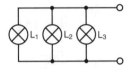

Fig. KA.4

11 With reference to Fig. KA.4, if lamp L_2 should
   fail then
   (a) lamps L_1 and L_3 will also go out
   (b) lamps L_1 and L_3 will become dim
   (c) lamps L_1 and L_3 will be unaffected
   (d) only lamp L_3 will remain alight

12 With reference to Fig. KA.4, if the supply
   voltage is 6 V and lamps L_1, L_2 and L_3 are
   each rated at 3 W the total current drawn
   from the supply will be
   (a) 0.5 A
   (b) 0.67 A
   (c) 1.5 A
   (d) 18 A

13 With reference to Fig. KA.5, the value of the
   single resistor that can replace R_1 and R_2 is
   (a) $\frac{1}{3}$ Ω
   (b) 9 Ω
   (c) 24 Ω
   (d) 36 Ω

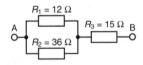

Fig. KA.5

14 With reference to Fig. KA.5, the total resistance between A and B is
   (a) $1\frac{2}{3}$ Ω
   (b) 6 Ω
   (c) 24 Ω
   (d) 63 Ω

15 Which diagram in Fig. KA.6 shows the correct connection of three cells of 2 V each to make a 6 V battery?

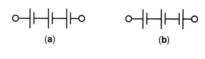

(a)   (b)

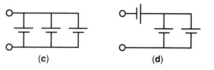

(c)   (d)

Fig. KA.6

L1 Magnets

Figure L1.1 shows two typical permanent magnets. Although they only look like pieces of straight or bent steel, they are capable of picking up small pieces of iron and steel such as tacks, nails and paper-clips. This is because they are surrounded by an invisible force field, their magnetic flux. Let's see if we can find the shape of this magnetic flux field using a simple experiment.

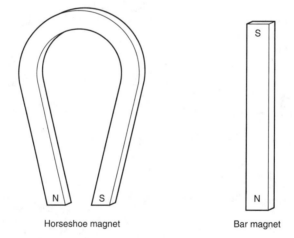

Horseshoe magnet   Bar magnet

Fig. L1.1 Caption

 Activity L1.1

Place a horseshoe magnet on a flat, horizontal surface and cover it with a piece of stiff but thin, smooth card.

• Sprinkle iron filings lightly onto the card over the area covering the magnet.

- Lightly tap the card so that the filings can move into position.
- Sketch the pattern into which the filings arrange themselves. This is the shape of the flux field. Repeat the experiment using a bar magnet.

Now check your response

You should have seen from the experiment you performed in Activity L1.1 that the magnetic flux fields seemed to flow from the ends of the magnet. These ends are called the **poles** of the magnet. All magnets have two poles. If a bar magnet is cut into pieces, as shown in Fig. L1.2, each piece will still have two poles. I have labelled the poles N and S (north and south), let's see why.

Original bar magnet

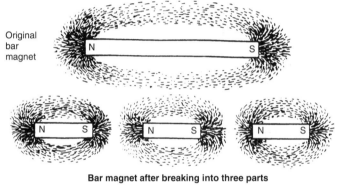

Bar magnet after breaking into three parts
Each part becomes a magnet in its own right with two poles

Fig. L1.2

If a bar magnet is freely suspended as shown in Fig. L1.3, it will take up a position along a line running approximately north–south, that is, it will point to the Earth's magnetic north and south poles. The magnetic poles lie a little to the side of their corresponding geographical poles.

The end of the bar magnet that points to the Earth's magnetic north pole is correctly called the north-seeking pole of the magnet. Usually, for convenience, it is simply referred to as the magnet's **north pole**.

The end of the magnet that points to the Earth's south magnetic pole is correctly called the south-seeking pole of the magnet. Usually, for convenience, it is simply referred to as the magnet's **south pole**.

A bar magnet suspended or pivoted at its centre so that it is free to rotate and align itself with the Earth's magnetic field is the basis of a practical **magnetic compass**.

If we bring a magnetic compass near to the north-seeking pole of a bar magnet, the north-seeking pole of the compass turns away from the magnet, as shown in Fig. L1.4(a). But if the compass is brought towards the south-seeking pole of the magnet, the north-seeking pole of the compass swings

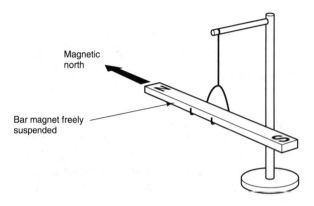

Magnetic
north

Bar magnet freely
suspended

Fig. L1.3

towards the magnet as shown in Fig. L1.4(b). This is because:

- Like poles repel each other.
- Unlike poles attract each other.

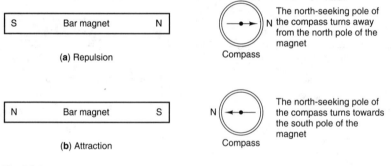

| S | Bar magnet | N |

(a) Repulsion

Compass

The north-seeking pole of the compass turns away from the north pole of the magnet

| N | Bar magnet | S |

(b) Attraction

Compass

The north-seeking pole of the compass turns towards the south pole of the magnet

Fig. L1.4

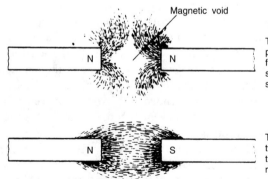

Magnetic void

The lines of force of two similar poles repel each other and try to force the magnets apart. Two south poles would produce the same effect

The lines of force between two opposite poles bridge the gap and try to attract the magnets together

Fig. L1.5

It is conventional magnetic theory that magnetic flux fields flow from north-seeking poles to south-seeking poles in any magnetic circuit. Let's now repeat our iron filings experiment using two bar magnets arranged as shown in Fig. L1.5.

- See what happens when like poles face each other.
- See what happens when unlike poles face each other.

Activity L1.2

These diagrams show some magnets arranged in different ways. For each example, state in your notebook whether the pole marked * is north seeking (N) or south seeking (S). Remember that like poles attract each other, unlike poles repel each other. And remember that magnetic flux is assumed to flow from north-seeking poles to south-seeking poles. Do the same for the poles marked **.

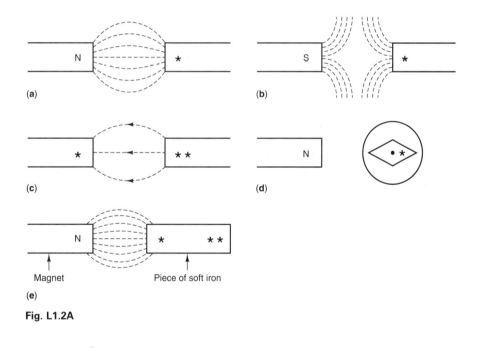

Fig. L1.2A

***

Now check your response

***

So far we have only considered permanent magnets. However, in the response to the last activity, you found that a piece of soft iron (annealed mild steel) placed in a magnetic field would also become magnetised but only for as long as it was in the magnetic field. Remove the field and it becomes just a piece of soft iron again. It no longer behaves like a magnet.

This is the principle of the electromagnet. When a current flows through a conductor, as shown in Fig. L1.6(a), a magnetic flux field is created around that conductor. When the current ceases to flow, the magnetic flux field ceases to exist. And the greater the current flowing through the conductor, the stronger will be the magnetic field.

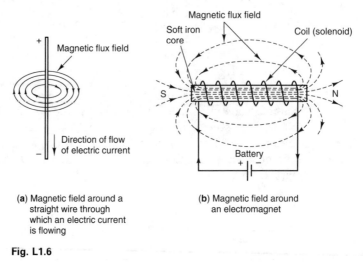

(a) Magnetic field around a straight wire through which an electric current is flowing

(b) Magnetic field around an electromagnet

Fig. L1.6

The strength of the magnetic field can be concentrated by winding the conductor into a coil. This coil is called a **solenoid**; it is also called a winding. The strength of the magnetic flux field can be increased still further by inserting a piece of soft iron into the centre of the solenoid (coil or winding) as shown in Fig. L1.6(b).

- When the current is flowing, as shown, the soft iron core behaves like a bar magnet.
- If the current ceases to flow, the magnetic field collapses. The soft iron core ceases to behave like a magnet.

Electromagnets are very useful because they can be turned on and off as required. Large and powerful electromagnets mounted on cranes are used for handling steel scrap in scrapyards.

Current flow

When I first introduced you to the flow of electrons as an electric current, we saw how the negatively charged electrons flowed towards the positively charged terminal of a battery or other source of electrical energy. This directed flow of electrons is the modern concept of an electric current.

However, when Michael Faraday was setting the ground rules for electromagnetic theory in the nineteenth century, atomic theory was unheard of. Because contact with the positive of a source of electrical energy gave people a shock, it was assumed that this was the terminal from which electricity flowed. People were beginning to understand how to generate electricity by various means and how to apply it to produce various effects but they had no means of knowing what constituted an electric current.

Therefore, all the electromagnetic theory was based on the assumption that electricity flowed from positive to negative. We still use this assumption in our electromagnetic calculations and theory. We call this direction of flow **conventional current flow**. The correct, modern concept of current flow is referred to as **electron current flow**; this is shown in Fig. L1.7.

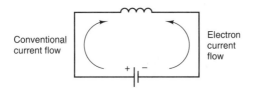

Conventional current flow

Electron current flow

Fig. L1.7

Right-hand grip rule

Look back to Fig. L1.6. The arrowheads on the solenoid (coil) indicate the direction of conventional current flow. Now, in your imagination, grasp the solenoid in your **right hand** so that your fingers curl round the coil in the direction of conventional current flow (the direction of the arrowheads). Your **thumb**, extended sideways, will point to the **north** pole of the magnet.

 Activity L1.3

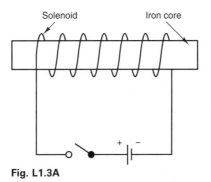

Solenoid   Iron core

Fig. L1.3A

Copy the circuit shown into your notebook.

(a)   What must you do to make the current flow through the solenoid?

(b)   Use arrowheads to show the direction of **conventional** current flow through the windings of the solenoid.

(c)   Apply the right-hand grip rule and mark the north (N) and south (S) ends of the iron core.

(d)   State what would happen if you reversed the connections to the cell.

Now check your response

L2   Magnetic materials

All materials are affected to some extent by strong magnetic fields. Only certain materials have such pronounced magnetic properties that they can be made into permanent magnets or electromagnets; they are the **ferromagnetic** materials. Only ferromagnetic materials are attracted to magnets. The ferromagnetic materials are iron, cobalt, nickel and gadolinium. They often appear in association with other metals and non-metals to form special magnetic alloys.

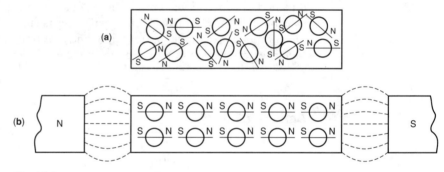

Fig. L2.1

Let's now see how a piece of ferromagnetic material becomes magnetised. Figure L2.1(a) shows a piece of iron or steel in the **unmagnetised** state. All the particles in the lattice structure of the material behave like little weak bar magnets. These particles are naturally magnetised by the spinning of the electrons within their atoms. Each particle has a north pole (N) and a south pole (S).

Figure L2.1(b) shows the same piece of material placed between the poles of a powerful magnet. The magnetised particles align themselves within this external field as shown. Although the individual particles are only weakly magnetised, they are present in such vast quantities in any piece of ferromagnetic material that all their fields added together produce a very powerful magnet.

Permanent magnets are made from hardened high carbon steels and steel alloys, electromagnets are made from soft iron and annealed low carbon steels. They have to be magnetised by placing them between the poles of a powerful magnet or by placing them within a solenoid through which an electric current is flowing.

Soft magnetic materials

Soft magnetic materials such as pure iron and low carbon steels behave as magnets when placed in strong external magnetic fields. They lose their magnetism as soon as the external field is removed. Consequently they are used for the cores of electromagnets, the cores of transformers and the rotors and stators of electromagnetic machines. In addition to soft iron and low carbon steels, alloys such as silicon–iron, μ-metal and permalloy are also used.

Hard magnetic materials

To make a simple permanent magnet, take a piece of high carbon steel (e.g. silver steel rod) and heat it to red heat. Immediately, cool it quickly (quench it) from red heat in cold water. The steel will now be hard and brittle. If it is placed in a powerful magnetic field, it will become magnetised. Unlike soft magnetic materials, its particle magnets will remain in alignment even after the external magnetising field has been removed. Very powerful permanent magnets can be made using alloys such as Columax. A permanent magnet made from Columax alloy is 30 times more powerful than a magnet made from quench-hardened high carbon steel of the same physical size.

Activity L2.1

Piece of mild
steel rod

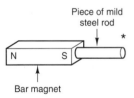

Bar magnet

Fig. L2.1A

The figure shows a piece of mild steel rod placed against one pole of a bar magnet. Use a compass to carry out the following tests and record your results in your notebook:

(a)   Does the end of the mild steel rod marked * appear to be magnetised?
(b)   If the answer to (a) is yes, what is the polarity of the end marked *?
(c)   Repeat the experiment with the piece of mild steel rod touching the opposite end of the bar magnet. What has happened to the polarity of the end marked *?
(d)   Remove the magnet. Does the piece of mild steel still appear to be as strongly magnetised?
(e)   Do you think mild steel is a hard or a soft magnetic material? Give reasons for your answer based upon your findings in (a) to (d) above.

Now check your response

Activity L2.2

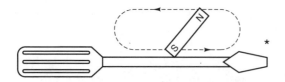

Fig. L2.2A

Using one pole of a bar magnet, stroke the blade of a screwdriver about 25 times as shown. Lift the magnet well clear of the screwdriver as you reach the handle at the end of each stroke. Use a compass to determine the following:

(a)   Has the blade of the screwdriver become magnetised?
(b)   If the blade has become magnetised, what is the polarity at *?
(c)   Does the screwdriver remain magnetised after the bar magnet has been removed?
(d)   Do you think the blade of the screwdriver has been made from a hard or a soft magnetic material?

Now check your response

L3 Electromagnetic induction

When a magnet is plunged into a coil of wire, an emf is induced in the coil. If the coil forms part of an electric circuit, as shown in Fig. L3.1, an electric current will flow. A centre-zero galvanometer will detect this current and indicate its direction of flow.

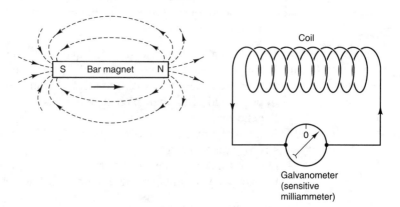

Fig. L3.1

The galvanometer will indicate that:

- The current only flows as long as the magnet is moving.
- The direction of current flow depends upon:
  (i)   which pole of the magnet is plunged into the coil
  (ii)   the direction of movement of the magnet–whether it is moving into or out of the coil
  (iii) The 'hand' of the coil winding
- The magnitude of the induced emf (and therefore the induced current) will depend upon:
  (i)   the speed with which the magnet moves
  (ii)   the number of turns of wire in the coil
  (iii) the strength of the magnet

Although the arrangement shown in Fig. L3.1 is a convenient means of demonstrating electromagnetic induction, it would be a very inconvenient method of generating electricity on a commercial scale. We use rotating machinery (e.g. turbines) to drive our generators, so the relative movement of the magnet and coil must also be rotary. Figure L3.2 shows how this is done.

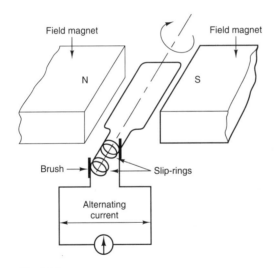

Fig. L3.2

A single-loop conductor is arranged so that it can be rotated between the poles of a powerful magnet. The electric current is drawn from the loop by means of hard copper slip-rings which are connected to the loop and rotate with it. Carbon brushes press against the slip-rings and conduct the electric current into the external circuit. Carbon is used for the brushes because its high contact resistance prevents arcing which would burn and damage the slip-rings. Also carbon is self-lubricating and this reduces the frictional wear of the slip-rings.

Activity 3.1

Take a good look at Fig. L3.2 then answer the following questions in your notebook:

(a) Consider what you think would happen to the induced emf if:
   (i)   the strength of the magnetic field were increased
   (ii) the speed of rotation were decreased
(b) Consider what you think would happen to the induced current flow if:
   (i)   the polarity of the magnets were reversed
   (ii) the direction of rotation were reversed

Now check your response

Figure L3.3 shows what happens as the loop rotates. Sometimes it will be moving at right angles to the magnetic flux field and the induced emf will have a maximum value. Sometimes it will be moving parallel to the magnetic flux field and the induced emf will be zero. Sometimes it will be moving at an angle to the magnetic flux field and the induced emf will have some intermediate value between zero and the maximum.

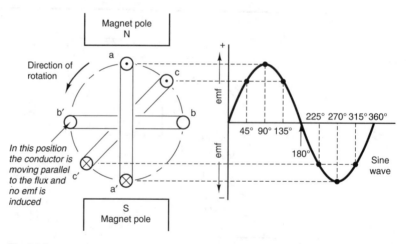

Fig. L3.3

Let's now examine the magnitude of the induced emf in more detail with the help of Fig. L3.3.

*   When moving at **right angles** to the magnetic field (aa′ in Fig. L3.3) the emf induced in the loop will have a **maximum** value.
*   When moving **parallel** to the magnetic field (bb′ in Fig. L3.3) a **zero emf** value will be induced in the loop.
*   When moving at an **angle** to the magnetic field (cc′ in Fig. L3.3) an **intermediate emf** value is induced in the loop.

These conditions can be plotted graphically as shown in Fig. L3.3. This graph is identical to the shape of the graph you would get if you plotted the sine of an angle against the angle itself for the range 0° to 360°. Therefore the graph of the emf (and current) generated by a rotating machine is called a **sine wave**. A graph of the current flowing in the external circuit of the single-loop generator would also have the shape of a sine wave. The current commences at a zero value, rises to a maximum positive value then falls back to a zero value at 180° at the end of the first half-revolution. It rises to a maximum value in the negative direction and falls to zero again at 360°. A current that constantly and cyclically changes direction in this manner is called an **alternating** current (ac). A generator that produces alternating current electricity is called an alternator.

Instead of slip-rings, some generators have a rotary switch called a commutator. This reverses the connections of the external circuit every half-revolution (for a single-loop generator) and the current in the external circuit flows in the same direction all the time. This is called a **direct** current (dc). A generator that produces direct current is called a dynamo.

In practice, more than one loop is used and each loop has many turns of wire. Also there will be more than one pair of magnetic poles. So far we have only considered one complete revolution of the loop. To produce a useful alternating current the rotor will have many loops and will be kept rotating continuously at high speed. We could no longer observe what is happening with a galvanometer. It would not be able to swing backwards and forwards quickly enough to keep up with the changes of direction in the current. Even if it could, our eyes could not keep up with the movements of the needle. Therefore we use a device called an oscilloscope. It works rather like a television set and we can see the shape of the induced emf on the screen. With our alternator rotating continuously we would see a succession of sine waves standing side by side as shown in Fig. L3.4.

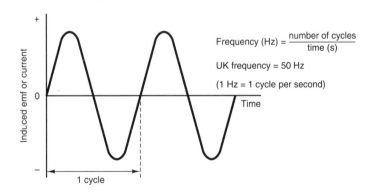

$$\text{Frequency (Hz)} = \frac{\text{number of cycles}}{\text{time (s)}}$$

UK frequency = 50 Hz

(1 Hz = 1 cycle per second)

Fig. L3.4

Each complete sine wave (360° rotation) is called a **cycle**. The **frequency** (f) of an alternating emf or an alternating current is the number of complete cycles that occur in one second. The unit of frequency is the hertz (Hz). One hertz (Hz) equals one cycle per second as shown in Fig. L3.4.

Activity L3.2

(a)   An alternating current completes 1000 cycles in 5 seconds. Calculate its frequency.

(b)   How quickly must a single-loop alternator rotate to produce 50 Hz alternating current? Assume the field magnet has two poles and state your answer in revolutions per minute (rpm).

(c)   Sketch the emf–time curve for a 1.5 V primary cell over a period of 60 seconds.

Now check your response

L4   The transformer

At the start of Section L3, I introduced you to the principle of electomagnetic induction, that is, to induce an emf in a conductor, the magnetic flux linked with the conductor must change. In Fig. L3.1 we achieved this change by plunging a bar magnet into a coil and then withdrawing it. Figure L4.1 shows an alternative way of changing the magnetic flux linkage.

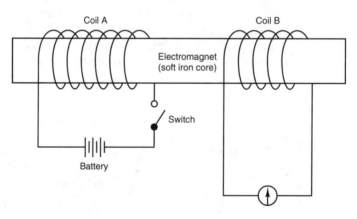

Fig. L4.1

Instead of a bar magnet we can use an electromagnet and keep switching it on and off. In Fig. L4.1 the coil (solenoid) A is wound round a soft iron core. When the switch is closed an electric current flows through coil A and the soft iron core becomes magnetised.

The magnetic flux field of the soft iron core is linked with coil B, which is also wound on the core. When you switch on, the magnetic flux linked with coil B builds up. This induces an emf in coil B and the galvanometer flicks to one side from its central zero position. If the switch is left on, the magnetic flux in the core will settle down to a steady value. The galvanometer needle will return to zero because there is no change in the magnetic flux linked with coil B.

When the switch is opened, the electric current ceases to flow and coil A ceases to produce a magnetic field. The soft iron core ceases to be magnetised, so there is a collapse of the magnetic flux field linked with coil B. This too is a change in the field and again an emf is induced in coil B. But the galvanometer will flick in the opposite direction. By switching the current on and off we can make the needle flick from side to side.

Instead of using a switch to change the strength and direction of the flux field linked with coil B, we can connect coil A to an alternating current source as shown in Fig. L4.2. The strength and direction of the magnetic flux field produced by coil A, in the soft iron core, will vary directly with the changes in strength and direction of the alternating current supply. If the alternating current supply to coil A is derived from the mains supply, the strength and direction will change twice per cycle, that is, 100 times per second for a 50 Hz supply.

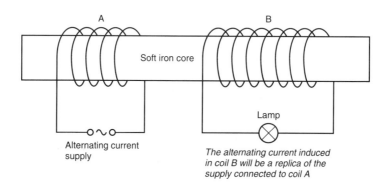

Fig. L4.2

Thus the magnetic flux field linked with coil B will also be constantly changing and a corresponding 50 Hz alternating emf will be induced in coil B. This can be detected with an electric light-bulb as shown. It all happens too fast for a galvanometer to follow the changes. Alternatively an oscilloscope could be used as described previously. What we have produced is the **transformer** effect.

We can make a practical **transformer** by completing the magnetic circuit to increase the efficiency of the device. Different core arrangements to produce an efficient closed magnetic path are shown in Fig. L4.3. The magnitude of the induced emf can easily be calculated if we know the number of turns on each coil. This is shown in Fig. L4.4.

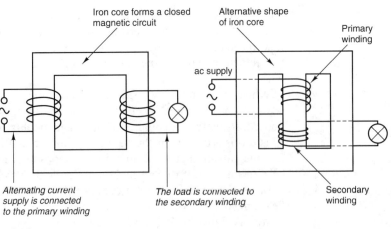

Fig. L4.3

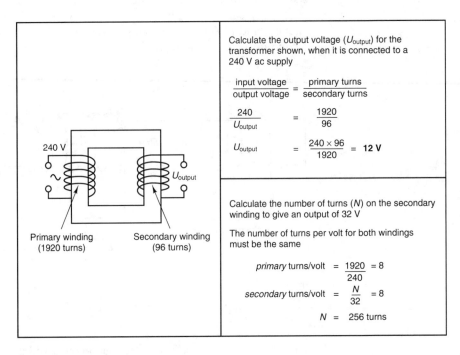

Fig. L4.4

The table content of Fig. L4.4:

Calculate the output voltage (U_{output}) for the transformer shown, when it is connected to a 240 V ac supply

$$\frac{\text{input voltage}}{\text{output voltage}} = \frac{\text{primary turns}}{\text{secondary turns}}$$

$$\frac{240}{U_{output}} = \frac{1920}{96}$$

$$U_{output} = \frac{240 \times 96}{1920} = \mathbf{12\ V}$$

Calculate the number of turns (N) on the secondary winding to give an output of 32 V

The number of turns per volt for both windings must be the same

$$primary\ \text{turns/volt} = \frac{1920}{240} = 8$$

$$secondary\ \text{turns/volt} = \frac{N}{32} = 8$$

$$N = 256\ \text{turns}$$

240 V

U_{output}

Primary winding
(1920 turns)

Secondary winding
(96 turns)

Activity L4.1

(a)   The primary winding of a transformer has 2490 turns and the secondary winding has 144 turns. Calculate the output voltage of the transformer if it is connected to a 415 V alternating current supply.

(b)   For the same transformer calculate the number of turns for the secondary winding if the output voltage is to be 45 V.

Now check your response

In a perfect transformer (100% efficient):

$I \times U$ (primary) = $I \times U$ (secondary)

Now comes the hard bit. You are going to ask why can't we use power (watts) instead of $I \times U$?

   This is because in alternating current theory and practice power in watts can only apply to circuits containing pure resistance. Here the sine wave for the pd and the sine wave for the current are in step. As soon as you include coils (such as a transformer winding) within the circuit, the pd and the current get out of step and the power (watts) equation no longer applies. If you look on the maker's data plate on a transformer you will find that the power rating is given in kVA, and not in kW, so we will stick with $I \times U$.

Example

Calculate the output current for a perfect transformer given:

   primary current   = 2 A
   primary voltage   = 240 V
   secondary voltage = 12 V

Solution

   $I \times U$ (primary) = $I \times U$ (secondary)
   2 A $\times$ 240 V   = $I \times$ 12 V

   I (secondary) $= \dfrac{2 \text{ A} \times 240 \text{ V}}{12 \text{ V}}$

   $= \mathbf{40\ A}$

In practice 100% efficiency is not attained, although transformers do have very high efficiencies. The efficiency of a transformer (as a percentage) is given by the expression:

$$\eta = \frac{I \times U \text{ (secondary)} \times 100}{I \times U \text{ (primary)}}$$

Example

Calculate the efficiency of a transformer given:

   primary voltage   = 240 V

primary current   = 2 A

secondary voltage = 12 V

secondary current = 36 A

Solution

$$h = \frac{I \times U \ (\text{secondary}) \times 100}{I \times U \ (\text{primary})}$$

$$= \frac{36 \ \text{A} \times 12 \ \text{V} \times 100}{2 \ \text{A} \times 240 \ \text{V}}$$

$$= 90\%$$

So what has happened to the missing 10%? This represents the various losses that occur in the transformer and cause the core and the windings to heat up. Large transformers, such as those used at electricity substations, are filled with a special oil. This not only acts as an insulator but also as a coolant. The oil circulates through the transformer and then through a heat exchanger where it is cooled down before returning to the transformer. The heat exchanger often takes the form of the vertical pipes you can see on the outside of the transformer casing.

Activity L4.2

Calculate the secondary (output) current for the transformer in Activity L4.1(a) if the primary (input) current is 2 A and the efficiency of the transformer is reduced to 84%.

Now check your response

That concludes Module L. Before proceeding complete the following assignment and hand it to your tutor for assessment. Don't forget to put your name and assignment code on all your answer sheets.

Assignment for Module L

1   Fig. LA.1 shows
    (a) an electromagnet
    (b) a horseshoe magnet
    (c) a bar magnet
    (d) a compass

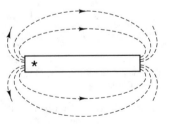

Fig. LA.1

2 **With reference to Fig. LA.1, the end of the magnet marked * is**
   (a) a north pole
   (b) a south pole
   (c) a positive pole
   (d) a negative pole

3 **A permanent magnet is made from**
   (a) a soft magnetic material
   (b) a hard magnetic material
   (c) a silicon–iron alloy
   (d) μ-metal

4 **The north-seeking pole of a compass is attracted to**
   (a) the north pole of a magnet
   (b) the south pole of a magnet
   (c) either pole of a magnet
   (d) neither pole of a magnet

5 **In Fig. LA.2 the symbol * indicates**
   (a) the south pole of a magnet
   (b) the north pole of a magnet
   (c) a piece of soft iron
   (d) a piece of hard steel

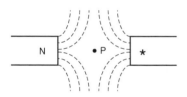

Fig. LA.2

6 **In Fig. LA.2 the point P represents**
   (a) maximum magnetic field strength
   (b) a magnetic void
   (c) the average magnetic field strength
   (d) a rotating m agnetic field

Fig. LA.3

7 **The magnets shown in Fig. LA.3 will be**
   (a) attracted to each other
   (b) repelled by each other
   (c) unaffacted by each other
   (d) demagnetised by each other

8 **For the electromagnet shown in Fig. LA.4 the symbol * indicates**
   (a) a south pole
   (b) a positive pole
   (c) a north pole
   (d) a negative pole

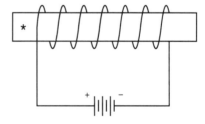

Fig. LA.4

9 **If the direction of current flow in Fig. LA.4 is reversed, the polarity of * will**
 (a) remain the same
 (b) reverse
 (c) rise to a maximum value
 (d) fall to a minimum value

10 In electromagnetic theory we assume that current flows
 (a) from negative to positive (electron flow)
 (b) from positive to negative (conventional flow)
 (c) from north to south
 (d) from south to north

11 The strength of an electromagnet will depend upon
 (a) the number of turns in the coil alone
 (b) the current flowing through the coil alone
 (c) the current value multiplied by the number of turns
 (d) the current value plus the number of turns

12 Figure LA.5 shows a bar magnet being used to induce a current in a coil of wire. If the poles of the magnet are reversed, the current flow will
 (a) reverse
 (b) remain the same
 (c) cease
 (d) become stronger

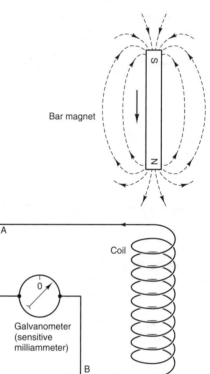

Fig. LA.5

13 With reference to Fig. LA.5, if the speed with which the magnet is moved into and out of the coil is increased, the emf across the points AB will
 (a) reverse
 (b) remain the same
 (c) decrease
 (d) increase

14 Which of the diagrams in Fig. LA.6 represents an alternating current?

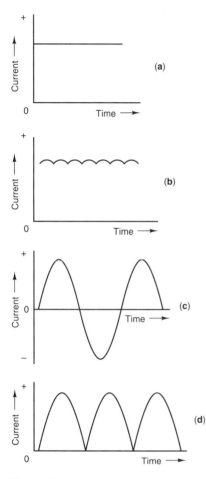

Fig. LA.6

15 An alternating current makes 3.6×10^6 complete cycles in 2 seconds. Its frequency is
(a) 1.8 kHz
(b) 1.8 MHz
(c) 3.6 MHz
(d) 7.2 MHz

16 A transformer has a primary winding of 2400 turns and a secondary winding of 120 turns. If it is connected to a 240 V supply its output emf will be
(a) 2 V
(b) 12 V
(c) 480 V
(d) 4800 V

17 A transformer with 1440 turns on its primary winding has an output emf of 50 V when connected to a 240 V supply. Therefore its secondary winding will have
(a) 48 turns
(b) 50 turns
(c) 288 turns
(d) 300 turns

18 Given:
primary pd = 110 V
primary current = 5 A
secondary pd = 33 V
secondary current = 15 A

The efficiency of the transformer will be
(a) 10%
(b) 11.1%
(c) 90%
(d) 111%

19 Increasing the rotational speed of a single-loop slip-ring generator will
(a) increase the emf and increase the frequency
(b) decrease the emf and increase the frequency
(c) increase the emf and decrease the frequency
(d) have no effect on either the emf or the frequency

20 Increasing the strength of the field magnet of a single loop generator will
(a) decrease the induced emf
(b) increase the frequency
(c) decrease the frequency
(d) increase the induced emf

M1 Tools using the lever principle

Before commencing this section I would like you to revise Module F. Figure M1.1 shows a lever (crowbar) being used to move a heavy load. From what you have already learnt in Module F, you should know that for the effort force to balance the load:

$$F \times l_F = W \times l_W$$

Any further increase in F will cause the load to move.

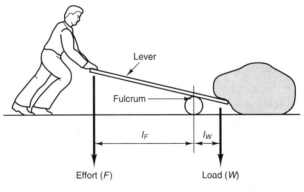

Fig. M1.1

 Activity M1.1

Calculate the force (F) required just to balance the weight (W) of the box using the data given in the figure over page.

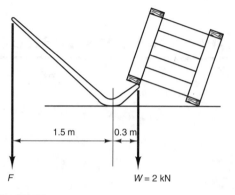

1.5 m   0.3 m

F   W = 2 kN

Fig. M1.1A

Now check your response

There are **three** orders of levers depending upon the relative positions of the load, effort and fulcrum; they are shown in Fig. M1.2.

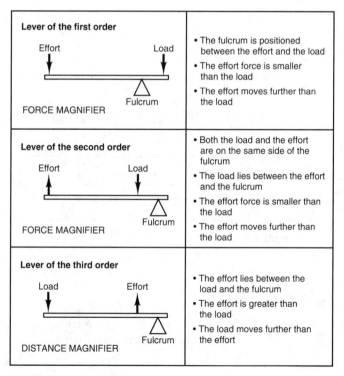

Lever of the first order	
Effort Load Fulcrum FORCE MAGNIFIER	• The fulcrum is positioned between the effort and the load • The effort force is smaller than the load • The effort moves further than the load
Lever of the second order	
Effort Load Fulcrum FORCE MAGNIFIER	• Both the load and the effort are on the same side of the fulcrum • The load lies between the effort and the fulcrum • The effort force is smaller than the load • The effort moves further than the load
Lever of the third order	
Load Effort Fulcrum DISTANCE MAGNIFIER	• The effort lies between the load and the fulcrum • The effort is greater than the load • The load moves further than the effort

Fig. M1.2

Activity M1.2

The figure shows some practical examples of levers. For each example:

(a)   Indicate the point of application of the effort force (F).
(b)   Indicate the point of application of the load force (W).
(c)   Indicate the position of the fulcrum (pivot).
(d)   State the order of lever the example represents.

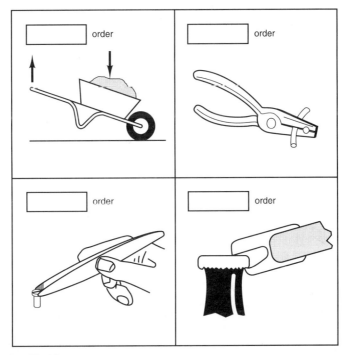

Fig. M1.2A

Now check your response

Figure M1.3 shows some further examples of hand-tools that depend upon the lever principle in order to work. In each example the device shown is using the lever principle to magnify the effort force being applied by the user.

The effectiveness of any of the devices shown in Fig. M1.3 depends upon the relative distances from the pivot point of the user's hand and the work being gripped or turned. In Fig. M1.4 you will see how this affects the correct use of a pair of hand-shears (snips). Figure M1.4(a) shows the correct way to hold a pair of snips. Figure M1.4(b) shows the relative positions of the forces and the pivot. The metal being cut should be kept as close to the

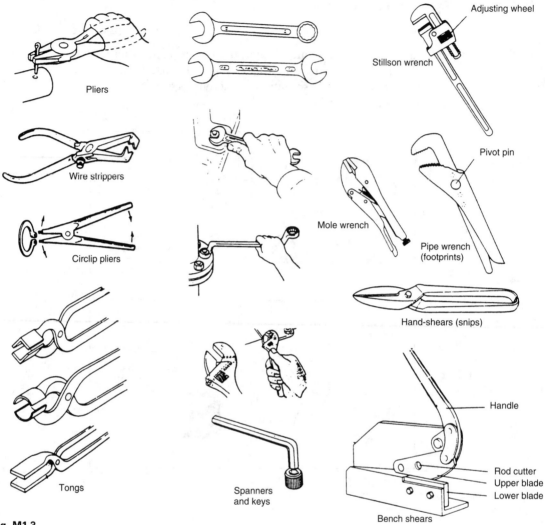

Pliers

Wire strippers

Circlip pliers

Tongs

Stillson wrench

Adjusting wheel

Mole wrench

Pivot pin

Pipe wrench
(footprints)

Hand-shears (snips)

Spanners
and keys

Handle

Rod cutter
Upper blade
Lower blade

Bench shears

Fig. M1.3

pivot as possible. You will see the reason for this from the following example.

Example

Calculate the forces F_1 and F_2 from the data given in Fig. M1.4 and so decide which position is the most efficient for cutting.

Solution

(a) Shearing force (F_1) near the pivot:

clockwise moments = anticlockwise moments

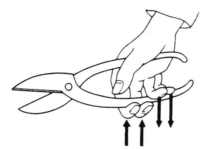

(a) Correct grip: the scissors action is provided by the finger
movement indicated by the arrows

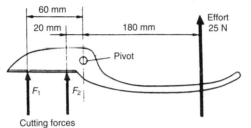

Cutting forces

(b) Correct grip: relative positions of the forces and the pivot

Fig. M1.4

$$F_1 \times 20 \text{ mm} = 25 \text{ N} \times 180 \text{ mm}$$

$$F_1 = \frac{25 \text{ N} \times 180 \text{ mm}}{20 \text{ mm}}$$

$$= \textbf{225 N}$$

(b)   Shearing force (F_2) remote from the pivot:

clockwise moments = anticlockwise moments

$$F_2 \times 60 \text{ mm} = 25 \text{ N} \times 180 \text{ mm}$$

$$F_2 = \frac{25 \text{ N} \times 180 \text{ mm}}{60 \text{ mm}}$$

$$= \textbf{75 N}$$

The force exerted by the shears on the metal being cut is very much less in
the second position, so for any given effort force, the metal being cut should
be kept as close to the pivot as possible.

 Activity M1.3

With reference to Fig. M1.4, recalculate the forces F_1 and F_2 if F_1 lies
15 mm from the pivot, F_2 lies 50 mm from the pivot and the effort force is
20 N.

Now check your response

Another important application of the lever principle is in the clamping of work to be machined. An example is shown in Fig. M1.5

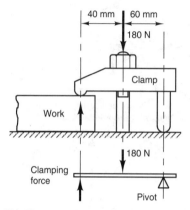

Fig. M1.5

Let's now calculate the force exerted on the workpiece by the clamp for the conditions shown in Fig. M1.5.

$$\text{clockwise moments} = \text{anticlockwise moments}$$

$$\text{clamping force} \times (40 \text{ mm} + 60 \text{ mm}) = 180 \text{ N} \times 60 \text{ mm}$$

$$\text{clamping force} \times 100 \text{ mm} = 180 \text{ N} \times 60 \text{ mm}$$

$$\text{clamping force} = \frac{180 \text{ N} \times 60 \text{ mm}}{100 \text{ mm}}$$

$$= \textbf{108 N}$$

The balance of the force exerted on the clamp by the nut and stud (180 N − 108 N = 72 N) is exerted on the packing under the rear of the clamp and is wasted.

Activity M1.4

With reference to Fig. M1.5:

(a)   Recalculate the clamping force when the stud and nut are moved 10 mm nearer to the work (10 mm further from the packing).
(b)   Recalculate the clamping force when the stud and nut are moved 10 mm further from the work (10 mm nearer to the packing).
(c)   Which position gives the most effective clamping.

Now check your response

A less obvious application of the lever principle for magnifying forces is to be found in the windlass or winch. Figure M1.6 shows a simple hand-operated winch.

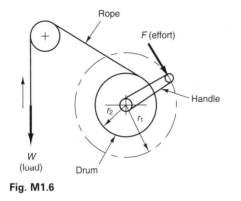

Fig. M1.6

As drawn, clockwise rotation of the handle will wind the rope onto the drum. This will raise the load *W*. Applying the principle of moments:

$$F \times r_1 = W \times r_2$$

  Activity M1.5

With reference to Fig. M1.6, calculate the effort required to balance a load of 1 kN if $r_1 = 600$ mm and $r_2 = 150$ mm.

Now check your response

There are practical limits to the force magnification that can be achieved in a simple windlass or winch:

- The smaller the drum radius; the greater the force magnification. However, if the drum radius is reduced too much, the rope fibres will be bent too sharply and they will become fractured.
- The magnification can also be increased by lengthening the radius of the handle. In practice, this is limited by how far the operator can conveniently reach.

When the required force magnification is greater than obtainable from this simple arrangement, the handle can be geared to the drum as shown in Fig. M1.7.

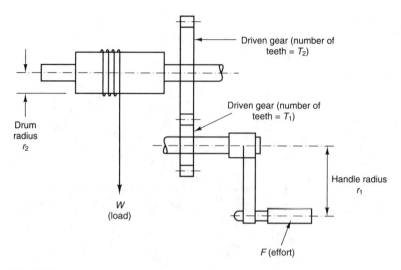

Driven gear (number of teeth = T_2)

Driven gear (number of teeth = T_1)

Drum radius r_2

W (load)

Handle radius r_1

F (effort)

Fig. M1.7

This time the force magnification equals the winch magnification multiplied by the gear ratio. Expressed mathematically this becomes:

$$F \times r_1 \times \frac{T_2}{T_1} = W \times r_2$$

where: T_1 = number of teeth on the driver gear
T_2 = number of teeth on the driven gear

 Activity M1.6

With reference to Fig. M1.7, calculate the effort force required to balance a 1kN load, given:

$r_1 = 600$ mm

$r_2 = 150$ mm

$T_1 = 45$ teeth

$T_2 = 90$ teeth

Now check your response

In theory we appear to have halved the effort required to raise the load of 1 kN. However, no machine is perfect (100% efficient), and every time we introduce some additional mechanism we increase the frictional losses. Even allowing for the additional frictional losses, introducing the gears would make it a lot easier for the person turning the handle to raise the load. But the time taken would increase because the drum would revolve more slowly.

M2 Pulley systems

Pulley systems can also be used to magnify forces. They enable heavy loads to be raised safely without undue effort. The basic principles are shown in Fig. M2.1.

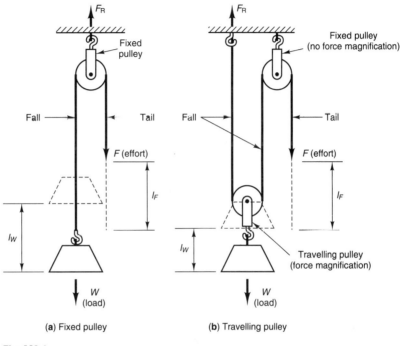

(a) Fixed pulley   (b) Travelling pulley

Fig. M2.1

In Fig. M2.1(a) there is only one pulley (a fixed pulley) and the distance moved by the load equals the distance moved by the effort; there is no force magnification:

- $l_W = l_F$ and $F = W$
- $F \times l_F = W \times l_W$
- reaction force $(F_R) = W + F + $ (weight of the fixed pulley block)

In Fig. M2.1(b) there is one fixed pulley block and one travelling pulley block. This time the distance moved by the tail rope and, therefore, the effort force is twice the distance moved by the load. The introduction of a travelling pulley provides force magnification. The top and bottom pulleys together with their mountings are called **sheave blocks**. This time:

- $l_F = 2l_W$ and $W = 2F$
- $F \times l_F = W \times l_W$
- reaction force $(F_R) = W + F + $ (combined weight of the fixed and travelling pulley blocks)

In Fig. M2.1 the fixed and travelling pulleys have been spaced for clarity. Figure M2.2 shows a more usual and practical arrangement for two pulleys and two falls of rope. When calculating the force magnification we do not include the tail rope. The relationships between the effort force, the load and the distances travelled by the effort force and the load are the same as for Fig. M2.1.

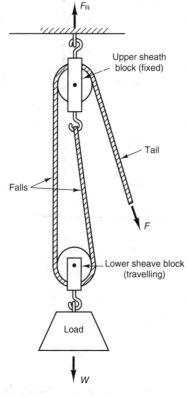

Fig. M2.2

By increasing the number of pulleys in the upper and lower sheaves, the pulley tackle can provide even greater force magnification:

- With an even number of falls the end of the rope is fastened to the upper sheave.
- With an odd number of falls the end of the rope is fastened to the lower sheave.
- The effort force can be calculated using the expression:

$$F = \frac{W}{n}$$

where: n = the number of falls

- There can never be more than a difference of 1 between the number of pulleys in the sheaves. Some typical combinations are shown in Table M2.1.

Table M2.1

Upper sheave	Lower sheave	Number of falls
1	1	2
2	1	3
2	2	4
3	2	5
4	2	a

[a] This one does not work because the difference in the number of pulleys is greater than 1.

Activity M2.1

(a) Calculate the effort force (F) required to just raise a load of 2 kN if the pulley tackle used has three pulleys in the upper sheave and two pulleys in lower sheave.

(b) If the load in (a) is raised by 2 m, calculate the distance the tail rope has to be pulled through the tackle.

(c) If the total weight of the tackle is 0.5 kN, calculate the reaction force (F_R) at the point where the tackle is suspended from the beam.

Now check your response

Weston (differential) pulley blocks

Weston (differential) pulley blocks work on a different principle. The layout of the pulleys is shown in Fig. M2.3. The lower (travelling) sheave never has more than one pulley. The upper (fixed) sheave always has two pulleys fixed to the same shaft so that they rotate together at the same speed. The force magnification depends upon the difference in diameter between these two pulleys. Chain is used instead of rope, to prevent slip over the pulleys in the upper sheave, and the flanges of the pulleys are formed to engage with the chain links.

To raise the load, the effort force (F) is applied to the endless chain in the direction as shown. As the chain is drawn in over the larger pulley, it is let out over the smaller pulley. The pulleys rotate at the same speed, so the movement ratio depends upon their relative circumferences and can be calculated as follows. That part of the chain supporting the load is shortened by an amount equal to:

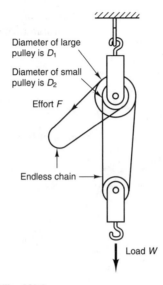

Diameter of large pulley is D_1

Diameter of small pulley is D_2

Effort F

Endless chain

Load W

Fig. M2.3

(circumference of pulley diameter D_1) − (circumference of pulley diameter D_2)

The load is raised by half this amount because there are two falls of chain and a single pulley in the lower (travelling) sheave. Since the circumference of a pulley is equal to πD, we can now develop equations for calculating the movement ratio and the force magnification of any differential pulley tackle. Let's consider the distances moved during one revolution of the upper two pulleys:

$$\text{amount load is raised} = \frac{\pi D_1 - \pi D_2}{2} \qquad (1)$$

At the same time, the effort force (F) moves through a distance equal to the circumference of the larger pulley:

$$\text{distance moved by effort} = \pi D_1 \qquad (2)$$

So we finally have an expression for the movement ratio:

$$\text{movement ratio} = \frac{\text{distance moved by effort}}{\text{distance moved by load}}$$

$$= \frac{\pi D_1}{\frac{1}{2}(\pi D_1 - \pi D_2)}$$

$$= \frac{2D_1}{D_1 - D_2}$$

Since the relationship $F \times l_F = W \times l_W$ also applies to this equipment, we can calculate the force magnification as follows:

$$F = \frac{W \times (D_1 - D_2)}{2D_1}$$

Activity M2.2

Calculate the effort force required to raise a load of 3 kN using Weston differential tackle, given:

  large pulley diameter (D_1) = 300 mm
  small pulley diameter (D_2) = 200 mm

Assume the tackle is 100% efficient.

Now check your response

M1   The inclined plane

Figure M3.1 shows a load (W) being raised by an effort force (F) using a wedge. A wedge is an application of an inclined plane. An inclined plane can be used to magnify the effort force or the effort movement. Like all mechanical devices it is impossible to magnify both at the same time.

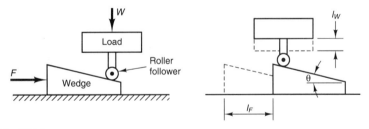

Fig. M3.1

Before I show you the mathematical relationships applied to the inclined plane, I want to remind you of some of the symbols I am going to use.

  $a = b$ means a is equal to b
  $a > b$ means a is greater than b
  $a < b$ means a is less than b

Again we have our basic relationship:

  $F \times l_F = W \times l_W$

- When wedge angle $\theta = 45°$, then $l_F = l_W$ and $F = W$.
- When wedge angle $\theta < 45°$, then $l_F > l_W$ and $F < W$.
- When wedge angle $\theta > 45°$, then $l_F < l_W$ and $F > W$.

You will use this information in the next activity.

Activity M3.1

Using a wedge, calculate the effort force (F) required to raise a load (W) of 4 kN given $l_F = 500$ mm and $l_W = 10$ mm.

Now check your response

A simple wedge is a useful device for levelling a machine or for levelling large and heavy work on a machine. In these applications the movement required for W is very small, so the length of the wedge can be kept to a reasonable value for a substantial force magnification.

Where the load has to be raised through a greater distance, we have to convert our inclined plane into a screw thread to make it more compact and convenient to use. Let's see how this is done. Since a screw thread is an application of a helix, we have to convert our inclined plane into a helix. When an inclined plane is wrapped around a cylinder it becomes a helix. Figure M3.2 shows a long paper wedge wrapped around a broom handle. I hope you can see how it starts to look like a scew thread. Why not try it for yourself?

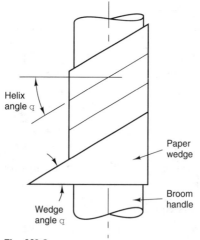

Helix angle q

Paper wedge

Broom handle

Wedge angle q

Fig. M3.2

A screw thread is a practical application of a helical groove cut into a metal cylinder (metal rod). Notice how the wedge angle (θ) becomes the helix angle of the thread measured perpendicular to the axis of the cylinder.

- The smaller the helix angle, the finer the thread.
- The smaller the helix angle, the smaller the equivalent wedge angle and the greater the force magnification.
- Therefore fine threads give large force magnification. Unfortunately fine threads are weaker than coarse threads, so any device using screw threads as a force magnifier has to be a compromise between strength and magnification.

Before we move on and look at a screw-jack (a device that uses a screw thread to lift heavy loads) let's see what we mean by fine threads and coarse threads. These are terms related to the **pitch** and **lead** of a thread.

Single-start thread

Figure M3.3 shows the basic helix of a single-start thread. This sort of thread is associated with nuts and bolts and is by far the most common. There is only a single helix and **the lead equals the pitch**.

Pitch is the distance between similar points on adjacent threads measured parallel to the axis.

Lead is the axial distance moved by a nut along the screw thread in one revolution.

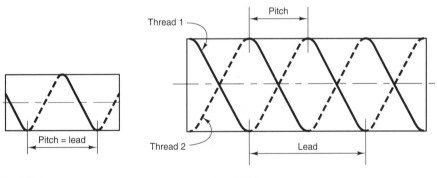

Fig. M3.3   **Fig. M3.4**

Multi-start thread

A multi-start thread is used when the lead needs to be increased without increasing the pitch and, therefore, the depth of the thread. The basic helices of a two-start thread are shown in Fig. M3.4. Thread number 1 is cut first. Then thread number 2 is cut between the first thread. When viewed from the end, the threads appear to be 180° apart. Threads may be cut with more than two starts. When viewed from the end, the individual threads of a three-start thread appear to be 120° apart:

lead = pitch × number of starts

Activity M3.2

Copy out and complete the table in your notebook.

Table M3.2A

Pitch	Number of starts	Lead
4 mm	1	–
4 mm	3	–
–	2	6 mm
2.5 mm	–	10 mm
6 mm	–	6 mm

Now check your response

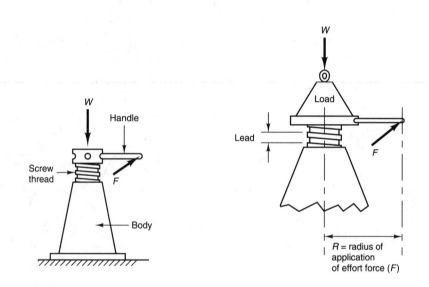

Fig. M3.5

Fig. M3.6

Figure M3.5 shows a practical screw-jack. When the handle is rotated in an anticlockwise direction, the screw is unscrewed from the nut fixed in the body of the jack. This movement raises the load. The effort force (F) acts at right angles to the handle of the jack; it moves further than the load (W) so there is force magnification. Using Fig. M3.6 let's see how we can calculate this force magnification.

For one revolution of the screw:

$$F \times l_F = W \times l_W$$

where: $l_F = 2\pi R$
l_W = the lead of the screw

Example

Calculate the effort force (F) required to raise a load (W) of 2 kN if the effort force acts on the handle at a radius of 250 mm and the single-start screw has a pitch of 4 mm.

Solution

$$\text{lead} = \text{pitch} \times \text{number of starts}$$

$$= 4 \text{ mm} \times 1$$

$$= 4 \text{ mm}$$

$$F \times l_F = W \times l_W$$

$$F \times 2\pi \times 250 \text{ mm} = 2000 \text{ N} \times 4 \text{ mm}$$

(I have converted 2 kN into 2000 N)

$$F = \frac{2000 \text{ N} \times 4 \text{ mm}}{2\pi \times 250 \text{ mm}}$$

$$= \mathbf{5.09 \ N} \ (2 \text{ d.p.})$$

Remember that 2 d.p. means there is no exact answer; the answer is given correct to two decimal places.

This example assumes that the jack is 100% efficient. In practice there would be friction between the screw and the nut. Therefore the effort force would be greater than the ideal value calculated.

Activity M3.3

(a) Recalculate the previous example assuming the screw-jack to have a two-start thread with a 4 mm pitch with all the other data unchanged;

(b) Recalculate the previous example assuming the screw-jack to have a single-start thread of 4 mm pitch, a handle now 200 mm long and all the other data unchanged.

(c) Describe the effect these changes have on the effort force and why.

Now check your response

Now let's return to the inclined plane in use as a ramp. This will involve the use of some simple trigonometry, so we had better revise it. When solving problems by trigonometry we use the notation shown in Fig. M3.7. We use upper case (capital) letters for the angles and lower case (small) letters for the sides. So side a is opposite angle A, side b is opposite angle B and side c is opposite angle C.

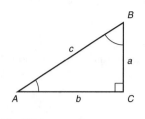

Fig. M3.7

Since the triangle shown in Fig. M3.7 is a right-angled triangle, side c must be the **hypotenuse** since it lies opposite the right angle C. Let's now consider angle A.

- Side a is **opposite** angle A.
- Side b is **adjacent** to angle A.

Therefore, the basic ratios are:

- tangent (tan) $A = \dfrac{\text{opposite}}{\text{adjacent}} = \dfrac{a}{b}$

- sine (sin) $A = \dfrac{\text{opposite}}{\text{hypotenuse}} = \dfrac{a}{c}$

- cosine (cos) $A = \dfrac{\text{adjacent}}{\text{hypotenuse}} = \dfrac{b}{c}$

 Activity M3.4

With reference to Fig. M3.7, write down the corresponding ratios for angle B.

Now check your response

The theorem of Pythagoras is also useful for inclined plane calculations. Expressed mathematically for the triangle shown in Fig. M3.7:

$$c^2 = a^2 + b^2$$

Activity M3.5

With reference to Fig. M3.7, and applying the theorem of Pythagoras, calculate the length of:

(a)   side c, given that side $a = 5$ cm and side $b = 12$ cm
(b)   side a, given that side $c = 50$ mm and side $b = 40$ mm

Now check your response

Having revised the necessary mathematics, let's now consider the inclined plane as a ramp for raising or lowering heavy bodies. Figure M3.8 shows the forces acting on a body on a ramp.

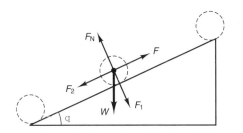

Fig. M3.8

The weight of the body (W) acts vertically downwards because it is the force of gravity acting on the mass of the body. The weight of the body (W) can be resolved into forces F_1 and F_2. We can find the magnitude of these forces graphically as shown in Section E8 or, more accurately, by the use of trigonometry. Referring to Fig. M3.8:

- $F_1 = F_N = W \cos \theta$, where F_N is the reaction force normal (at $90°$) to the inclined plane.
- $F_2 = F = W \sin \theta$, where F is the effort force dragging the body up the ramp and F_2 is the force trying to slide the body down the ramp.
- Work in joules (J) is said to be done when a force moves a body through a distance.

Let's now see if there are any free lunches when we compare the work done in moving a body up the inclined plane in Fig. M3.9 with the work done when the same body is raised up the vertical side.

Example

With reference to Fig. M3.9, angle $\theta = 30°$ and $W = 500$ N. Calculate:

(a)   the work done when raising the body up the inclined plane
(b)   the work done when raising the body through the same height vertically

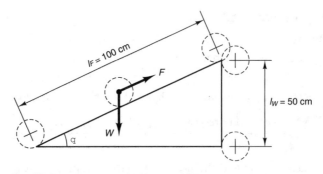

Fig. M3.9

Solution

(a)   First find the force F:

$F = W \sin \theta = 500 \text{ N} \times \sin 30° = 250 \text{ N}$

Next we find the work done raising the body 50 cm up the inclined plane:

work done $= F \times l_F = 250 \text{ N} \times 0.1 \text{ m} = \textbf{25 J}$

(b)   Now to raise the body vertically:

work done $= W \times l_W = 500 \text{ N} \times 0.05 \text{ m} = \textbf{25 J}$

So again, $F \times l_F = W \times l_W$

Sorry, there was no free lunch; you have to do as much work raising the body up the ramp as you do lifting it vertically. Use of a ramp (inclined plane) only reduces the force needed to raise the body.

 Activity M3.6

(a)   Calculate the effort force (F) required to move the body up the inclined plane using the data given in the Figure.

(b)   Calculate the work done in raising the body through the vertical height of 100 cm.

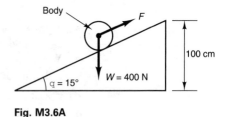

Fig. M3.6A

Now check your response

So we can use a ramp as a force magnifier when raising a heavy load. As on previous occasions, the greater the force magnification, the smaller the effort force (F) required to raise a given load. And the smaller the value of the effort force (F), the greater the distance it has to travel and the greater the time taken to raise the load (W) through a given height.

M4   Hydraulic equipment

Before commencing this section you should revise Section I7. By way of revision you should now complete Activity M4.1. Remember that Pascal's law states:

> **If a pressure is exerted on a liquid in a full, closed container, the pressure will disperse itself equally in all directions.**

The pressure will be exerted equally on all surfaces of the container.

 Activity M4.1

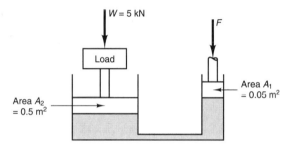

Fig. M4.1A

With reference to the figure:

(a) Calculate the magnitude of the effort force (F) required to raise the load of 5 kN.

(b) Calculate the distance through which the force (F) must travel to raise the load 0.4 m.

Now check your response

The response to Activity M4.1 shows that the movement ratio between the effort force and the load becomes excessive if we require a large force magnification. We can overcome this problem by using the effort force to operate a pump such as the hand-pump in Fig. M4.1, used to operate a simple upstroke hydraulic press.

There are two stages of magnification:

• The pump operating handle is a lever of the second order.
• The area of the ram of the press is very much greater than that of the pump ram.

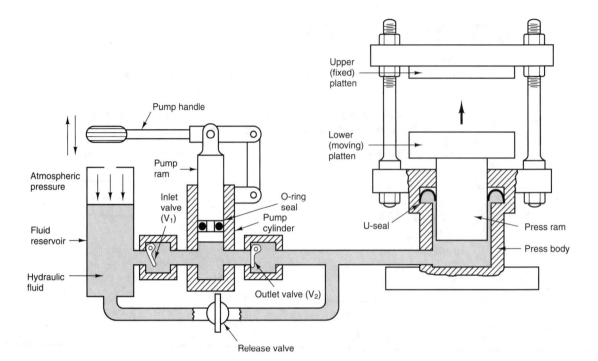

Fig. M4.1

Upstroke of the press ram

Let's now follow the sequence of events for raising the press ram.

- Close the release valve.
- Operate the pump handle.
- The pump ram is raised on the upstroke of the handle, creating a partial vacuum in the pump cylinder.
- Atmospheric pressure acting on the surface of the hydraulic fluid in the reservoir will cause the fluid to open valve V_1 and flow into the pump cylinder. The back pressure from the press will keep valve V_2 closed.
- On the downstroke of the pump handle, the pump ram will exert a force on the hydraulic fluid in the pump cylinder. This will cause the hydraulic fluid to exert pressure equally on valves V_1 and V_2 (Pascal's law).
- The pressure exerted by the fluid will close valve V_1 and open valve V_2. Hydraulic fluid will now be transferred from the pump cylinder into the press cylinder. This will raise the press ram by a small amount.
- This cycle of events is repeated. Each time the pump handle is raised, more fluid is drawn into the pump cylinder. Each time the pump handle is lowered, the press is raised by another small amount (increment). The valve V_2 prevents the press ram from falling back during the upstroke of the pump handle.
- Pumping is continued until sufficient hydraulic fluid has been transferred from the reservoir to the press cylinder to raise the press ram by the required amount.

Downstroke of the press ram

- Simply stop pumping and carefully open the release valve. The weight of the press ram and moving platten will force the hydraulic fluid back into the reservoir and the press will open.
- Open the release valve slowly. It controls the rate at which the press ram will fall. The ram should not be allowed to fall too quickly or damage may occur.
- The release valve must be closed before the press ram can be raised again.

The O-ring seal on the pump ram prevents the pressurised fluid from leaking past the pump ram. The inverted U-seal on the press ram prevents fluid escaping past the press ram. The greater the pressure acting on the seal, the more tightly it will press against the ram and the sides of the press body. If the area of the pump ram is 1/10 the area of the press ram, then the incremental rise of the press ram will be 1/10 the stroke of the pump ram (assuming no leakage and fluid loss). For example, if the stroke of the pump ram is 50 mm the incremental rise of the press ram will be (50 mm)/10 mm, which equals 5 mm per double stroke (once up and once down) of the pump. Therefore, to raise the press ram by 100 mm will take 20 double strokes of the pump (20 × 5 mm = 100 mm).

 Activity M4.2

The figure below shows the principles of a trolley jack of the type used in garages to raise vehicles for maintenance and repairs.

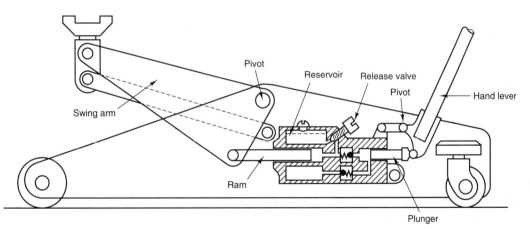

Fig. M4.2A

(a) Copy the figure into your notebook and indicate:

(i)   the pump inlet valve
(ii) the pump outlet valve.
(b) Describe how the jack works.
(c) State the order of the hand lever.
(d) State whether the hand lever is a force magnifier or a distance magnifier.
(e) State whether the swing-arm is a force magnifier or a distance magnifier.
(f) State the order of lever represented by the swing-arm.

Now check your response

That concludes Module M. Before proceeding, complete the following assignment and hand it to your tutor for assessment. Don't forget to put your name and assignment code on all your answer sheets.

Assignment for Module M

1 The clamp shown in Fig. MA.1 is a lever of
(a) the first order
(b) the second order
(c) the third order
(d) no order

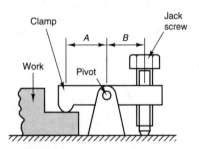

Fig. MA.1

2 With reference to Fig. MA.1, efficient clamping of the work requires that
(a) A is greater than B ($A > B$)
(b) A equals B ($A = B$)
(c) A is less than B ($A < B$)
(d) any of the above is satisfied – they are equally effective

3 In Fig. MA.1, force magnification is provided by
(a) the lever action of the clamp only
(b) the screw-jack only
(c) the clamp and the screw-jack together
(d) a compound lever

4 In Fig. MA.1 $A = 50$ mm, $B = 75$ mm and the jack screw exerts a force of 900 N. The clamping force is
(a) 600 N
(b) 1350 N
(c) 1500 N
(d) 2250 N

5 Which of the tools shown in Fig. MA.2 is not solely dependent on the lever principle for its force magnification.

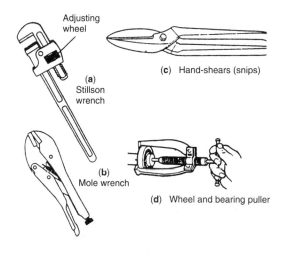

(a) Stillson wrench

(b) Mole wrench

(c) Hand-shears (snips)

(d) Wheel and bearing puller

Fig. MA.2

6 A simple winch has a drum diameter of 400 mm and a handle radius of 800 mm. To raise a load of 1.2 kN the effort force is
(a) 0.3 kN
(b) 0.6 kN
(c) 9.6 kN
(d) 480 kN

7 A geared winch has a drum diameter of 300 mm, a handle radius of 300 mm, a driver gear with 50 teeth and a driven gear with 150 teeth. An effort force of 500 N will raise a load of
(a) 750 N
(b) 1000 N
(c) 1500 N
(d) 3000 N

8 Table MA.1, taken from a manufacturer's catalogue, shows the number of pulleys in sets of pulley block sheaves. Which combination is incorrect?

Table MA.1

Set	Upper sheath	Lower sheath
(a)	2	3
(b)	3	2
(c)	3	4
(d)	3	5

9 A set of pulley blocks has three pulleys in the upper sheave and two pulleys in the lower sheave. The number of falls of rope is
(a) 2
(b) 3
(c) 5
(d) 6

10 A pulley block has two pulleys in both the upper and lower sheaves. To raise a load of 800 N the effort force is
(a) 200 N
(b) 400 N
(c) 1600 N
(d) 3200 N

11 A set of Weston differential pulley blocks has a large pulley 400 mm diameter and a small pulley 300 mm diameter. To raise a load of 2 kN requires an effort force of
(a) 250 N
(b) 333 N
(c) 500 N
(d) 1750 N

12 A screw-jack has a screw with a 6 mm lead and a handle 600 mm long. To raise a load of 3 kN the effort force is
(a) 4.8 N
(b) 9.4 N
(c) 30 N
(d) 48 N

13 To move a 600 N load up a 30° inclined plane requires a force acting parallel to the inclined plane of
(a) 20 N
(b) 300 N
(c) 346 N
(d) 519 N

14 A pulley block has three pulleys in both sheaves. To raise the load 2 m, the tail rope will have to be pulled through the tackle by
(a) 2 m
(b) 6 m
(c) 12 m
(d) 18 m

15 Figure MA.3 shows a hydraulic bottle-jack. Briefly describe how the jack works, paying particular attention to how force magnification is achieved.

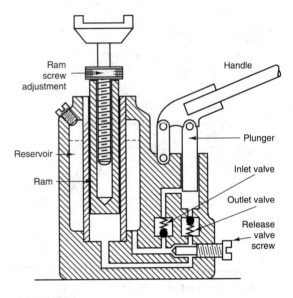

Fig. MA.3

N1 Tension in materials

Figure N1.1 shows a load suspended from a fixed beam by a metal hook. The load is trying to stretch the hook; therefore the hook is in a state of **tension**. The load is applying a **tensile** force to the hook. Any force that is stretching or trying to stretch a component is said to be a **tensile** force, regardless of its direction.

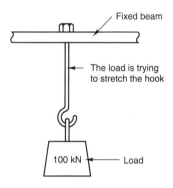

Fig. N1.1

Engineers need to know:

- How easily a material stretches.
- How far it can stretch yet spring back to its original size and shape when the deforming force is removed.
- The maximum tensile load a material can withstand without breaking and with what margin of safety.
- The tensile load at which a sample of the material breaks.

This information can be found by carrying out a tensile test on a specimen of the material. We will now consider how a tensile test is carried out and how to interpret the results.

N2 Tensile test

Tensile tests are performed using a universal testing machine. This machine can apply controlled tensile, compression and shear loads to appropriate specimens and also measure and record the behaviour of the specimens under load conditions.

Figure N2.1 shows a standard tensile test specimen. It is proportioned so that it will stretch and eventually fracture within its marked gauge length. The thickened ends are gripped in the jaws of the testing machine. The gauge length and diameter of the test piece should be measured accurately before testing begins.

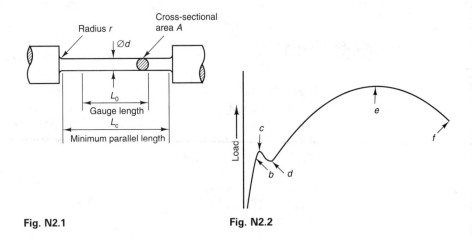

Fig. N2.1   **Fig. N2.2**

The tensile force is applied gradually to the specimen. For each incremental increase in tensile force, the correponding increase in length is measured and recorded. The force is gradually increased until the specimen eventually breaks. The corresponding measurements of force and extension are recorded on a graph as shown in Fig. N2.2. Most modern machines do this automatically as the test proceeds. Let's now examine the load–extension graph shown in Fig. N2.2 in greater detail. This graph is typical of annealed (softened) low carbon steels.

Elastic zone

- From a to b extension is proportional to load and the graph is a straight line.
- The straight line relationship finishes at point b. The material has reached its **limit of proportionality**. All components made from this

material must be designed so that the conditions at *b* are never exceeded in service.

- From *a* to *c* the material behaves in an elastic manner. Any extension of the material produced by the tensile load is lost when the load is removed. The specimen returns to its original length.
- The **elastic limit** is reached at point *c*. Any further increase in the tensile load will result in permanent distortion of the specimen. It will no longer show elastic properties.

Ductile zone

- The material suddenly gives way at point *d* and the specimen stretches without any increase in load.
- The material recovers and the load can again be increased until the point *e* is reached. From *d* to *e* the specimen stretches very much more rapidly for each incremental increase in load. And, if the load were removed, the specimen would not return to its original length. The material has taken a permanent set. It has been permanently deformed by a tensile load. It has shown the property of **ductility**.
- From point *e* the specimen commences to thin down at some local point within the gauge length. This is called necking. The reduction in cross-section prevents the specimen from supporting the load; further extension occurs even though the load has to be reduced. Eventually the specimen fractures (breaks) at point *g*. The test is complete.

N3 Elongation

The elongation of the specimen is an indication of the ductility of the material from which it was made. The ductility of a material is its ability to be stretched into a shape or to be drawn out into a wire. Copper has a high ductility and a copper specimen would show a high elongation value. Figure N3.1 shows a specimen before and after testing. The two pieces of the fractured specimen have been placed together to measure the final length.

Using the information given in Fig. N3.1 we can express elongation as a percentage:

$$\text{percentage elongation} = \frac{\text{increase in length} \times 100}{\text{original length}}$$

$$= \frac{(L_U - L_0) \times 100}{L_0}$$

where: L_0 = gauge length before testing
         L_U = gauge length after testing

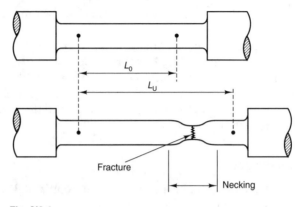

Fig. N3.1

Activity N3.1

Calculate the percentage elongation for a brass specimen if its original gauge length was 56 mm and its length at fracture is 95.2 mm.

Now check your response

| N4 | Reduction of cross-sectional area |

The percentage reduction of cross-sectional area of a specimen is also an indication of ductility. To find the original and final areas requires accurate measurements of the specimen diameter before and after testing. The original diameter of the specimen should be measured with a micrometer calliper within the gauge length. The final diameter is measured across the necked portion of the specimen at the point of fracture. This is awkward to measure and a vernier caliper may be found more convenient than a micrometer.

$$\text{percentage reduction of area } (\psi) = \frac{\text{reduction of area} \times 100}{\text{original area}}$$

$$= \frac{(A_0 - A_U) \times 100}{A_0}$$

where: A_0 = cross-sectional area within gauge length before testing
         A_U = cross-sectional area at point of fracture
         (ψ is the Greek letter psi)

Remember:

$$\text{area} = \frac{\pi D^2}{4}$$

Activity N4.1

Calculate the percentage reduction in area for a specimen if the original diameter was 10 mm and the final diameter at point of fracture is 8.5 mm.

Now check your response

N5   Tensile stress

When a tensile force is applied to a specimen, it distributes itself uniformly over the entire cross-section of the material. We give this load (force) per unit area a special name; we call it **stress**. Stress is denoted by lower case Greek sigma (σ); tensile stress is indicated by a subscript letter t:

$$\text{tensile stress } (\sigma_t) = \frac{\text{tensile force } (F_t)}{\text{original cross-sectional area } (A_0)}$$

Have you noted the similarity between the calculation of stress in a solid and pressure in a fluid? We give both of them the same unit, the **pascal**. (1 Pa = 1 N/m²). Most engineering materials are so strong that we work mainly in megapascals (MPa).

Activity N5.1

Calculate the stress in a 25 mm diameter steel rod when it is subjected to a tensile force (pull) of 35.7 kN. Express your answer in MPa. Remember that 1 MPa = 1 N/mm².

Now check your response

Figure N2.3 showed a load–extension curve for a low carbon (mild) steel. Such a curve is of limited use because it refers to only one size of specimen. It is much more usual and much more useful to plot stress against strain. The stress axis replaces the load axis and the strain axis replaces the extension axis. We have just seen how to calculate stress. Now let's see how we calculate strain:

$$\text{strain} = \frac{\text{extension}}{\text{original length}}$$

It is a ratio so there are no units. Note how the calculation of strain is similar to the calculation of percentage elongation except that we do not express it as a percentage. Both stress and strain are calculated for each increase in load on the specimen in a tensile test and they are plotted as shown in Fig. N5.1

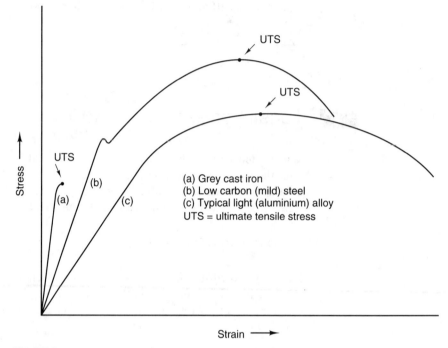

Fig. N5.1

Let's now consider the curves shown in Fig. N5.1 in some detail.

Cast iron

- Cast iron has the most upright elastic zone for the three metals shown, indicating that it is the most rigid of them.

- Cast iron fractures with negligible ductile distortion or thinning. It is a brittle metal. It also shows a low value of ultimate tensile strength (UTS). It is weak in tension. Although not shown from these results, it is as strong as steel in compression. Its rigidity and strength in compression make cast iron a good material for machine-tool beds.

Low carbon (mild) steel
- This curve has been fully described in Section N2.
- The elastic zone for low carbon steel is less upright than for cast iron therefore low carbon steel is less rigid than cast iron; it has more give.
- Low carbon steel has an appreciable ductile zone. It can be drawn into rods and wires, bent into complicated shapes or formed into car body panels. This is indicated by the long curved part of the graph.

- Low carbon steel is much stronger in tension than cast iron. This is shown by its higher value of ultimate tensile stress (UTS) – the highest value of tensile stress recorded for the steel during its tensile test.

Light alloy

- This curve is typical of many metals, especially the ductile non-ferrous metals. It does not show a distinct yield point and it is difficult to determine the elastic limit precisely.
- It has the least upright elastic zone and is therefore the least rigid of the three metals shown.
- It is the most ductile of the metals shown because it has the longest curved zone.
- It has a lower ultimate tensile stress than low carbon steel and is therefore weaker than low carbon steel.

 Activity N5.2

The figure shows the tensile test curves for two different types of steel. Copy it into your notebook and answer the following questions:

(a)   Which steel is the more ductile?
(b)   Which steel is the more rigid?
(c)   Which steel has the higher elastic limit?
(d)   Which steel has the lower UTS?
(e)   Which steel is the stronger?

In each case give the reason for your answer.

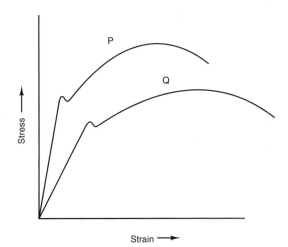

Fig. N5.2A

Now check your response

N6 # Factor of safety

The working tensile stress must never exceed the **limit of proportionality** under any service conditions. The safe working tensile stress is usually taken as 50% of the stress at the limit of proportionality. It is determined by dividing the ultimate tensile stress for a given material by the factor of safety set by the designer for a specific job. This can be expressed mathematically as:

$$\text{safe working stress } (\bar{\sigma}_t) = \frac{\text{ultimate tensile stress } (\sigma_{t,\,max})}{\text{safety factor } (s)}$$

 Activity N6.1

With reference to the tensile test curve shown in the figure:

(a) Calculate the safe working stress for the steel if the factor of safety is 3.2. (Estimate the UTS from the figure to the nearest 100 MPa.)

(b) How does your calculated safe working tensile stress relate to the limit of proportionality for this steel?

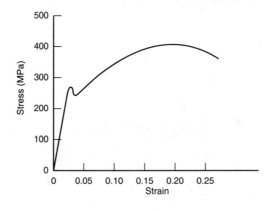

Fig. N6.1

Now check your response

N7 Compression

Figure N7.1 shows a piece of soft metal, such as lead, being squeezed in a vice. The piece of lead is reduced in length but increases in cross-sectional area. There is no change in volume. The piece of lead is being subjected to **compressive** forces; it is in **compression**.

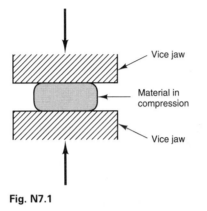

Fig. N7.1

Most materials are equally strong in tension and compression. Two notable exceptions are cast iron and concrete. They are very strong in compression but very weak in tension.

 Activity N7.1

With reference to the figure, state whether items 1 to 3 are in tension or compression and give reasons for your choice.

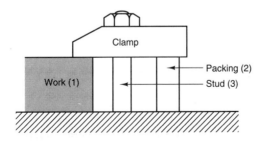

Fig. N7.1A

Now check your response

The formulae for materials in compression are similar to the formulae for materials in tension, except the compressive force (F_C) is trying to shorten (squash) the material. Here are some of the formulae you should remember:

- compressive stress (σ_C) $= \dfrac{F_C}{A}$

- ultimate compressive stress ($\sigma_{C,\,max}$) $= \dfrac{F_{C,\,max}}{A_0}$

- safe working compressive stress ($\bar{\sigma}_C$) $= \dfrac{\sigma_{C,\,max}}{s}$

where:

F_C = compressive force
A = cross-sectional area
$F_{C,\,max}$ = maximum compressive force achieved during a compressive test on the material
A_0 = initial cross-sectional area of specimen
s = safety factor

Note that brittle materials such as cast iron and concrete will eventually fracture if the compressive force becomes sufficiently great. However, most ductile materials are also malleable and may be squashed flat without fracturing.

 Activity N7.2

The ultimate compressive stress for a material is 400 MPa.

(a) Calculate the safe working compressive stress if the factor of safety is 4.
(b) Calculate the safe working compressive load (F_C) if the cross-sectional area (A) of the material is 5420 mm^2.

Now check your response

N8 Shear

Tensile or compressive forces act in line with each other, but shear forces are **offset**. The difference between tension, compression and shear is shown in Fig. N8.1

Shear testing can be performed on a tensile testing machine using special jaws as shown in Fig. N8.2. In this arrangement the specimen is in double shear, that is, the shear force (F_S) acts on both the shear planes at the same time.

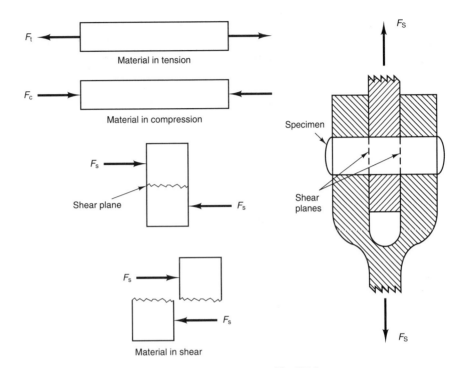

Fig. N8.1

Fig. N8.2

$$\text{shear stress } (\tau) = \frac{F_S}{A}$$

where: F_S = shear force
A = area in shear
(τ is the Greek letter tau)

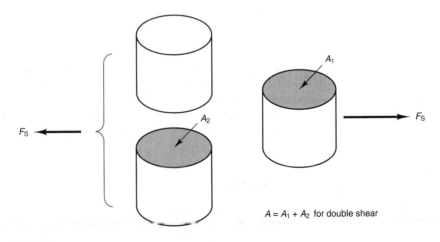

$A = A_1 + A_2$ for double shear

Fig. N8.3

The shear force is increased slowly until the specimen breaks. The specimen is in double shear for this test, so the combined areas of the shear planes have to be used as shown in Fig. N8.3

Figure N8.4 shows a rivet in single shear. Riveted joints should always be designed so that the rivet is in shear. Rivet heads are only intended to keep the rivets in place. The heads should not have to take the major load on the rivet. Because the rivet is in single shear, the area in shear is just the cross-sectional area of the rivet.

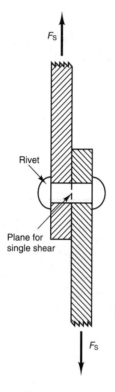

Fig. N8.4

Components must not normally fail in shear, except where a shear-pin is used as a safety device to prevent a mechanism being overloaded. To ensure that shear does not occur, the safe working shear stress is taken as between 0.5 and 0.8 times the safe working tensile stress. This value must never be exceeded under normal service conditions.

 ## Activity N8.1

(a) Calculate the shear stress for a 12 mm diameter rivet in single shear if the shear force (F_S) is 11.3 kN.

(b) Calculate the safe working shear stress for a material given:

UTS for material   = 400 MPa

factor of safety (tensile) = 4

factor of safety (shear) = 0.5

Now check your response

Sometimes we want the material to fail in shear, for example, when cutting sheet metal and plate in a shearing machine as shown in Fig. N8.5.

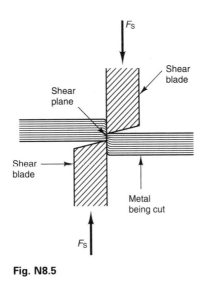

Fig. N8.5

Shaped components can be cut out by using a blanking tool such as shown in Fig. N8.6(a). The blanking tool is mounted in a press which exerts a force on the tool. This force drives the punch through the metal to be cut into a die. In this example the tool will stamp out circular blanks as shown in Fig. N8.6(b). The area in shear is equal to the circumference of the blank times its thickness. Let's now look at an example based on the dimensions given in Fig. N8.6(b).

Example

Calculate the blanking (shear) force required to produce a circular blank from the tools shown in Fig. N8.6 if the material has an ultimate shear stress value of 450 MPa. Take $\pi = 3.14$.

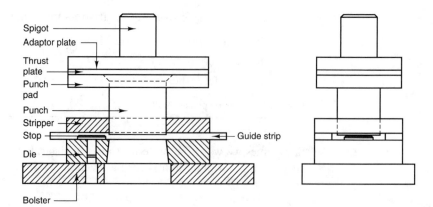

Spigot
Adaptor plate
Thrust plate
Punch pad
Punch
Stripper
Stop
Die
Bolster

Guide strip

(a) Blanking tool

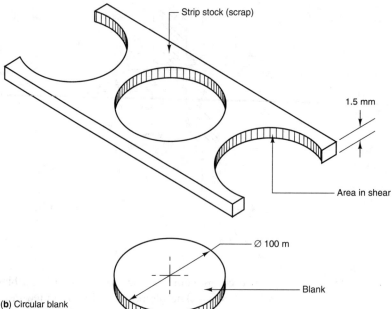

Strip stock (scrap)

1.5 mm

Area in shear

Ø 100 m

Blank

(b) Circular blank
produced by tool (a)

Fig. N8.6

Solution

$$\begin{aligned}
\text{area in shear} &= \text{circumference of blank} \times \text{thickness of metal} \\
&= \pi D \times \text{thickness} \\
&= 3.14 \times 100 \text{ mm} \times 1.5 \text{ mm} \\
&= 471 \text{ mm}^2
\end{aligned}$$

$$\text{blanking force} = \text{area in shear} \times \text{ultimate shear stress}$$
$$= 471 \text{ mm}^2 \times 450 \text{ N/mm}^2$$
$$= \mathbf{212\ kN} \text{ (3 s.f.)}$$

Remember that $450 \text{ MPa} = 450 \text{ N/mm}^2$

 Activity N8.2

Calculate the blanking force required to cut (shear) a square blank from 2 mm thick material, given:

side length of square = 50 mm

ultimate shear stress of material = 300 MPa

Now check your response

That concludes Module N. Now complete the final assignment and hand it to your tutor for assesment. Don't forget to put your name and the assignment code on each of your answer sheets.

Assignment for Module N

1 In Fig. NA.1 the load places the draw-bar in a state of
(a) compression
(b) tension
(c) shear
(d) torsion

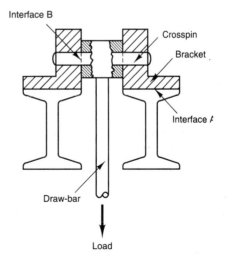

Fig. NA 1

2 In Fig. NA.1 the metal at interface A is in a state of
(a) compression
(b) tension
(c) shear
(d) torsion

3 In Fig. NA.1 the metal at interface B is in a state of
(a) compression
(b) tension
(c) shear
(d) torsion

4 In Fig. NA.2 the limit of proportionality is at the point
(a) *a*
(b) *b*
(c) *c*
(d) *d*

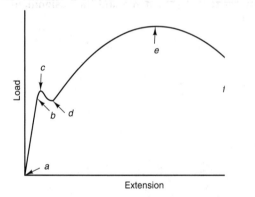

Fig. NA.2

5 In Fig. NA.2 the material behaves in an elastic manner between points
(a) *a* and *c*
(b) *c* and *d*
(c) *d* and *e*
(d) *e* and *f*

6 In Fig. NA.2 the yield point is
(a) *b*
(b) *c*
(c) *d*
(d) *f*

7 In Fig. NA.2 the ultimate tensile stress for the material occurs at the point
(a) *c*
(b) *d*
(c) *e*
(d) *f*

8 In Fig. NA.3 the most rigid material is represented by curve
(a) A
(b) B
(c) C
(d) D

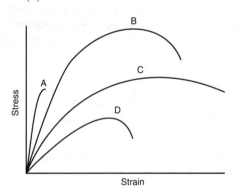

Fig. NA.3

9 In Fig. NA.3 the most ductile material is represented by curve
(a) A
(b) B
(c) C
(d) D

10 In Fig. NA.3 the most elastic material is represented by curve
(a) A
(b) B
(c) C
(d) D

11 In Fig. NA.3 the material with the lowest UTS
is represented by curve

(a) A

(b) B

(c) C

(d) D

12 A tensile test specimen, gauge length 50
mm, measures 80.2 mm at fracture. Its
elongation is

(a) 16.04%

(b) 37.75%

(c) 60.40%

(d) 80.02%

13 A tensile test specimen, initial diameter
10 mm, has diameter 9.1 mm at the point of
fracture. The reduction in area is

(a) 13.5%

(b) 17.2%

(c) 17.9%

(d) 20.8%

14 A metal rod of 20 mm² cross-sectional area
is subjected to a tensile force of 14 kN. The
stress in the rod is

(a) 0.7 N/mm^2

(b) 314 N/mm^2

(c) 700 N/mm^2

(d) 700 kN/mm^2

15 A stress of 17 N/mm² is equivalent to

(a) 17 Pa

(b) 17 kPa

(c) 17 MPa

(d) 17 GPa

16 The safe working tensile stress is given by
the expression

(a) (yield stress)/(safety factor)

(b) (UTS)/(safety factor)

(c) (safety factor)/(elastic limit)

(d) (safety factor)/(UTS)

17 A metal blank of 300 mm circumference is
stamped from metal 1.2 mm thick. If the
ultimate shear stress of the metal is 350
MPa, the blanking force is

(a) 102 kN

(b) 126 kN

(c) 360 kN

(d) 972 kN

18 Given that the UTS for a material is 500
MPa, its tensile factor of safety is 4, and its
shear factor of safety is 0.6, then its safe
working shear stress is

(a) 75 MPa

(b) 125 MPa

(c) 208 MPa

(d) 300 MPa

Responses

Response A1.1
- Your response to Activity A1.1 is correct if you wrote down any number from the list 1, 2, 3, 4, 5, 6, 7, 8, 9.
- I have written down the number 5. Standing alone it does not tell us very much. We need more information.
- For example, if I said that my office is 5 metres long, the number 5 takes on a whole new significance. It is now part of a complete statement. This complete statement consists of:

a quantity	in this case length
a unit	in this case the metre
a size (magnitude)	in this case number 5

- Therefore the length (l) of my office = 5 metres.

  Expressed in symbols: $l = 5$ m

- Have you noticed that I have used an italic (sloping) letter to represent the quantity (l) and a roman (upright) letter for the unit (m)? This is normal practice and will be referred to in more detail later.

Now return to the text

Response A2.1
At the time of publication, a first-class stamp costs 25p and the maximum mass that can be sent under a first class stamp by letter post is 60 grams. You are asked to give your answer in kilograms, therefore your response should read:

(a) The maximum mass of a letter that can sent under a first class stamp is **0.06** kilogram (kg).

Planet Earth rotates about its axis once every 24 hours. This is the same as 24 × 60 minutes or 24 × 60 × 60 seconds. Since you have to give your answer in seconds, your response should read:

(b) The time taken for the Earth to rotate once is 24 × 60 × 60 = **86400** seconds (s)

Looking up the pitch of an ISO M10 fine series thread in a set of workshop tables, I find that the pitch is 1.5 millimetres. The activity asks you to express the pitch in metres, so your response should read:

(c) The pitch of an ISO M10 fine series thread is **0.0015** metre (m).

Remember: 1000 grams (g)   = 1 kilogram (kg)

1000 millimetres (mm) = 1 metre (m)

60 minutes (min)   = 1 hour (h)

3600 seconds (s)   = 1 hour (h)

60 seconds (s)   = 1 minute (min)

Now return to the text

Response A3.1   Your answers to the calculations should read as follows:

(a)   14 km   = 14 × 1000 m   = **14 000 m**
(b)   14.3 km = 14.3 × 1000 m = **14 300 m**
(c)   25 kg   = 25 × 1000 g   = **25 000 g**
(d)   12 da g = 12 × 10 da g   = **120 g**
(e)   1.75 hm = 1.75 × 100 m   = **175 m**
(f)   12 t   = 12 × 1000 kg   = **12 000 kg**
(g)   3 Mt   = 3 × 1 000 000 t = **3 000 000 t**
(h)   0.5 Mt = 0.5 × 1 000 000 t
              = 0.5 × 1 000 000 × 1000 kg
              = **500 000 000 kg**

There are two most likely sources of error in this activity:

• The position of the decimal point when writing the answers out in full.
• Writing down the wrong number of place-holding zeros.

It is easier to use **standard form**. The answer to (h) in standard form becomes:

500 000 000 kg = **5 × 10⁸ kg**

Standard form will now be considered in the text.

Now return to the text

Response A3.2   Your response should read as follows:

(a)   14 000 m = 1.4 × 10 000 m   = **1.4 × 10⁴ m**
(b)   14 300 m = 1.43 × 10 000 m   = **1.43 × 10⁴ m**
(c)   25 000 g = 2.5 × 10 000 g   = **2.5 × 10⁴ g**
(d)   120 g   = 1.2 × 100 g   = **1.2 × 10² g**
(e)   175 m   = 1.75 × 100 m   = **1.75 × 10² m**
(f)   12 t   = 1.2 × 10 000 kg   = **1.2 × 10⁴ kg**
(g)   3 Mt   = 3 × 1 000 000 t   = **3 × 10⁶ t**
(h)   0.5 Mt   = 5 × 100 000 000 kg = **5 × 10⁸ kg**

If you had any difficulty with this activity, I hope that my solutions have helped you. Remember, if you are really stuck, consult your tutor. Never move on until you are satisfied that you understand the current section. Well done if you have been successful so far.

Now return to the text

Response A3.3 (a) Your response to this first part of the activity should read as follows:

    (i)   Express 1 450 000 grams in kilograms.

         1 450 000 g = 1 450 000/1000   = **1450 kg**

    (ii)   27 000 g   = 27 000/1000   = **27 kg**

    (iii) 3 000 000 g = 3 000 000/1 000 000 = **3 kg**

    (iv) 2.5 m   = 2.5/10   = **0.25 da m**

    (v)   75 hm   = 75/10   = **7.5 km**

    (vi) 2.7×10^5 m = 270 000/1000   = **270 km**

(b) Now let's consider the second part of the activity. You are asked to convert the answers in part (a) into standard form where **appropriate**. Although there is no technical reason why you cannot state: 27 kg = 2.7×10^1 kg or 3 kg = 3×10^0 kg, it would not be considered normal or correct practice. We only use standard form when the multiplying factor is $\times 10^2$ or larger, or $\times 10^{-2}$ or smaller. Using these criteria, we only have to convert (i) and (vi) from part (a) into standard form.

    (i)   1450 kg = 1.45 × 1000 = **1.45×10^3 kg**

    (ii)   270 km = 2.7 × 100   = **2.7×10^2 km**

That was a bit tricky, but I wanted to emphasise the need to be selective when deciding whether or not to use standard form.

Now return to the text

Response A4.1 (a) In this part of the activity I have shown alternative methods for each calculation. Your response is correct if you have used either method.

    (i)   15 mm = 15 × 0.001   = **0.015 m**

                     = 15/1000   = **0.015 m**

    (ii)   5.7 mm = 5.7 × 0.001   = **0.0057 m**

                    = 5.7/1000   = **0.0057 m**

    (iii) 5.0 μs = 5.0 × 0.000 001   = **0.000 005 s**

                    = 5.0/1 000 000   = **0.000 005 s**

    (iv) 1.7 ns = 1.7 × 0.000 000 001 = **0.000 000 0017 s**

                    = 1.7/1 000 000 000 = **0.000 000 0017 s**

I hope that you are remembering to put the unit or unit symbol after the number. Remember that a physical quantity is a number times a unit. If you omit the unit then the statement is incomplete. In an examination, such a satement would be marked as wrong.

(b) Your response to the second part of this Activity should read as follows.

    (i)   0.015 m   = 1.5/100   = **1.5×10^{-2} m**

    (ii)   0.0057 m   = 5.7/1000   = **5.7×10^{-3} m**

    (iii) 0.000 005 s   = 5.0/1 000 000   = **5.0×10^{-6} m**

    (iv) 0.000 000 0017 s = 1.7/1 000 000 000 = **1.7×10^{-9} m**

Well done if you got these correct, it is very easy to lose track of the zeros. If you had any difficulties, I hope my solutions have helped you.

Now return to the text

Response A4.2   Your response should read as follows:

(a) 0.0012 m $= 0.0012 \times 1000$ $= \textbf{1.2 mm}$
(b) 0.017 m $= 0.017 \times 1000$ $= \textbf{17 mm}$
(c) 1.57×10^{-2} m $= 1.57 \times 10^{-2} \times 10^3$ $= 1.57 \times 10^1$ mm $= \textbf{15.7 mm}$
(d) 0.000 08 s $= 0.000\,08 \times 1\,000\,000 = \textbf{80 } \mu\textbf{s}$
(e) 9.4×10^{-8} s $= 9.4 \times 10^{-8} \times 10^9$ $= 9.4 \times 10^1$ mm $= \textbf{94 ns}$

Two of these were particularly tricky. In both (c) and (e) you had to remember to **add** the powers of 10 in order to **multiply**. (I hope you did not rely on your calculator to sort it out for you.) I will run through (e) once more for you:

$$10^9 \times 10^{-8} = 10^{9+(-8)} = 10^{9-8} = 10^1 = 10$$

Remember that any number raised to the power of 1 is itself: $5^1 = 5$, $6^1 = 6$, etc. Also, any number raised to the power of 0 is one: $5^0 = 1$, $6^0 = 1$, etc.
Finally, any number raised to a negative power becomes the reciprocal of that number:

$$10^6 \times 10^{-8} = 10^{6+(-8)} = 10^{6-8} = 10^{-2} = \frac{1}{10^2} = \frac{1}{100}$$

In the previous activities I have used multiples and submultiples such as deci-, centi-, deca-, and hecto-. In engineering and technology, they are rarely used in practice. The preferred multiples and submultiples move up in steps of 10^3 or down in steps of 10^{-3}. For example:

micrometre (μm) $= 10^{-6}$ m

millimetre $= 10^{-3}$ m

metre $=$ base unit

kilometre $= 10^3$ m

That completes the base units for the time being. We are now going to consider the derived units.

Now return to the text

Response A5.1   Your completed table should read as follows.

Table A5.1R

Length	Width (breadth)	Area	Calculation
5 m	4 m	**20 m^2**	5 m $\times$ 4 m $=$ 20 m^2
3 m	2 m	**6 m^2**	3 m $\times$ 2 m $=$ 6 m^2
12 m	**3 m**	36 m^2	(36 m^2)/(12 m) $=$ 3 m
50 mm	5 mm	**250 mm^2**	50 mm $\times$ 5 mm $=$ 250 mm^2
15 mm	**3 mm**	45 mm^2	(45 mm^2)/(15 mm) $=$ 3 mm
10 km	2 km	**20 km^2**	10 km $\times$ 2 km $=$ 20 km^2
40 km	20 km	800 km^2	(800 km^2)/(20 m) $=$ 40 km
100 m	2 km	**200 000 m^2**	100 m $\times$ 2000 m $=$ 200 000 m^2
300 mm	0.5 m	**150 000 mm^2**	300 mm $\times$ 500 mm $=$ 150 000 mm^2

(continued overleaf)

Table A5.1R (*continued*)

Diameter	Area
5 m	$A = \dfrac{1}{4}(\pi D^2) = \dfrac{1}{4}(\pi \times 5^2) = \dfrac{1}{4}(\pi \times 25) = \mathbf{19.6\ m^2}$
8 m	$A = \dfrac{1}{4}(\pi D^2) = \dfrac{1}{4}(\pi \times 8^2) = \dfrac{1}{4}(\pi \times 64) = \mathbf{50.3\ m^2}$
7 km	$A = \dfrac{1}{4}(\pi D^2) = \dfrac{1}{4}(\pi \times 7^2) = \dfrac{1}{4}(\pi \times 49) = \mathbf{38.5\ km^2}$
40 mm	$A = \dfrac{1}{4}(\pi D^2) = \dfrac{1}{4}(\pi \times 40^2) = \dfrac{1}{4}(\pi \times 1600) = \mathbf{1256.7\ mm^2}$

The answers to the circular areas are given correct to one decimal place (1 d.p.).

I hope you noticed that the last two calculations in the first batch had mixed units. Before calculating the area you should have converted them to common units. I chose metres and millimetres as shown in the table. You may have chosen kilometres and metres. If you did, your answers should read 0.2 km² and 0.15 m² respectively.

Now return to the text

Response A5.2

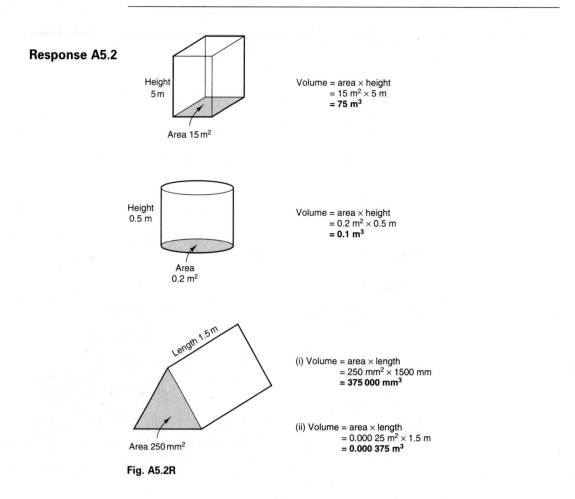

Volume = area × height
= 15 m² × 5 m
= **75 m³**

Volume = area × height
= 0.2 m² × 0.5 m
= **0.1 m³**

(i) Volume = area × length
= 250 mm² × 1500 mm
= **375 000 mm³**

(ii) Volume = area × length
= 0.000 25 m² × 1.5 m
= **0.000 375 m³**

Fig. A5.2R

I hope you noticed that the dimensions in (c) had mixed units. This is why I have given you two answers, one in mm³ and one in m³.

Remember $1 \text{ m}^2 = 1\,000\,000 \text{ mm}^2 \quad = 1 \times 10^6 \text{ mm}^2$

$1 \text{ m}^3 = 1\,000\,000\,000 \text{ mm}^3 = 1 \times 10^9 \text{ mm}^3$

Now return to the text

Response A5.3

The answers to your calculations should read as follows:

(a) speed = distance/time = (80 km)/(2 h) = **40 km/h** or **40 km h⁻¹**
(b) speed = distance/time = (80 mm)/(5 s) = **16 mm/s** or **16 mm s⁻¹**
(c) time = distance/speed = (90 m)/(45 m/s) = **2 s**
(d) distance = speed × time = 45 km/h × 4.5 h = **202.5 km**

Did you manage to rearrange the relationship between speed, distance and time correctly? I hope so, but if not, perhaps my solutions have helped you.

Now return to the text

Response A5.4

Remember the rules:

• Quantity symbols (variables) are in italics (sloping) letters. All other letters and numbers are in roman (upright) characters.
• Rules for units based on the names of famous people:
  (i) Units written in full use lower case (small) initial letters.
  (ii) Unit symbols use upper case (capital) letters (e.g. N) or a capital letter followed by a small letter (e.g. Pa).
  (iii) Names of persons associated with units use a capital initial letter as in normal writing (e.g. James Watt).

I will now show you how the sentences should have been written using these rules.

(a) The unit of force (F) is called the newton (N) in honour of the famous British scientist Sir Isaac Newton.
(b) The unit of energy (Q) is called a joule (J) in honour of the British scientist James Joule.
(c) The unit of electrical resistance (R) is called an ohm (Ω) in honour of the German scientist Georg Simon Ohm.
(d) The unit of electrical potential (U) is called a volt (V) in honour of the Italian scientist Alessandro Volta.
(e) The unit of electric current (I) is called an ampere (A) in honour of André-Marie Ampère, the French physicist.

I hope you now understand when to use capital and small letters and when to use italic and roman characters when writing out the units and physical quantities.

Now return to the text

Response A6.1

• The correct answer is **yes**.
• Mass is the quantity of matter in an object.

- The quantity of matter in an object is the same when it is on planet Earth or when it is on the Moon.
- The object and the known masses will still be made of the same number of atoms having the same mass whether they are on the Earth or on the Moon.
- The reason why things **weigh** less on the Moon will be considered in Section C4.

Now return to the text

Response B1.1   Your sentences should have been completed as follows:

(a) The number of electrons in an atom **equals** the number of protons in the **nucleus** of the atom.
(b) There is **no** relationship between the number of electrons and the number of neutrons in an atom.
(c) **Electrons** orbit around the nucleus of an atom.
(d) The nucleus of an atom can contain either **protons** alone or both **protons** and **neutrons**.
(e) Of the atoms shown in Fig, B1.4, the atoms of **beryllium** has the greatest mass.

I hope you got these correct. If not, I hope my response has helped you. If you have any outstanding queries, clear them up with your tutor before moving on. It is important that you thoroughly understand this groundwork.

Now return to the text

Response B1.2   Your completed sentences should read as follows:

(a) Electrons have **negative** charges.
(b) Protons have **positive** charges.
(c) Electrostatically charged particles are only attracted together if they have **unlike** charges.
(d) Neutrons have virtually the same mass as **protons** but carry **no** charge.
(e) Electrons are held in their orbits by **electrostatic** forces.
(f) The mass of an atom is said to be the sum of the masses of the **protons** and **neutrons** in the atom.
(g) Atoms which have gained or lost one or more electrons are called **ions**.
(h) An atom is said to be **isotopic** if its mass changes but its chemical properties remain **unchanged**.
(i) Protons and neutrons are only found in the **nucleus** of an atom.

Again you must make sure you understand this essential groundwork before moving on.

Now return to the text

Response B2.1   Given $^{56}_{26}$Fe is an iron atom.

(a) The relative atomic mass for iron is **56**. The relative atomic mass is always the larger of the two numbers.
(b) We now have to compare the relative atomic mass for iron (56) with the relative atomic mass for carbon-12 as this is our standard atom. As its name suggests, it has a relative atomic mass of 12. Therefore, by proportion:

the mass of an iron atom is $56/12 =$ **4.67** times greater than the mass of a standard carbon-12 atom.

(c) The atomic number for an iron atom is **26**. (The atomic number is the smaller of the two numbers.) If there are no neutrons present, the relative atomic mass and the atomic number will be the same.

(d) The atomic number is the number of electrons present in the atom. There are as many protons in an atom as there are electrons. Therefore the atomic number (Z) also indicates the number of protons present in the nucleus of the atom. For iron there are **26** protons in the nucleus.

(e) For electrical balance, there must always be as many negatively charged electrons orbiting the nucleus as there are positively charged protons in the nucleus. Therefore there are **26** electrons in an iron atom. If this balance is disturbed, the atom becomes an **ion**.

(f) If the relative atomic mass for iron is 56, yet there are only 26 protons present in the nucleus, the number of neutrons present must make up the difference. Therefore:

number of neutrons present = relative atomic mass − atomic number

$$= 56 - 26 = \textbf{30 neutrons}$$

Now return to the text

Response B3.1

Your completed statement should read as follows:

Molecules consist of groups of **atoms** bonded together in different ways by means of **electrostatic charges**. The molecules may consist of the **same** type of atoms or of different types of **atoms**. For example, a table salt (sodium chloride) molecule contains atoms of the elements **sodium** and **chlorine**. Very large molecules are called **macromolecules**. They are hard and brittle and consist of **large** numbers of **non-metallic** atoms. They have **high** melting and boiling temperatures. They **do not** conduct electricity.

Now return to the text

Response B4.1

(a) False The atoms of metallic substances do not form molecules with each other. They are grouped together in large, three-dimensional lattice structures.

(b) True Pure metals can be bent; they are ductile. (More about ductility in Module N.)

(c) True Pure metals are good conductors of electricity.

(d) True In losing electrons, which are negatively charged, the atom has a surplus of positively charged protons. It becomes a positively charged ion.

(e) False The 'layers' of metal ions can be displaced by sufficiently large, external, mechanical forces. However great the displacement the ionic bond is not destroyed until the metal fractures.

(f) True The forces between the ions and the free electrons are electrostatic. Remember that unlike forces attract each other, therefore the negative electrons and the positive ions are attracted together (see Fig. B4.2).

Response B5.1   Sodium chloride appears to be a compound for the following reasons.

(a)   Sodium chloride is the product of a chemical reaction. Sodium metal burns in chlorine gas giving out heat.

(b)   The substance produced by the reaction (sodium chloride) is quite unlike the elements from which it is made. Sodium chloride is common table salt. It is a white powder and can be safely used in the preparation of food, whereas sodium is a highly reactive metal and chlorine is a poisonous gas.

(c)   Sodium chloride can only be converted back into its constituent elements by complex chemical and electrochemical processes.

Well done if you got this correct. Sodium chloride not only appears to be a compound, it *is* a compound. I did not give you enough data to work out the proportions of sodium and chlorine present. As a matter of interest, I can tell you that, to the nearest whole number, in every 59 grams of table salt there is **always** 23 grams of sodium and 36 grams of chlorine. This constant proportion is yet another indication that sodium chloride is a compound.

Now return to the text

Response B5.2   The iron filings and sawdust can be separated quite simply as follows:

●   Wrap cling film round one end of a bar magnet or both legs of a horseshoe magnet.

●   Dip the magnet into the mixture.

●   The iron filings will be attracted to the magnet. The sawdust will not be attracted.

●   The purpose of the cling film is to make it easier to remove the iron filings from the magnet.

●   The iron filings and sawdust can be separated from each other by a simple physical operation. No chemical reactions are involved.

●   The filings and sawdust can be mixed in any proportions.

For all these reasons the iron filings and sawdust merely form a mixture, not a compound.

Now return to the text

Response B5.3   (a)   Your response to this first part of the activity is correct if you chose any five of the six differences listed below. The order is not important and I expect you will have used different wording. However, if the meaning is the same, well done.

(i)   When two or more substances react together to form a compound, heat is taken in or given out. When two or more substances form a mixture, no heat is involved.

(ii)   When two or more substances form a compound, an entirely new substance is formed. When two or more substances form a mixture, no new substance is formed.

(iii)   The properties of a compound are dissimilar to those of its constituents. The properties of a mixture are the average of the properties of its constituents.

(iv)   Compounds can only be converted back into their constituent substances by chemical or electrochemical means. Mixtures can be separated by simple physical processes.

(v) Compounds have fixed melting and boiling temperatures. Mixtures do not have fixed melting and boiling temperatures.

(vi) The substances which make up a compound are always present in the same, fixed proportions. The substances in a mixture can be in any proportion.

(b) The second part of the activity asked you to explain why the metal zinc is an element. Zinc is an element because, in any piece of the pure metal, only zinc atoms will be present. A piece of pure zinc cannot be broken down into two or more simpler substances. Substances that are elements consist of only one type of atom.

Now return to the text

Response B7.1 Your completed sentences should read as follows:

(a) All substances can be solids, liquids or gases depending on their **temperatures**.
(b) Heat energy is **gained** or **lost** during a change of **state**.
(c) Solids have definite **shape** and **volume**.
(d) Considerable **force** is required to change the shape of a solid.
(e) The particles of a solid are **closely** packed together.

Now return to the text

Response B7.2
(a) True   The particles in a solid do vibrate about fixed points.
(b) False   The higher the temperature, the greater the agitation of the particles. At the melting temperature of a solid, the agitation of the particles becomes so great that they break away from their fixed positions and the solid becomes a liquid. If the solid is cooled down, the agitation of the particles becomes less. At $-273\,°C$ all movement stops. This temperature is called **absolute zero**. At the melting temperature of a solid, the agitation of the particles becomes so great that they break away from their fixed positions and the solid becomes a liquid.
(c) False   Metals expand when they are heated. The increased agitation of the particles in the metal, as the temperature rises, causes them to 'nudge' each other apart slightly and take up more room.
(d) True   Most metals become softer and more malleable when their temperatures are raised. This is again due to the greater agitation of their particles. The further the particles move apart, the lower the attractive forces between them. This is why a blacksmith heats up the metal to red heat before forging it to shape on an anvil.
(e) False   As stated above, any increase in temperature results in greater agitation of the metal particles. This, in turn, causes the particles to 'nudge' each other apart and the increased distances between their locations reduces the attractive forces between them.

As well as giving you the correct answers, I hope my explanations have helped you to understand them. If you have any problems, consult your tutor before moving on.

Now return to the text

Response B8.1   (a)   Liquids have definite volume but they adopt the shape of the vessels in which they are stored. A pint of milk in a bottle has the same volume as a pint of milk in a supermarket carton but its shape is different.

(b)   No, the particles in a liquid are free to move about at random in straight lines. They are bounded only by the walls of the vessel containing the liquid and also the surface of the liquid.

(c)   Yes, because of the greater distances between the particles in a liquid, the attractive forces are weaker than for the same substance in the solid state.

(d)   No, liquids and solids are **not** compressible; only gases are compressible.

(e)   No, the particles in a liquid are not closely packed as in a solid. Nor are the particles in a liquid arranged in any definite pattern; they are free to move about. This freedom of movement creates the liquid state of a substance.

(f)   Yes, any reduction in temperature results in less activity by the particles in the liquid and they congregate closer together. This results in the liquid becoming 'thicker' (more viscous). This is why the oil in the engine of your car or motor cycle becomes thicker on a cold winter morning and makes starting more difficult.

(g)   Yes, see my response to (a).

As well as giving you the correct answers, I hope my explanations have helped you to understand them.

Now return to the text

Response B9.1   (a)   Gas particles have complete freedom of movement and will disperse throughout the atmosphere unless kept in sealed containers.

(b)   No, gas particles are even further apart than the particles in a liquid. The attractive forces between gas particles are therefore correspondingly less. For all practical purposes the attractive forces between gas particles are considered to be non-existent except at very high pressures.

(c)   Yes, gases always fill any totally enclosed vessel in which they are contained.

(d)   Yes, only gases are compressible; solids and liquids are not compressible.

(e)   Yes, once a gas escapes, its particles disperse throughout the atmosphere.

Vapours

A lot of confusion arises about the difference between gases and vapours. Before I return you to the text I will try and explain the difference to you. In the text I have implied that if a liquid is heated to a sufficiently high temperature it will become a gas. This is true providing the temperature is high enough. At first the liquid becomes a vapour before it becomes a gas, if evaporation takes place over a range of temperatures. Let's consider water.

Like most liquids, water starts to evaporate well below its boiling point. A puddle of rainwater will evaporate quite quickly on a warm sunny day as shown in the figure. Evaporation is taking place even though the water is not boiling. There is sufficient heat energy from the sun to warm the water and make its particles agitate sufficiently that they break through the surface of the liquid and disperse into the atmosphere. What escapes consists mostly of very fine water droplets together with some gas particles. If there is no wind to disperse these droplets, they will hang about just above the ground level as a mist. The mist is water vapour. As the sun gets hotter these droplets start to disperse.

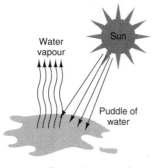

Evaporation

Fig. B9.1R

When the boiling point of water is reached the evaporation becomes very rapid. The water bubbles and steam is given off. However, we still have a vapour, not a gas. We are just producing a lot of vapour very rapidly. The steam we get from an open pan or, to a lesser extent, in a low pressure boiler is called wet steam. It is a mixture of gas particles and water droplets. It is not very efficient for driving a steam engine and the water droplets can cause a lot of damage.

From an engineering point of view we consider a vapour to be a partially evaporated liquid which consists of particles of gas together with liquid droplets in suspension, hence the expression wet steam. Such a vapour does not behave like a gas; it does not obey the gas laws.

To convert a vapour into a gas it is essential to heat it further to complete the evaporation process. This is called **superheating**. The greater the degree of superheating, the nearer the vapour becomes to being a true gas.

- Vapours are associated with substances that are liquids at room temperature, such as water, propane, butane and petrol.
- True gases (which obey the gas laws) – oxygen, hydrogen, nitrogen, argon, neon, carbon dioxide, etc. – are only liquids at very low temperatures approaching absolute zero. By the time they reach room temperature they have become true gases.

Now return to the text

Response B10.1   (a)   Here are some special properties that distinguish between oil and water, both of which have the general properties of liquids.

Water   Water has only very limited lubricating properties and causes corrosion in some metals after contact for a period of time. Water is non-flammable.

Oil   Oils are very good lubricants. While in contact with metals, they protect them from corrosion. Oils are flammable.

(b)   Here are some special properties that distinguish between acetylene and carbon dioxide, both of which have the general properties of gases.

Acetylene   Acetylene is a highly flammable gas used as the fuel gas in oxy-acetylene welding. It has a characteristic garlic smell.

Carbon dioxide   Carbon dioxide gas is non-flammable and is used in fire extinguishers. It has no smell.

Now return to the text

Response C1.1   Yours calculations should be as follows:

(a)   From Fig. C1.1 you can see that 1 dm^3 of water has a mass of 1 kg. Therefore, by proportion, 5 dm^3 of water has a mass of 5×1 kg = **5 kg**.

(b)   From Fig. C1.1 you can see that 1 litre of water has a mass of 1 kg. Therefore, by proportion, 7 kg of water occupies 7×1 litres = **7 l**.

(c)   We know that 1 dm = 10 cm, therefore 1 dm^3 = 1000 cm^3 so 5000 cm^3 = 5 dm^3. Since 5 dm^3 of water has a mass of 5 kg, then 5000 cm^3 of water must also have a mass of **5 kg**.

(d)   From Fig. C1.1 we know that 1 kg of water occupies 1 litre. That is, 1000 g of water occupies 1000 millilitres of water. Therefore, by proportion, 10 g of water has a volume of **10 millilitres**.

(e)   We know that 12×10^3 dm^3 of water is the same as 12 000 dm^3 of water. Therefore, since 1 dm^3 of water has a mass of 1 kg, 12 000 dm^3 of water will have a mass of 12 000 kg. We also know that 1000 kg equals 1 tonne. Therefore, 12 000 kg = **12 t**.

I hope you managed to reason your way through these calculations using the relationships given in Fig. C1.1 and your mathematical experiences throughout the previous modules. If you have had any difficulties I hope my responses have helped you.

Strictly speaking, 1 litre of pure water has a mass of 1.000 028 kg at 4°C. For all practical purposes we can take 1 litre of pure water as having a mass of 1 kg.

Now return to the text

Response C2.1   (a)   If the force (F) is removed, the trolley will cease to move. An applied force is always required to cause motion.

(b)   When two forces of equal strength act in opposite direction along the same line of action, they cancel each other out. Thus there will be no force left to move the trolley. It will again cease to move.

This is what I expected you to answer in your own words. However, I am impressed if you carried the argument further as follows:

Although the trolley is not moving, the forces are still acting on it and trying to cause movement. If the forces are large enough, they will squeeze the trolley flat. One of the other properties of a force is to change or try to change the shape of a body.

Now return to the text

Response C3.1   (a)   We are using a scale of 1 cm = 10 N, so 50 N = 5 cm. Therefore the vector is an arrow, 5 cm long, drawn due north from point P as shown in part (a) of the figure.

(b)   We are using a scale of 1 cm = 10 N, so 40 N = 4 cm. Therefore the vector is an arrow, 4 cm long, drawn at 45° to the horizontal line as shown in part (b) of the figure. The method of doing this is as follows:

(i)   Draw a line at 45% from the point P as shown. This is the line of action of the force.

(ii)   Set your compasses to a radius of 4 cm.

(iii)   With the point of your compasses on point P, strike an arc to cut the line of action of the force at the point A. This will mark off the length of the vector.

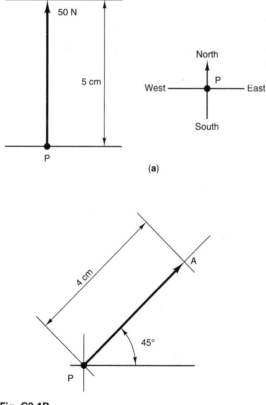

Fig. C3.1R

Now return to the text

Response C4.1   Your completed table should read as follows.

Table C4.1R

Earth		Moon	
Mass	**Weight**	**Mass***	**Weight**
6 kg	**58.86 N**	6 kg	**9.81 N**
100 kg	981 N	100 kg	163.5 N
3 tonnes†	**29.43 kN**	3 tonnes	**4.91 N**
100 tonne	981 kN	100 tonnes	163.5 kN
500 kg	**4.905 kN**	500 kg	**817.5 N**

* Remember that mass is constant for any given body. It is the same on the Moon as it is on planet Earth.

† Remember that 3 tonnes = 3000 kg. Therefore the **weight** of the body = 3000 kg $\times$ 9.81 m/s^2 = 29 430 N = **29.43 kN** on planet Earth. Since the force of gravity on the moon is only $\frac{1}{6}$ the force of gravity on Earth, the weight of the body will be (29.43)/(6) = **4.9 kN**. The mass of a body does not change, so the body still has a mass of **3 tonnes** on the moon.

Now return to the text

Response C5.1   The following calculations ignore wind resistance:

(a) $v = u + at$

$\quad = 0 + (9.81 \text{ m/s}^2 \times 3 \text{ s})$

$\quad = \textbf{29.43 m/s}$

where: $u = 0$ m/s since the ball starts from rest
$\qquad a = 9.81$ m/s^2
$\qquad t = 3$ s

(b) $v = u + at$

$\quad = 0 + (9.81 \text{ m/s}^2 \times 4 \text{ s})$

$\quad = \textbf{39.24 m/s}$

where: $u = 0$ m/s since the ball starts from rest
$\qquad a = 9.81$ m/s^2
$\qquad t = 4$ s

(c) $v = u + at$

$\quad = 0 + (9.81 \text{ m/s}^2 \times 5 \text{ s})$

$\quad = \textbf{49.05 m/s}$

where: $u = 0$ m/s since the ball starts from rest
$\qquad a = 9.81$ m/s^2

Notice how the speed increases with time. This indicates that the ball is accelerating. Had the speed of the ball been decreasing with time, it would have been decelerating.

Now return to the text

Response D1.1 Your calculations of mass per unit volume should be as follows:

(a) volume of solid $= 4$ m $\times$ 5 m $\times$ 3 m $= 60$ m^3

mass of solid $= 600$ t (given)

mass per unit volume $= \dfrac{600 \text{ t}}{60 \text{ m}^3} = 10$ t/m^3

But there are $1\,000\,000$ g in 1 t

And there are $1\,000\,000$ cm^3 in 1 m^3

Mass per unit volume expressed in g/cm^3 $= \dfrac{600 \times 1\,000\,000 \text{ g}}{60 \times 1\,000\,000 \text{ cm}^3} = \mathbf{10}$ **g/cm**^{3}

(b) volume of solid $- 4$ mm $\times$ 5 mm $\times$ 3 mm $= 60$ mm^3

mass of solid 0.6 g $=$ (given)

mass per unit volume $= \dfrac{0.6 \text{ g}}{60 \text{ mm}^3} = 0.01$ g/mm^3

But there are 1000 mm^3 in 1 cm^3

Therefore, mass per unit volume in g/cm^3 $= 0.01 \times 1000$ g/cm^3 $= \mathbf{10}$ **g/cm**^{3}

So, regardless of the body's dimensions and mass, its mass per unit volume is constant; it is 10 g/cm^3. The mass per unit volume for any body depends solely upon the material from which it is made.

Now return to the text

Response D1.2 Your completed statement should read:

Density is the name given to **mass** per unit **volume** of a substance. That is, **mass divided** by the **volume** of a solid made of that substance.

Now return to the text

Response D1.3 In this activity you have to find density, mass and volume. To do this you have to rearrange the formula as follows and then correctly select and apply the appropriate data:

$$\rho = \frac{M}{V} \qquad V = \frac{M}{\rho} \qquad M = \rho \times V$$

where: $\rho =$ density
$M =$ mass
$V =$ volume

Using this information, Table D1.3R should read as follows.

Table D1.3R

Mass (m)	Volume (V)	Density (ρ)	Calculation
500 g	50 mm^3	**10 g/mm^3**	$\rho = m/V = (500\text{ g})/(50\text{ mm}^3) = 10\text{ g/mm}^3$
20 kg	10 m^3	**2 kg/m^3**	$\rho = m/V = (20\text{ kg})/(10\text{ m}^3) = 2\text{ kg/m}^3$
532.5 g	35.5 cm^3	15 g/cm^3	$15\text{ g/cm}^3 \times 35.5\text{ cm} = 532.5\text{ g}$
13 kg	**2 m^3**	6.5 kg/cm^3	$(13\text{ kg})/(6.5\text{ kg/m}^3) = 2\text{ m}^3$
800 g	**20 cm^3**	40 g/cm^3	$(800\text{ g})/(40\text{ g/cm}^3) = 20\text{ cm}^3$
105 kg	70 m^3	1.5 kg/cm^3	$1.5\text{ kg/m}^3 \times 70\text{ m}^3 = 105\text{ kg}$
250 g	50 mm^3	**5 g/mm^3**	$(250\text{ g})/(50\text{ mm}^3) = 5\text{ g/mm}^3$

If you had any difficulty in rearranging and/or applying the formulae, I hope that my response has helped you. If you still have any areas of uncertainty please consult your tutor before moving on.

Now return to the text

Response D1.4   (a) $M = p \times V$

$$= 7.2\text{ g/cm}^3 \times 300\text{ cm}^3$$
$$= 2160\text{ g}$$
$$= \textbf{2.16 kg}$$

where: $\rho = 7.2\text{ g/cm}^3$
$V = 300\text{ cm}^3$

(b) $V = \dfrac{M}{\rho}$

$$= \frac{2120\text{ kg}}{8480\text{ kg/m}^3}$$
$$= \textbf{0.25 m}^3$$

where: $M = 2.12\text{ t} = 2120\text{ kg}$
$\rho = 8480\text{ kg/m}^3$

(c) $V = \dfrac{M}{\rho}$

$$= \frac{3200\text{ kg}}{800\text{ kg/m}^3}$$
$$= \textbf{4 m}^3$$

where: $M = 3.2\text{ t} = 3200\text{ kg}$
$\rho = 800\text{ kg/m}^3$

Paraffin is a liquid, so it is more usual to express the volume in litres (l). Remember:

1 cubic metre (m^3) = 1000 cubic decimetres (dm^3)

1 cubic decimetre (dm^3) = 1 litre (l)

Therefore the answer to (c) expressed in litres is as follows:

$V = 4\text{ m}^3 = 4000\text{ dm}^3 = \textbf{4000 l}$

(d) $M = \rho \times V$

$\qquad = 1.25 \text{ kg/m}^3 \times 20 \text{ m}^3$

$\qquad = \textbf{25 kg}$

where: $\rho = 1.25 \text{ kg/m}^3$
$\qquad\quad V = 20 \text{ m}^3$

(e) Since the density (ρ) is given in kg/m^3, we have to convert the volume (V) from litres to cubic metres:

1 litre = 1 cubic decimetre, therefore 50 litres = 50 cubic decimetres

but 1 m^3 = 1000 cubic decimetres, therefore 50 cubic decimetres

$$= \frac{50}{1000} \text{ m}^3 = 0.05 \text{ m}^3$$

We can now calculate the mass as follows:

$M = \rho \times V$

$\qquad = 720 \text{ kg/m}^3 \times 0.05 \text{ m}^3$

$\qquad = \textbf{36 kg}$

where: $\rho = 720 \text{ kg/m}^3$
$\qquad\qquad V = 0.05 \text{ m}^3$ (calculated above)

Some of these calculations required quite a lot of thought to get into the appropriate units. I hope you managed to find a path to the appropriate units and obtained the correct solutions. If not, I hope my responses have helped you. If you are not confident, please consult your tutor before moving on.

Now return to the text

Response D3.1 (a) Rectangular solid:

volume = length $\times$ breadth $\times$ height

$\qquad = 8 \text{ cm} \times 4 \text{ cm} \times 6 \text{ cm}$

$\qquad = \textbf{192 cm}^3$

(b) Spherical solid:

$$\text{volume} = \frac{4}{3} \times \pi \times \text{radius}^3$$

$$= \frac{4}{3} \times \pi \times 10^3 \text{ cm}$$

$$= \textbf{4189 cm} \text{ (4 s.f.)}$$

(c) Triangular prism:

volume = area of triangle $\times$ length

$$= \frac{1}{2} \times \text{base} \times \text{height} \times \text{length}$$

$$= \frac{1}{2} \times 50 \text{ mm} \times 60 \text{ mm} \times 80 \text{ mm}$$

$$= \mathbf{120\,000 \text{ mm}^3}$$

$$\text{density} = \frac{\text{mass}}{\text{volume}}$$

$$= \frac{240\,000 \text{ g}}{120\,000 \text{ mm}^3}$$

$$= \mathbf{2 \text{ g/mm}^3}$$

where: mass $= 0.24$ t $= 240\,000$ g

volume $= 120\,000$ mm^3

I hope you remembered to convert tonnes into grams before substituting in the formula.

Now return to the text

Response D4.1   (a)   volume of solid = (volume of water plus solid) — (volume of water)

$$= 0.75 \text{ l} - 0.5 \text{ l}$$

$$= 0.25 \text{ l}$$

Remember that only the volumes of fluids should be expressed in litres. Volumes of solids should be expressed in mm^3, cm^3, or m^3.
   Since 1 litre = 1 decimetre, the volume of our solid (0.25 l) is 0.25 dm^3.
   But we require our answer in g/cm^3. So we must convert dm^3 into cm^3:

$$0.25 \text{ dm}^3 = 0.25 \times 1000 \text{ cm}^3 = 250 \text{ cm}^3$$

We now have our data in the correct units to calculate the density of the solid:

$$\text{density} = \frac{\text{mass}}{\text{volume}}$$

$$= \frac{680 \text{ g}}{250 \text{ cm}^3}$$

$$= \mathbf{2.72 \text{ g/cm}^3}$$

where: mass = 680 g (given)
         volume = 250 cm^3

(b)   No, the result would have been the same. The volume of a liquid displaced by a solid is not affected by the density of the liquid. Nor is it affected by the mass of the solid if the solid is wholly submerged.

Now return to the text

Response D5.1

mass of liquid = mass of full bottle − mass of empty bottle

$$= 190 \text{ g} - 150 \text{ g}$$

$$= 40 \text{ g}$$

density (ρ) $= \dfrac{\text{mass}}{\text{volume}}$

$$= \dfrac{40 \text{ g}}{50 \text{ cm}^3}$$

$$= \textbf{0.8 g/cm}^3$$

where: mass = 40 g (calculated)
volume = 50 cm³ (given)

Now return to the text

Response D6.1

The apparent density of the gas, ignoring standard temperature and pressure (STP) can be calculated as follows:

$$\rho = \frac{\text{mass}}{\text{volume}} = \frac{(150.25 \text{ g} - 150.00 \text{ g})}{125 \text{ cm}^3} = \frac{0.25 \text{ g}}{125 \text{ cm}^3} = \textbf{0.002 g/cm}^3$$

This is the density of the gas calculated from data obtained when the atmospheric conditions were:

pressure = 755 mm of mercury

temperature = 15°C.

We now have to find the density under conditions of standard temperature and pressure (STP), that is, 760 mm mercury and 0°C. We have to use the general gas law formula:

$$\frac{P_1 \times V_1}{T_1} = \frac{P_2 \times V_2}{T_2}$$

As for all gas law calculations we have to use the **absolute** scale of temperature. That is, we have to add 273 to the temperature in celsius. This gives us the temperature on the **kelvin** (K) scale. Note that we do not use the degree symbol (°) when expressing a temperature using the kelvin scale. So:

15°C = 288 K   and   0°C = 273 K

Our data now becomes:

$P_1 = 755 \text{ mm}$ $P_2 = 760 \text{ mm}$
$V_1 = 125 \text{ cm}^3$ $V_2 = \text{volume corrected to STP}$
$T_1 = 288$ $T_2 = 273 \text{ K}$

Inserting this data in our formula, we get:

$$\frac{755 \text{ mm} \times 125 \text{ cm}^3}{288 \text{ K}} = \frac{760 \text{ mm} \times V_2}{273 \text{ K}}$$

Therefore $V_2 = \dfrac{755 \text{ mm} \times 125 \text{ cm}^3 \times 273 \text{ K}}{760 \text{ mm} \times 288 \text{ K}}$

$$= \textbf{118 cm}^3$$

We can now use this corrected volume to find the density under STP conditions:

$$\rho = \frac{\text{mass}}{\text{corrected volume}} = \frac{0.25 \text{ g}}{118 \text{ cm}^3} = \textbf{0.002 119 g/cm}^3$$

I hope you found this diversion into STP interesting. Don't worry, I won't be asking you to do it at this level.

Now return to the text

Response D8.1   Your completed table should read as follows, providing you remembered that **weight per unit volume** is density multiplied by the gravitational constant (g) which equals 9.81 m/s^2.

Table D8.1R

	Density	Weight per unit volume
(a)	2.72 g/cm^3	0.02668 N/cm^3
(b)	7820 kg/m^3	76.7142 kN/m^3
(c)	7747 kg/m^3	0.076 N/cm^3
(d)	8481 kg/m^3	83.2 kN/m^3

(a)   Since weight (N) = mass (kg) $\times$ g (9.81 m/s^2) we have to work in kilograms, **not** in grams as given. Therefore 2.72 g/cm^3 = 2720 kg/m^3. Thus weight per unit volume = 2720 kg/m^3 $\times$ 9.81 m/s^2 = 26 683.2 N/m^3 However, since we started in g/cm^3, we had better finish in N/cm^3:

$$26\,683.2 \text{ N/m}^3 = \frac{26\,683.2 \text{ N/m}^3}{1\,000\,000} \text{ N/cm}^3$$

$$= \textbf{0.2668 N/cm}^3$$

(b)   This time the density is already given in kg/m^3, so

$$\text{weight} = \text{density} \times g$$
$$= 7820 \text{ kg/m}^3 \times 9.81 \text{ m/s}^2$$
$$= 76714.2 \text{ N/m}^3$$
$$= \textbf{76.7142 kN/m}^3$$

(c) $$\text{mass} = \frac{\text{weight per unit volume}}{g}$$

$$= \frac{0.076 \text{ N/cm}^3}{9.81 \text{ m/s}^2}$$

$$= 0.007\,747 \text{ kg/cm}^3$$

This is better expressed in kg/m^3, so we have to multiply our previous answer by 1 000 000, thus:

$$\text{mass} = 0.007\,747 \text{ kg/cm}^3 \times 1\,000\,000$$

$$= \textbf{7747 kg/m}^3$$

(d) This time we are already in kg/m³, so we only have to divide by 9.81 m/s² after converting 83.2 kN into 83 200 N.

$$\text{density } (\rho) = \frac{\text{weight per unit volume}}{9.81 \text{ m/s}^2}$$

$$= \mathbf{8481 \text{ kg/m}^2}$$

These examples needed quite a lot of thought to get into the correct units before and after conversion. Well done if you are getting most of them correct. Brilliant if you got them all.

Now return to the text

Response D9.1   volume = area × length

$$= \frac{\pi D^2}{4} \times \text{length}$$

$$= \frac{\pi \times 20^2 \text{ mm}}{4} \times 25 \text{ mm}$$

$$= 7854 \text{ mm}^3$$

where: $D = 20$ mm
$\quad\quad\quad l = 25$ mm

$$\text{weight per unit volume} = \frac{\text{weight}}{\text{volume}}$$

$$= \frac{0.85 \text{ N}}{7854 \text{ mm}^3}$$

$$= 0.000\,108 \text{ N/mm}^3$$

$$= 0.000\,108 \times 1000 \text{ N/cm}^3$$

$$= \mathbf{0.108 \text{ N/cm}^3} \quad (1000 \text{ mm}^3 = 1 \text{ cm}^3)$$

where: weight = 0.85 N (given)
$\quad\quad\quad\quad\quad\quad = 7854 \text{ mm}^3$

Now return to the text

Response E2.1   (a) Figure E2.1R(a) shows the vector for a force of 40 N acting towards point P at an angle of 30° to the horizontal. (Scale: 1 cm = 10 N)
(b) Figure E2.1R(b) shows the vector for the 45 N force acting at 60° to the horizontal away from the point P. It also shows the vector for the 30 N force acting at 30° to the horizontal away from the point P.

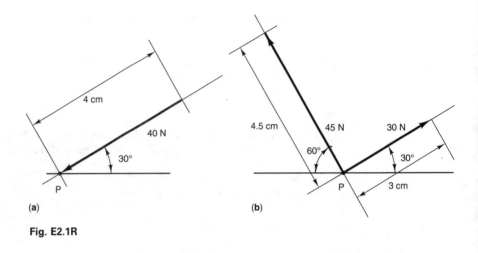

(a)

(b)

Fig. E2.1R

Now return to the text

Response E2.2

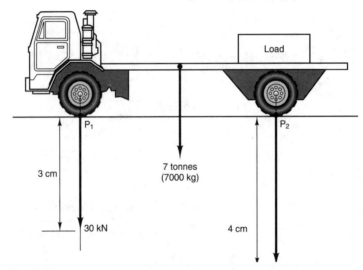

Fig. E2.2R

Using the data given in the figure we can complete the following calculations:

$$\text{weight of the truck} = W = 7000 \text{ kg} \times 10 \text{ m/s}^2$$
$$= 70\,000 \text{ N}$$

The ratio of the forces at P_1 and P_2 is $3 : 4$.

Therefore the force acting at $P_1 = 30\,000 \text{ N} = \textbf{30 kN}$
and at $P_2 = 40\,000 \text{ N} = \textbf{40 kN}$

At a scale of 1 cm = 10 kN, the force vector acting at P_1 will be 3 cm long and the force vector acting at P_2 will be 4 cm long. The forces are the result of gravitational attraction, so they will act vertically downwards.

Now return to the text

Response E3.1   (a)   The vectors are acting in the same direction, so the resultant force that can replace them is the addition of the vectors F_1 and F_2 in (a). Since $F_1 + F_2 = $ 15 N + 20 N = 35 N, the resultant force F_R is 35 N. At a scale of 1 cm = 5 N, the resultant vector will be 7 cm long. Remember that the resultant vector can be identified by its double arrowhead.

  (b)   The vectors are acting in opposite directions so, this time, they are subtracted to obtain the resultant force that can replace them, as shown in (b). Since $F_2 - F_1 = $ 20 N − 10 N = 10 N, the resultant force F_R is 10 N. At a scale of 1 cm = 5 N, the resultant vector will be 2 cm long.

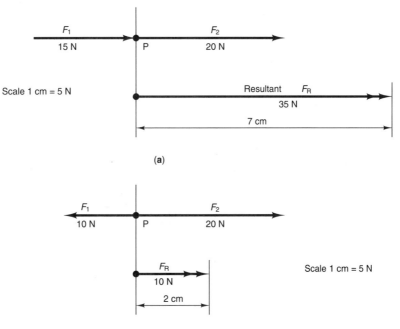

Fig. E3.1R

Now return to the text

Response F4.1   Your completed parallelograms of forces should be as shown. Your answers will depend upon the accuracy of your drawing and measuring. However, they should closely approximate to my answers, which I have checked by calculation.

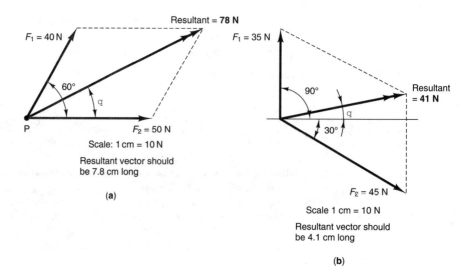

Scale: 1 cm = 10 N

Resultant vector should
be 7.8 cm long

(a)

Scale 1 cm = 10 N

Resultant vector should
be 4.1 cm long

(b)

Fig. E4.1R

Now return to the text

Response E5.1

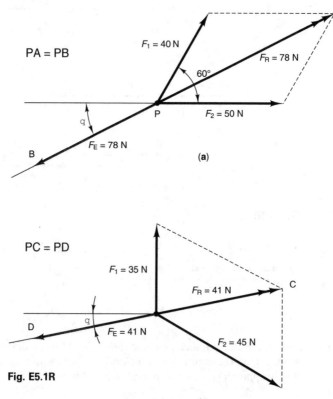

PA = PB

(a)

PC = PD

Fig. E5.1R

(b)

In each case the equilibrant force (F_E) is equal and opposite to the resultant force (F_R). Therefore length PA = length PB and length PC = length PD. The arrowheads on the equilibrant force vectors point in the opposite direction to the arrowheads on the resultant force vectors.

Response E6.1

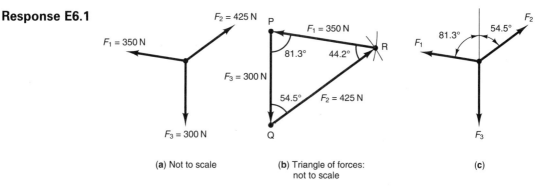

(a) Not to scale   (b) Triangle of forces: not to scale   (c)

Fig. E6.1R

A system of three forces acting on the same point is shown in (a). To draw the triangle of forces shown in (b), we adopt the following procedure using a scale of 1 mm = 5N:

- Draw the vector for F_3 to a suitable scale. This is the easiest as it is acting vertically downwards. Your vector should be 60 mm long.
- Next we will tackle the vector for F_2. We know it is 85 mm long to our scale and we know that it starts form the point Q. For the moment we do not know where it finishes. So, with the point of your compass at Q, strike an arc of 85 mm radius. The end of the vector for force F_2 will lie somewhere on this arc.
- Now for vector F_1. We use the same procedure as for F_2 but, this time, the radius will be 70 mm. So, with the point of your compass on the point P, strike your arc to cut the previous arc at the point R.
- By joining the points P, Q and R, as shown, you complete the triangle of forces.
- Add the arrowheads to show the directions in which the forces are acting.
- If the system is in equilibrium you should have a closed triangle with all the arrowheads following each other around. Now measure the angles with a protractor. Because of the limitations of space on this page I have not been able to draw my diagrams to our chosen scale. Therefore, for accuracy, I have calculated the values of the angles. This will give you an accurate result with which to compare your measured answers. Your angles should add up to 180° because the internal angles of all triangles always add up to 180°.
- These angles have been transferred back to the original figure (a). Acting at these angles the forces are in equilibrium. There will be no movement of the point on which they are acting; the forces balance each other out. If the direction of any of the forces were changed, we would no longer have equilibrium, and movement would occur.

Now return to the text

Response E6.2

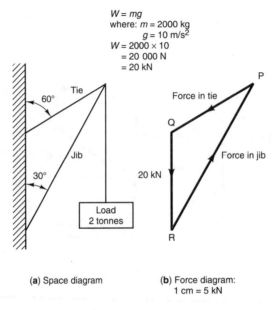

(a) Space diagram

(b) Force diagram:
    1 cm = 5 kN

Fig. E6.2R

A simple wall-mounted jib-crane is shown in (a). Before we can start to draw the force diagram, we have to calculate the gravitational force exerted on the load.

$$W = Mg$$

$$= 2000 \text{ kg} \times 10 \text{ m/s}^2$$

$$= 20\,000 \text{ N}$$

$$= \mathbf{20\,000 \text{ N}}$$

where: $M = 2\,\text{t} = 2000$ kg
                 $= 10 \text{ m/s}^2$

With a scale of 5 kN = 1 cm, draw the force diagram as follows:

- Start with the load vector because this acts vertically downwards and we know where it goes. Draw the force vector 4 cm long acting vertically downwards.
- Draw the line of action for the force in the jib parallel to the jib (30° to the vertical) from the point R.
- Draw the line of action for the force in the tie parallel to the tie (60° to the vertical) from the point Q.
- The lines of action intersect (cross) at the point P.
- PQ is the vector for the tie and PR is the vector for the jib.
- Measuring and scaling the vectors: the force in the jib = **34.6 kN**

                                                              the force in the tie = **20 kN**

Now return to the text

Response E7.1

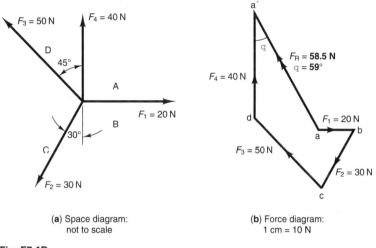

(a) Space diagram:
not to scale

(b) Force diagram:
1 cm = 10 N

Fig. E7.1R

First draw the space diagram as shown in (a). The arrows indicating the forces need not be drawn to scale. However, the **angles** between them **must be drawn to scale**. Add the capital letters in the spaces as shown; this is where the diagram gets its name. This method of lettering space and force diagrams is called Bowes notation. With reference to (a) and (b), we can now draw the force diagram:

- Draw the vector for force F_1 to scale and horizontal. Since this force lies between A and B in the space diagram we label it ab.
- Draw the vector for force F_2 to scale from the point b. The line of action for this vector is drawn parallel to the force F_2 in the space diagram. Since this force lies between B and C it is labelled bc in the force diagram.
- Draw the vector for force F_3 to scale from the point c. The line of action for this vector is drawn parallel to the force F_3 in the space diagram. Since this force lies between C and D it is labelled cd in the force diagram.
- Draw the vector for force F_4 to scale from the point d. The line of action for this vector is drawn parallel to the force F_4 in the space diagram. Since this force lies between D and A it is labelled da'.
- The vector joining aa' in the force diagram is the resultant force F_R. Note its distinguishing double arrowhead and the fact that is pointing in the opposite direction to the other vectors. This is the single force that can replace all the other forces and produce the same effect. If we reverse the direction of action of this force it becomes the equilibrant force and cancels out the effect of all the other forces.
- $F_R = 58.5$ N and the angle of its line of action (θ) is 59° to the horizontal.

Now return to the text

Response E7.2

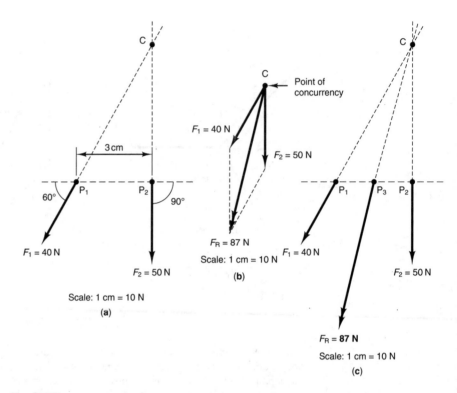

Fig. E7.2R

- Draw the figure given in the activity accurately to scale and extend the lines of action of the forces F_1 and F_2 so that they intersect at the point P as shown in (a). Point C is the **point of concurrency**.
- Draw the vectors for the forces F_1 and F_2 to scale from the point of concurrency C, as shown in (b).
- Complete the parallelogram of forces as shown in (b).
- The resultant force (F_R) is the diagonal of the parallelogram of forces. Measure and scale the drawing to find the magnitude of the force (**87 N**).
- Slide the vectors down their lines of action so that F_1 again acts at the point P_1 and the force F_2 again acts at the point P_2 as shown in (c).
- The point P_3 is where the line of action of the resultant vector F_R cuts a straight line joining the points P_1 and P_2.
- The vector of the resultant force is drawn so that it acts from the point P_3 as shown in (c).

As for all the previous constructions, your success will depend upon the quality and accuracy of your drawings. Always work to as large a scale as possible and try and gain access to a drawing-board and T-square or a portable drawing-board. I hope you are enjoying these graphical solutions as a rest from the earlier calculations.

Now return to the text

Response E8.1

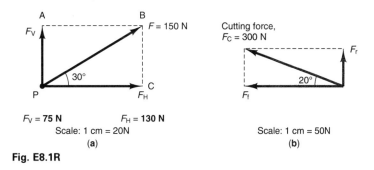

$F_V = 75$ N $F_H = 130$ N
Scale: 1 cm = 20N

(a)

Scale: 1 cm = 50N

(b)

Fig. E8.1R

For part (a):

- Draw the vector for the force F to scale from the point P.
- Draw the line of action for the force F_V perpendicular from the point P.
- Draw the line of action for the force F_H horizontal from the point P.
- Complete the parallelogram of forces, as shown, by drawing line AB parallel to line PC and line BC parallel to line AP.
- AP is the vector for the force F_V.
- CP is the vector for the force F_H.
- The magnitudes of the vectors can be determined by measuring and scaling the drawing.
- $F_V = 75$ N   and $F_H = 130$ N (to the nearest whole number)

For part (b):

Using the same procedure as has just been described for part (a), you draw the parallelogram of forces for the resolution of the cutting force F_C. The magnitudes of the resolved forces are:

$$\text{feed force } (F_f) \ \ = 282 \text{ N}$$
$$\text{radial force } (F_r) = 102 \text{ N}$$

Now return to the text

Response F1.1   Your completed table should read as follows.

Table F1.1R

	Force (F)	Length (l)	Turning moment (M)	Calculation
(a)	30 N	0.5 m	15 N m	$M = F \times l = 30 \text{ N} \times 0.5 \text{ m} = 15$ N m
(b)	20 N	0.4 m	8 N m	$M = 20 \text{ N} \times 0.4 \text{ m} = 8$ N m
(c)	50 N	750 mm	37.5 N m	$M = 50 \text{ N} \times 0.75 \text{ m} = 37.5$ N m
(d)	100 N	2.4 m	250 N m	$M = 100 \text{ N} \times 2.4 \text{ m} = 240$ N m
(e)	**64 N**	0.5 m	32 N m	$F = (32 \text{ N m})/(0.5 \text{ m}) = 64$ N
(f)	50 N	**0.2 m**	10 N m	$l = (10 \text{ N m})/(50 \text{ N}) = 0.2$ m

The most likely errors may have been:

- In (c) you forgot to convert millimetres into metres before multiplying by the force. Remember the unit we are using is the newton-metre (N m).
- In (e) you did not transpose the formula correctly. If $M = F \times l$, then $F = (M)/(l)$.
- In (f) you did not transpose the formula correctly. If $M = F \times l$, then $l = (M)/(F)$.

I hope you are remembering to use the correct units throughout the calculations. They are an essential part of each physical quantity. Failure to state the units correctly would cost you marks in an examination.

Now return to the text

Response F1.2   Your completed table should read as follows.

Table F1.2R

	Force (F)	Length (l)	Angle θ	Effective length (l_E)	Turning moment (M)
(a)	30 N	0.5 m	60°	**0.433 m**	**13 N m**
(b)	10 N	120 mm	45°	**0.085 m**	**0.85 N m**
(c)	120 N	250 mm	30°	**0.125 m**	**15 N m**

In case you had any difficulty with this activity, I will solve the first one in the table for you by graphical method. The following figure shows the layout of the lengths and angles.

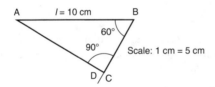

Fig. F1.2R

- Draw the line AB to a large scale. I have chosen 1/5 full size to fit my paper. Thus the real length (l) of 0.5 m becomes 10 cm on the drawing.
- Draw BD at 60° to AB as shown. This is the given angle. We don't yet know its length, but it won't be longer than AB.
- Draw a line from A to cut BD at 90°. It will cut the line BD at C. It helps if you have noticed that the angle at A is 30°. You can draw lines AC and BD using a 30°/60° set square.
- Line AC is the effective length (l_E) and, in this example, it should measure 8.66 cm.
- Thus the true effective length is 8.66 cm × 5 = 433 cm. Since we have to work in metres, the true effective length (l_E) is **0.433 m**.
- The turning moment (M) can be calculated by multiplying the force (F) by the effective length (l_E).

$$M = F \times l_E = 30 \text{ N} \times 0.433 \text{ m} = \textbf{13 N m} \text{ (to the nearest whole number)}$$

You may wonder how I can be so accurate about the sizes in my specimen solution. I calculate the values using trigonometry to cross-check my measurements.

Now return to the text

Response F2.1

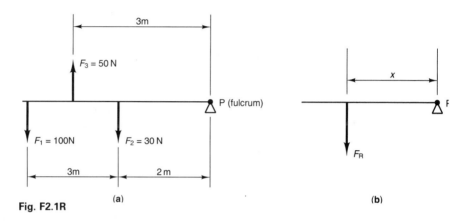

Fig. F2.1R

(a)   Forces F_1 and F_2 act in the same direction so they can be added together. Force F_3 acts in the opposite direction so it is subtracted from the sum of F_1 and F_2 in order to find the resultant force (F_R).

Therefore $F_R = (F_1 + F_2) - F_3 = (100 \text{ N} + 30 \text{ N}) - 50 \text{ N} = \textbf{80 N}$

Note that I have arranged the calculation to give me a positive answer for convenience. Taking moments about the pivot point P:

Clockwise moments

$M_3 = F_3 \times 3 \text{ m} = 50 \text{ N} \times 3 \text{ m} = \textbf{150 N m}$

Anticlockwise moments

$M_1 = F_1 \times (3 \text{ m} + 2 \text{ m}) = 100 \text{ N} \times 5 \text{ m} = \textbf{500 N m}$
$M_2 = F_2 \times 2 \text{ m} \qquad \quad = 30 \text{ N} \times 2 \text{ m} \ = \textbf{60 N m}$

Resultant moment

$M_R = M_3 - M_1 - M_2 = 150 \text{ N m} - 500 \text{ N m} - 60 \text{ N m} = \textbf{-410 N m}$

The minus sign indicates a tendency for the resultant moment to move the lever in an anticlockwise direction. It has no mathematical significance.

(b)   We can now find the distance x at which the resultant force (F_R) acts. Remember that the negative value of the moment (M_R) indicates a tendency for the force (F_R) to move the lever in an anticlockwise direction about the fulcrum point (P). And remember that we have already calculated a value for the resultant force $(F_R = 80 \text{ N})$.

Since
$$M_R = F_R \times x$$
$$410 \text{ N m} = 80 \text{ N} \times x$$
$$x = \frac{410 \text{ N m}}{80 \text{ N}}$$
$$= 5.125 \text{ m}$$

So, the system of forces we started with can be replaced by a single force of 80 N acting at a distance of 5.125 N from the fulcrum as shown in Fig. F2.1R(b).

That was a lot of work. It really tested your stamina. Well done if you got it. If not, I hope my solution helped you.

Now return to the text

Response F2.2   Activity F2.2 is further practice on the moments of forces, so much of the detailed explanation of the previous response also applies to this one. Therefore I have only emphasised the more important points.

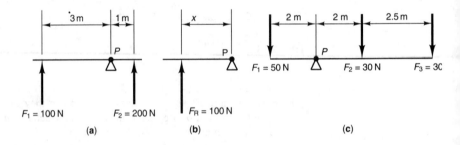

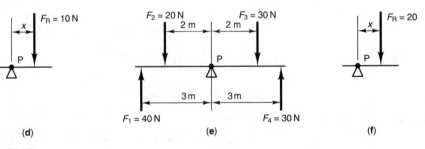

Fig. F2.2R

(a)   You can see that the resultant force can be calculated as follows:

$$F_R = F_2 - F_1 = 200 \text{ N} - 100 \text{ N} = \mathbf{100 \text{ N}}$$

Although the forces act in the same direction, they have to be subtracted because they lie on opposite sides of the pivot point (fulcrum) and therefore tend to rotate the lever in opposite directions.

Also note how I have organised this calculation to give me a positive answer for convenience. The direction of action of F_R is given by the sign of the **resultant moment** (M_R). It can be seen that:

$$M_R = M_1 - M_2$$
$$= (100 \text{ N} \times 3 \text{ m}) - (200 \text{ N} \times 1 \text{ m})$$
$$= 300 \text{ N m} - 200 \text{ N m}$$
$$= \textbf{100 N m}$$

Since M_R is positive, it is a **clockwise** moment and F_R will be so positioned that it will tend to move the lever in a clockwise direction.

(b) $$M_R = F_R \times x$$
$$100 \text{ N m} = 100 \text{ N} \times x$$
$$x = \frac{100 \text{ N m}}{100 \text{ N}}$$
$$= \textbf{1 m}$$

(c)   It can be seen that:
$$F_R = (F_2 + F_3) - F_1$$
$$= (30 \text{ N} + 30 \text{ N}) - 50 \text{ N}$$
$$= \textbf{10 N}$$

Taking moments about the pivot point P:

Clockwise moments $(+)$

$$M_2 + M_3 = (30 \text{ N} \times 2 \text{ m}) + (30 \text{ N} \times 4.5 \text{ m})$$
$$= 60 \text{ N m} + 135 \text{ N m}$$
$$= \textbf{195 N m}$$

Anticlockwise moments $(-)$

$$M_1 = 50 \text{ N} \times 2 \text{ m}$$
$$= \textbf{100 N m}$$

Therefore:

$$M_R = (M_2 + M_3) - M_1$$
$$= 195 \text{ N m} - 100 \text{ N m}$$
$$= \textbf{95 N m}$$

(d)   Since M_R is a positive moment, it will tend to rotate the lever in a clockwise direction:

$$M_R = F_R \times x$$
$$95 \text{ N m} = 10 \text{ N} \times x$$
$$x = \frac{95 \text{ N m}}{10 \text{ N}}$$
$$= \textbf{9.5 m}$$

(e)   It can be seen that:
$$F_R = (F_1 + F_4) - (F_2 + F_3)$$
$$= (40 \text{ N} + 30 \text{ N}) - (20 \text{ N} + 30 \text{ N})$$
$$= \textbf{20 N}$$

Taking moments about the pivot point P:

Clockwise moments (+)

$$M_1 + M_3 = (40 \text{ N} \times 3 \text{ m}) + (30 \text{ N} \times 2 \text{ m})$$
$$= 120 \text{ N m} + 60 \text{ N m}$$
$$= \textbf{180 N m}$$

Anticlockwise moments (−)

$$M_2 + M_4 = (20 \text{ N} \times 2 \text{ m}) + (30 \text{ N} \times 3 \text{ m})$$
$$= 40 \text{ N m} + 90 \text{ N m}$$
$$= \textbf{130 N m}$$
$$M_R = (M_1 + M_3) - (M_2 + M_4)$$
$$= 180 \text{ N m} - 130 \text{ N m}$$
$$= \textbf{50 N m}$$

Since M_R is again positive, the force (F_R) will tend to rotate the lever in a clockwise direction.

(f) $$M_R = F_R \times x$$
$$50 \text{ N m} = 20 \text{ N} \times x$$
$$x = \frac{50 \text{ N m}}{20 \text{ N}}$$
$$= \textbf{2.5 m}$$

Alternatively F_R could act upwards at a point 2.5 m to the left of the pivot. This would still produce a tendency to rotate the lever in a clockwise direction. Had M_R been negative, the dimension x would have positioned F_R so as to give a tendency to rotate the lever in an anticlockwise direction. That is, F_R would have acted downwards at a point 2.5 m to the left of the pivot point.

Next we are going to consider forces that are in equilibrium, that is, the clockwise moments exactly balance the anticlockwise moments and $M_R = 0$.

Now return to the text

Response F3.1

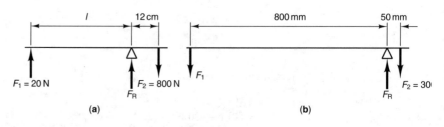

Fig. F3.1R

(a)   Taking moments about the pivot point, it can be seen that:

Clockwise moment

800 N $\times$ 12 cm = 9600 N cm

Anticlockwise moment

20 N $\times$ l

For equilibrium the clockwise moments and the anticlockwise moments must be equal. Therefore:

$$20 \text{ N} \times l = 9600 \text{ N cm}$$

$$l - \frac{9600 \text{ N cm}}{20 \text{ N}}$$

$$l = \textbf{480 cm}$$

$$F_R = F_1 + F_2$$

$$= 20 \text{ N} + 800 \text{ N}$$

$$= \textbf{820 N}$$

Thus F_R is equal and opposite to the sum of F_1 and F_2. In this case F_R is the **reaction force**, and not the resultant force. It is the force exerted at the fulcrum to support the forces acting downwards.

(b)   Taking moments about the fulcrum, it can be seen that:

Clockwise moment

300 N $\times$ 50 mm = 15 000 N mm

Anticlockwise moment

F_1 $\times$ 800 mm

For equilibrium

$$F_1 \times 800 \text{ mm} = 15000 \text{ N mm}$$

$$\text{Therefore} \quad F_1 = \frac{15\,000 \text{ N mm}}{800 \text{ mm}}$$

$$= \textbf{18.75 N}$$

$$F_R = F_1 + F_2 = 18.75 \text{ N} + 300 \text{ N} = \textbf{318.75 N}$$

This is the reaction force at the fulcrum supporting the sum of the downward forces. I hope my responses have helped you over any difficulties you may have had. If not, remember to consult your tutor before moving on. These activities are somewhat extended and a test of your mathematical stamina. If you have kept up with them, well done.

Now return to the text

Response R3.2

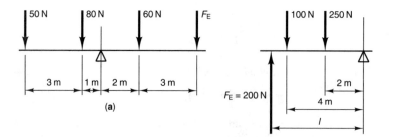

Fig. F3.2R

(a)   Taking moments about the fulcrum, you can see that:

clockwise moments $\qquad$ = anticlockwise moments

$(F_E \times 5 \text{ m}) + (60 \text{ N} \times 2 \text{ m})$ = $(80 \text{ N} \times 1 \text{ m}) + (50 \text{ N} \times 4 \text{ m})$

$(F_E \times 5 \text{ m}) + 120 \text{ N m}$ = $80 \text{ N m} + 200 \text{ N m}$

$(F_E \times 5 \text{ m})$ = $280 \text{ N m} - 120 \text{ N m}$

= 160 N m

Therefore F_E $= \dfrac{160 \text{ N m}}{5 \text{ m}}$

$= \textbf{32 N}$

reaction force at the fulcrum = the sum of the downward forces

Therefore F_R = $50 \text{ N} + 80 \text{ N} + 60 \text{ N} + 32 \text{ N}$

= $\textbf{242 N}$

(b)   Taking moments about the fulcrum, you can see that:

clockwise moments $\qquad$ = anticlockwise moments

$F_E \times l$ = $(100 \text{ N} \times 4 \text{ m}) + (250 \text{ N} \times 2 \text{ m})$

$l \times 200 \text{ N}$ = $400 \text{ N m} + 500 \text{ N m}$

= 900 N m

Therefore l $= \dfrac{900 \text{ N m}}{200 \text{ N}}$

$= \textbf{4.5 m}$

reaction force at the fulcrum = sum of the downward forces – the upward force

Therefore F_R = $100 \text{ N} + 250 \text{ N} - 200 \text{ N}$

= $\textbf{150 N}$

(c)   You can see from that the distances from the forces to the pivot of the bell-crank are measured at right angles to the lines of action of the forces. Therefore we can treat this example in the same way as the previous examples. Taking moments about the pivot:

clockwise moments = anticlockwise moments

$(100 \text{ N} \times 100 \text{ mm}) = (F_E \times 80 \text{ mm})$

$1000 \text{ N mm} \qquad = F_E \times 80 \text{ mm}$

Therefore $\quad F_E \quad = \dfrac{1000 \text{ N mm}}{80 \text{ mm}}$

$= \mathbf{125 \text{ N}}$

Again well done if you kept up with this one to the end. I hope you are able to follow the reasoning of my responses and find it helpful if you are having difficulty. Otherwise you must consult your tutor before moving on.

Now return to the text

Response F3.3

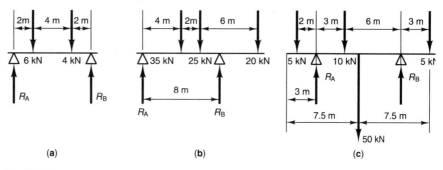

Fig. F3.3R

(a) Take moments about R_A:

clockwise moments $\qquad$ = anticlockwise moments

$(6 \text{ kN} \times 2 \text{ m}) + (4 \text{ kN} \times 6 \text{ m}) \quad = (R_B \times 8 \text{ m})$

$12 \text{ kN m} + 24 \text{ kN m} \quad = R_B \times 8 \text{ m}$

$36 \text{ kN m} \quad = R_B \times 8 \text{ m}$

Therefore $\quad R_B \quad = \dfrac{36 \text{ kN m}}{8 \text{ m}}$

$= \mathbf{4.5 \text{ k Nm}}$

Take moments about R_B:

clockwise moments = anticlockwise moments

$(R_A \times 8 \text{ m}) \quad = (6 \text{ kN m} \times 6 \text{ m}) + (4 \text{ kN m} \times 2 \text{ m})$

$R_A \times 8 \text{ m} \quad = 36 \text{ kN m} + 8 \text{ kN m}$

$R_A \times 8 \text{ m} \quad = 44 \text{ kN m}$

Therefore $\quad R_A \quad = \dfrac{44 \text{ kN m}}{8 \text{ kN m}}$

$= \mathbf{5.5 \text{ kN}}$

Check: $R_A + R_B$ = sum of the downward forces

$$5.5 \text{ kN} + 4.5 \text{ kN} = 6 \text{ kN} + 4 \text{ kN}$$

$$\mathbf{10 \text{ kN} = 10 \text{ kN}}$$

So our calculated reactions are correct. I must emphasise again that there is a temptation to take a short cut by only working out one reaction and then subtracting it from the sum of the downward forces to obtain the second reaction. The trouble is that if you get the first reaction wrong, the second reaction will also be wrong and you have no check. So the long way is the best way because, if it checks out, both answers are correct.

Note

Sometimes the following notation is used:

> CWM = clockwise moments
>
> ACWM = anticlockwise moments

(b) Take moments about R_A:

CWM $\qquad\qquad\qquad\qquad\qquad\qquad$ = ACWM

$(35 \text{ kN} \times 4 \text{ m}) + (25 \text{ kN} \times 6 \text{ m}) + (20 \text{ kN} \times 12 \text{ m}) = (R_B \times 8 \text{ m})$

$140 \text{ kN m} + 150 \text{ kN m} + 240 \text{ kN m} \qquad\qquad = \text{RB} \times 8 \text{ m}$

$\qquad\qquad\qquad 530 \text{ kN m} \qquad\qquad\qquad = R_B \times 8 \text{ m}$

Therefore $\qquad\qquad\qquad\qquad R_B \qquad\qquad = \dfrac{530 \text{ kN m}}{8 \text{ m}}$

$$= \mathbf{66.25 \text{ kN}}$$

Take moments about R_B:

CWM $\qquad\qquad\qquad\qquad$ = ACWM

$(R_A \times 8 \text{ m}) + (20 \text{ kN} \times 4 \text{ m}) \quad = (35 \text{ kN} \times 4 \text{ m}) + (25 \text{ kN} \times 2 \text{ m})$

$(R_A \times 8 \text{ m}) + 80 \text{ kN m} \qquad = 140 \text{ kN m} + 50 \text{ kN m}$

$R_A \times 8 \text{ m} \qquad\qquad\qquad = 140 \text{ kN m} + 50 \text{ kN m} - 80 \text{ kN m}$

$\qquad\qquad\qquad\qquad\qquad = 110 \text{ kN m}$

Therefore $\quad R_A \qquad\qquad = \dfrac{110 \text{ kN m}}{8 \text{ m}}$

$$= \mathbf{13.75 \text{ kN}}$$

Check: $R_A + R_B$ = sum of downward forces

$$66.25 \text{ kN} + 13.75 \text{ kN} = 35 \text{ kN} + 25 \text{ kN} + 20 \text{ kN}$$

$$\mathbf{80 \text{ kN} = 80 \text{ kN}}$$

So the reactions are correct as calculated.

In the next example, you have to take the weight of the beam into account. Remember that for a beam of uniform section, it is assumed that the weight of the beam acts vertically downwards through the centre of the beam.

(c)   Take moments about R_A:

CWM   = ACWM

$(10 \text{ kN} \times 3 \text{ m}) + (50 \text{ kN} \times 4.5 \text{ m}) + (5 \text{ kN} \times 12 \text{ m}) = (R_B \times 9 \text{ m}) + (5 \text{ kN} \times 2 \text{ m})$

$30 \text{ kN m} \qquad + 225 \text{ kN m} \qquad + 60 \text{ kN m} \qquad = (R_B \times 9 \text{ m}) + 10 \text{ kN m}$

$\qquad\qquad\qquad\qquad\qquad\qquad 315 \text{ kN m} \quad = (R_B \times 9 \text{ m}) + 10 \text{ kN m}$

$\qquad\qquad\qquad\qquad\qquad\qquad R_B \times 9 \text{ m} \quad = 315 \text{ kN m} - 10 \text{ kN m}$

$\qquad\qquad\qquad\qquad\qquad\qquad\qquad\qquad\quad = 305 \text{ kN m}$

Therefore $\qquad\qquad\qquad\qquad\qquad\qquad R_B \quad = \dfrac{305 \text{ kN m}}{9 \text{ m}}$

$\qquad\qquad\qquad\qquad\qquad\qquad\qquad\qquad\quad = \textbf{33.9 kN}\ (1 \text{ d.p.})$

Take moments about R_B:

CWM   = ACWM

$(R_A \times 9 \text{ m}) + (5 \text{ kN} \times 3 \text{ m}) = (50 \text{ kN} \times 4.5\text{m}) + (10 \text{ kN} \times 6 \text{ m}) + (5 \text{ kN} \times 11 \text{ m})$

$(R_A \times 9 \text{ m}) + 15 \text{ kN m} \quad = 225 \text{ kN m} + 60 \text{ kN m} + 55 \text{ kN m}$

$(R_A \times 9 \text{ m}) + 15 \text{ kN m} \quad = 340 \text{ kN m}$

$\qquad\qquad R_A \times 9 \text{ m} \quad = 340 \text{ kN m} - 15 \text{ kN m} = 325 \text{ kN m}$

Therefore $\quad R_A \qquad\quad = \dfrac{325 \text{ kN m}}{9 \text{ m}}$

$\qquad\qquad\qquad\qquad\qquad = \textbf{36.1 kN}\ (1 \text{ d.p.})$

Check: $R_A + R_B \qquad\qquad = $ sum of downward forces

$33.9 \text{ kN} + 36.1 \text{ kN} = 5 \text{ kN} + 10 \text{ kN} + 50 \text{ kN} + 5 \text{ kN}$

$\qquad\qquad\textbf{70 kN} = \textbf{70 kN}$

Therefore the reactions R_A and R_B are correct as calculated.

With all this practice, I hope that you have now mastered the taking of moments. The calculations tend to be rather long and tedious so I hope you have not been taking short cuts; they invariably lead to errors.

Now return to the text

Response G1.1   Your completed statement should read:

A body contains a large number of **particles** each of which has **mass**. The weight of each **particle** is the force of gravity acting on its **mass**. The lines of action of the **forces** acting on these particles can be considered to be **parallel** with each other. They can be replaced by a single resultant **force** called the **weight** of the body. The weight of the body acts through a point called the **centre** of **gravity** of the body.

Now return to the text

Response G4.1   The plumb bob shown in Activity G4.1 is in **stable** equilibrium. Any attempt to disturb the plumb bob can only raise its centre of gravity. Therefore it will always swing back to the position shown in the figure, with its centre of gravity vertically below the point of suspension (P).

Now return to the text

Response G5.1   (a)   Unstable   the line of action of the force of gravity **does not** pass through the base.
(b)   Stable   the line of action of the force of gravity **does** pass through the base.
(c)   Stable   the line of action of the force of gravity **does** pass through the base.
(d)   Unstable   the line of action of the force of gravity **does not** pass through the base.

Note that (b) is the most stable because it alone satisfies all the following criteria:

● The line of action of the force of gravity passes through its base.
● The base has a large area.
● The centre of gravity is low.

Now return to the text

Response G6.1

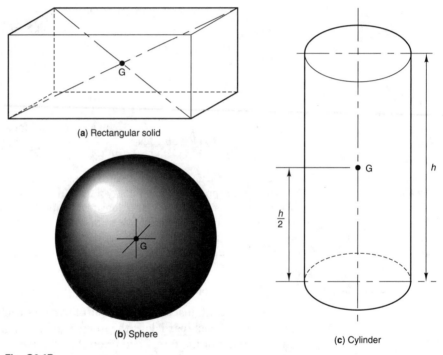

(a) Rectangular solid

(b) Sphere

(c) Cylinder

Fig. G6.1R

(a)   The centre of gravity (G) is at the centre of the solid at the point where the diagonals cross each other.
(b)   The centre of gravity (G) is at the centre of the sphere.
(c)   The centre of gravity (G) lies on the axis of the cylinder at a point halfway along the axis.

Now return to the text

Response G7.1

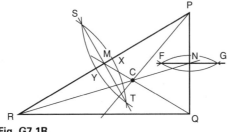

Fig. G7.1R

To bisect the side PR

- With centre R, use your compasses to strike an arc to cut side PR at X.
- With centre P, use your compasses to strike an arc of the same radius to cut side PR at Y.
- These arcs cut each other (intersect) at S and T.
- Join points S and T with a straight line.
- Line ST cuts side PR at M. This is the midpoint of side PR.

To bisect the side PQ

- Repeat the above construction using centres P and Q.
- The arcs will intersect at F and G.
- Join F and G with a straight line which cuts side PQ at N.
- N is the midpoint of side PQ.

To find the centre of area (C)

- Join point M to the opposite vertex Q with a straight line.
- Join point N to the opposite vertex R with a straight line.
- Lines QN and RN cut at the point C; this is the centre of area (centroid) of the triangle.

Side RQ could also have been used, in which case its midpoint would have been joined to vertex P.

Now return to the text

Response G8.1   (a)   The centre of area (centroid) of any triangle lies at a point measured one-third of the perpendicular distance from any side to the opposite angle, as shown.

$$y = \frac{1}{3} \times 6 \text{ cm} = \textbf{2 cm} \text{ measured at right angles (perpendicular) to QR}$$

$$x = \frac{1}{3} \times 9 \text{ cm} = \textbf{3 cm} \text{ measured at right angles (perpendicular) to PR}$$

C is the centroid of the triangle PQR.

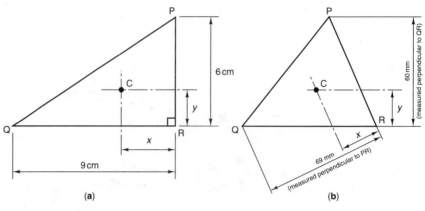

Fig. G8.1R

(b)

$$y = \frac{1}{3} \times 60 \text{ mm} = \textbf{20 mm} \text{ measured perpendicular to the side TU}$$

$$x = \frac{1}{3} \times 69 \text{ mm} = \textbf{23 mm} \text{ measured perpendicular to the side SU}$$

C is the centroid (centre of area) of the triangle STU.

Now return to the text

Response G10.1 The symmetrical plane figures complete with their lines of symmetry which I have added for you are shown in Fig. G10.1R(a). I hope that yours are the same. Note that the points where the lines of symmetry cross each other are the centres of area (C) for the figures.

So far we have only considered simple, symmetrical, geometric plane figures. Before we finish this section, I want to introduce you to a method of finding the centre of area for any irregular shape. We do this as follows.

- Cut the shape of the area from thin but stiff card then pierce the card with two holes near the edge as shown in Fig. G10.1R(b).
- Suspend the card from a pivot passing through one of the holes and suspend a plumb bob from the same pivot.
- The card, or lamina, to use its scientific name, will swing into such a position that its centroid (C) will lie directly beneath the pivot. It will lie somewhere along a line immediately behind the plumb line. Carefully mark this line on the card with a pencil.
- Now repeat the process using the second hole as shown in (C).
- Where the two lines cross is the centre of area (C) for the shape represented by the card.
- It is not as easy as it sounds to mark the lines accurately behind the plumb line. Therefore it is advisable to use more than two holes. The lines you mark are unlikely all to cross at the same point.
- The centroid (C) will lie at the centre of the space bounded by the lines you have marked, This is shown in (d).

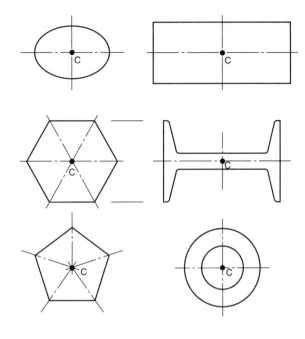

(a)

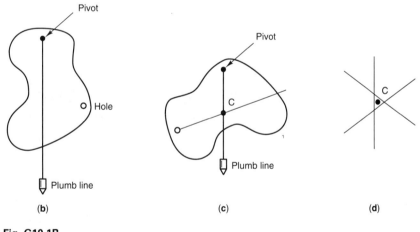

(b)   (c)   (d)

Fig. G10.1R

Compared with the calculations in the previous module, these geometrical solutions must seem like a rest cure. However, all good things come to an end and, before we finish this section, we have one calculation to solve using moments of forces.

Now return to the text

Response G11.1

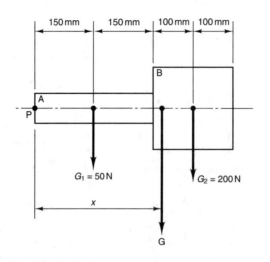

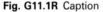

Fig. G11.1R Caption

With reference to the above figure, remember that:

G$_1$ acts through the midpoint of A

G$_2$ acts through the midpoint of B

So taking moments about P:

$$\text{CWM} = \text{ACWM}$$
$$(50 \text{ N} \times 150 \text{ mm}) + (200 \text{ N} \times 400 \text{ mm}) = (G \times x)$$
$$7500 \text{ N mm} + 80\,000 \text{ N mm} = (50 \text{ N} + 200 \text{ N}) \times x$$
$$87\,500 \text{ N mm} = 250 \text{ N} \times x$$

Therefore
$$x = \frac{87\,500 \text{ N mm}}{250 \text{ N}}$$

$$= \mathbf{350 \text{ mm}}$$

We are about halfway through the text and responses, so I am assuming that by now you are used to the system and that you are using my responses to back up the text when things go wrong and to give you confidence when things go right. I also hope that you are consulting your tutor when you get really stuck. I can't emphasise too often how important it is to resist moving on until you are really confident with the work you have just completed.

Now return to the text

Response H1.1   Here are some further examples where friction is desirable and where friction is undesirable. You may have thought of others. Mine are only a guide.

Desirable

Walking   It is easier to walk on a gravel path than on ice. You need friction to stop you from slipping.

Writing   You don't want your writing pad to keep slipping about on your desk or table while you are writing.

Screwed fastenings   You don't want the nut on a bolt to keep working loose. You need friction between the threads of the bolt and the threads of the nut to prevent this happening.

Undesirable

Metal cutting   Friction between the metal-cutting tool and the workpiece or between the chips removed by the tool and the toolface, can lead to wear and reduced tool life. It can also cause the tool to overheat and become soft. A cutting fluid with good lubricating and coolant properties should be used.

Space vehicles   Friction between a space vehicle and the Earth's atmosphere causes the vehicle to heat up on re-entry. Unless special precautions are taken, this heat is sufficient to burn up and destroy the space vehicle and its crew.

Sledge runners   Competitors in winter sports polish the runners of their vehicles so as to keep the friction to a minimum. This is necessary to gain maximum speed.

Now return to the text

Response H1.2

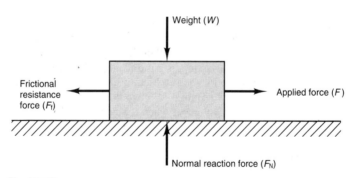

Fig. H1.2R

(a)   Given: the weight (W) of the body   = 200 kN

the applied force (F)   = 120 kN

the normal reaction force (F_N) = the weight (W) = 200 kN

$$\mu = \frac{F}{F_N} = \frac{120 \ \text{kN}}{200 \ \text{kN}} = 0.6$$

There are no units because coefficient of friction is a ratio and ratios have no units.

(b) From Table H1.1 we find that the coefficient of friction (μ) for brass on cast iron (or cast iron on brass) is 0.15. We are also given that the applied force (F) = 30 N.

Since $\mu = (F)/(F_N)$, then $F_N = (F)/(\mu)$ and we can now find the normal force F_N.

$$F_N = \frac{F}{\mu}$$

$$= \frac{30 \text{ N}}{0.15}$$

$$= \textbf{200 N}$$

where: $F = 30$ N
$\mu = 0.15$

In this example the weight of the body is equal to the normal reaction force, so:

$$W = F_N = 200 \text{ N}$$

You may wonder why we use the normal reaction force when it is equal to the weight. This is because in more complicated examples W and F_N are not always equal. For example, when the applied force (F) is not acting parallel to the friction surface, or when the friction surface is itself inclined. These situations are beyond the scope of this book but, providing we use the formula:

$$\mu = \frac{F}{F_N}$$

It will work correctly in any situation.

Now return to the text

Response H2.1 (a) Moving the boat over the rough shingle requires the greater force because the sharp edges of the stones bite into its bottom, causing considerable friction and wear. Once it has been launched, the water separates the boat from the shingle. The water is acting as a lubricant; it is keeping the friction surfaces separated. There is no longer any friction between the boat and the shingle. Much less force is now required to move the boat.

(b) Most wear will occur when the boat is dragged over the shingle. The stones will scour the bottom of the boat. Once in the water wear becomes negligible.

Now return to the text

Response H2.2 (a) Incorrect   A lubricant is used to reduce friction between bearing surfaces.

(b) Correct   A lubricant reduces friction by preventing the bearing surfaces from coming into contact with each other.

(c) Incorrect   A thick oil (an oil with a high viscosity) causes drag between the bearing surfaces and wastes energy. An oil should be no thicker than is necessary to support the load on the bearing. However, allowance must be made for the oil becoming thinner as it warms up. Generally, high speed bearing situations require a thinner oil than heavy-duty, low speed applications. Always use the grade of oil specified by the manufacturer of the machine.

(d) Correct   By keeping the bearing surfaces separated, there are no metal-to-metal contact points and no shearing takes place. This prevents wear of the shaft or the bearing.

(e) Correct   The contact area between the chip and the toolface is very small compared with a bearing and the cutting force is very large. Therefore the load per unit area is very much greater for metal cutting than the load per unit area for a bearing. Ordinary lubricating oils cannot support such high loads and are therefore unsuitable as cutting lubricants. Also, the high temperatures generated at the chip/tool interface would cause ordinary lubricating oil to vaporise and give off noxious fumes. Under extreme conditions it may even ignite. Special lubricants and coolants have been developed for metal-cutting applications which avoid these problems.

Now return to the text

Response I1.1   Your completed table should read as follows.

Table I1.1R

Force (F)	Area (A)	Pressure (p)	Calculation
(a) 300 N	2 m^2	**150 N/m^2**	$p = F/A = (800 \text{ N})/(2 \text{ m}^2) = 150 \text{ N/m}^2$
(b) 400 N	2 m^2	**200 N/m^2**	$p = (400 \text{ N})/(2 \text{ m}^2) = 200 \text{ N/m}^2$
(c) 600 N	2 m^2	**300 N/m^2**	$p = (600 \text{ N})/(2 \text{ m}^2) = 300 \text{ N/m}^2$
(d) 800 N	2 m^2	**400 N/m^2**	$p = (800 \text{ N})/(2 \text{ m}^2) = 400 \text{ N/m}^2$
(e) 1 kN	2 m^2	**500 N/m^2**	$p = (1000 \text{ N})/(2 \text{ m}^2) = 500 \text{ N/m}^2$

You can see from the table that the pressure increases as the force increases, while the area on which it acts is kept constant. With the area constant, the increase in pressure is proportional to the increase in force.

If the force is the weight of a body, the force will act vertically downwards and we can rewrite the formula as:

$$p = \frac{W}{A} \quad \text{or} \quad p = \frac{M \times g}{A}$$

where: W = weight of the body
M = mass of the body
g = gravitational constant (9.81 m/s^2)
A = area

Now return to the text

Response I1.2   Your completed table should read as follows.

Table I1.2R

Force (F)	Area (A)	Pressure (p)	Calculation
(a) 300 N	2 m^2	150 N/m^2	$p = F/A = (300 \text{ N})/(2 \text{ m}^2) = 150 \text{ N/m}^2$
(b) 300 N	4 m^2	75 N/m^2	$p = (300 \text{ N})/(4 \text{ m}^2) = 75 \text{ N/m}^2$
(c) 300 N	6 m^2	50 N/m^2	$p = (300 \text{ N})/(6 \text{ m}^2) = 50 \text{ N/m}^2$
(d) 300 N	1 m^2	300 N/m^2	$p = (300 \text{ N})/(1 \text{ m}^2) = 300 \text{ N/m}^2$
(e) 300 N	0.5 m^2	600 N/m^2	$p = (300 \text{ N})/(0.5 \text{ m}^2) = 600 \text{ N/m}^2$

You can see from Table I1.2R that, with constant force, the pressure decreases when the area increases. This is because you are spreading the load. Examples of this are shown on lines (a), (b) and (c) of the table. Note how a decrease in area, (d) and (e), increases the pressure. With constant force, the change in pressure is inversely proportional to the change in area or is inversely proportional to the square of the diameter.

To **increase the pressure**, increase the force or decrease the area or both.
To **decrease the pressure**, decrease the force or increase the area or both.

Now return to the text

Response I1.3   (a) $p = F_1/A_1 = (250 \text{ N})/(0.5 \text{ m}^2) = 500 \text{ N/m}^2 = \textbf{500 Pa}$

Remember that 1 N/m^2 = 1 Pa.

(b)   To prevent movement, F_2 must equal F_1. Therefore $F_2 = F_1 = 250$ N. So
$p = F_2/A_2 = (250 \text{ N})/(2.0 \text{ m}^2) = 125 \text{ N/m}^2 = \textbf{125 Pa}$

Now return to the text

Response I2.1   In liquids the pressure depends upon:

- The density of the liquid.
- The gravitational constant ($g = 9.81$ m/s^2 on planet Earth).
- The height of the column of liquid (the pressure head).

Therefore p_1 is the **greater** pressure because:

- The density is the same for the liquid in both flasks and, therefore, density does not affect the answer.
- In liquids the pressure is independent of area and, therefore, area does not affect the answer.
- In liquids the pressure depends upon the **height** of the liquid column, so p_1 is the greater pressure because h_1 is greater than h_2.

Now return to the text

Response I2.2   The pressure acting on the diver is calculated as follows:

$p = h \times p \times g$
$= 15 \text{ m} \times 1020 \text{ kg/m}^3 \times 9.81 \text{ m/s}^2$

$= 150093$ Pa

$= \textbf{150 kPa}$ (3 s.f.)

where: $h =$ pressure head $= 15$ m
$\rho =$ liquid density $= 1020$ kg/m
$g =$ gravitational constant $= 9.81$ m/s^2

For the next activity you will have to transpose the formula as follows:

$$h = \frac{p}{\rho \times g} \quad \text{and} \quad \rho = \frac{p}{h \times g}$$

Now return to the text

Response 12.3   Taking $g = 10$ m/s^2, your completed table should read as follows.

Table 12.3R

	Depth (h)	Density (ρ)	Pressure (p)
(a)	10 m	1000 kg/m^3	**100 kPa**
(b)	2 m	0.8 g/cm^3	**16 kPa**
(c)	**20 m**	720 kg/m^3	144 kPa
(d)	80 m	**1020 kg/m^3**	8.16×10^5 Pa

I will now take you through the calculations.

(a) $p = h \times p \times g$

$= 10$ m $\times 1000$ kg/m$^3 \times 10$ m/s^2

$= 100000$ Pa

$= \textbf{100 kPa}$

where: $h = 10$ m
$\rho = 1000$ kg/m^3
$g = 10$ m/s^2

(b) $p = h \times \rho \times g$

$= 2$ m $\times 800$ kg/m$^3 \times 10$ m/s^2

$= 16000$ Pa

$= \textbf{16 kPa}$

where: $h = 2$ m
$\rho = 0.8$ g/cm$^3 = 800$ kg/m^3
$g = 10$ m/s^2

I hope you remembered to convert density in g/cm^3 into kg/m^3.

(c) $h = \dfrac{p}{\rho \times g}$

$= \dfrac{144000 \text{ Pa}}{720 \text{ kg/m}^3 \times 10 \text{ m/s}^2}$

$= \textbf{20 m}$

where: $p = 144 \text{ kPa} = 144\,000 \text{ Pa}$
$\rho = 720 \text{ kg/m}^3$
$g = 10 \text{ m/s}^2$

I hope you remembered to convert pressure in kPa into Pa before substituting in the formula. I also hope that you transposed the formula correctly.

(d) $\rho = \dfrac{p}{h \times g}$

$= \dfrac{8.16 \times 10^5 \text{ Pa}}{80 \text{ m} \times 10 \text{ m/s}^2}$

$= \textbf{1020 kg/m}^3$

where: $p = 8.16 \times 10^5 \text{ Pa}$
$h = 80 \text{ m}$
$g = 10 \text{ m/s}^2$

I hope you managed to cope with the pressure in standard form. The pressure of 8.16×10^5 Pa is the same as $816\,000$ Pa. However, there was no need to make this conversion as all scientific calculators accept an input in standard form. Don't forget, if you are having any difficulties that you can't sort out with the help of my responses, you must seek help from your tutor before moving on.

Now return to the text

Response I2.4 (a) The area of the container base $= 3 \text{ m} \times 4 \text{ m} = 12 \text{ m}^2$.
The given pressure is $600 \text{ Pa} = 600 \text{ N/m}^2$.
Therefore, the force acting on the base is
$600 \text{ N/m}^2 \times 12 \text{ m}^2 = \textbf{7200 N}$ or **7.2 kN**

(b) The force of 7.2 kN will act through the centre of the base. Since the base is rectangular, its centre will be where the diagonals intersect at point P, as shown in the figure.

7.2 kN

Now return to the text   **Fig. I2.4R**

Response I2.5 Your response should be as follows:

$P_1 = 40 \text{ kPa}$ (given) at a depth of 4 m (given)

Since pressure is proportional to depth, the remaining pressures are:

$p_2 = \dfrac{3}{4} \times 40 \text{ kPa} = \textbf{30 kPa}$ (at 3 m from the surface)

$p_3 = \dfrac{2}{4} \times 40 \text{ kPa} = \textbf{20 kPa}$ (at 2 m from the surface)

$p_4 = \dfrac{1}{4} \times 40 \text{ kPa} = \textbf{10 kPa}$ (at 1 m from the surface)

$p_s = \dfrac{0}{4} \times 40 \text{ kPa} = \textbf{0 kPa}$ (at the surface)

At the surface there is no depth of liquid therefore there can be no pressure. Remember that height of liquid column, pressure head, and depth of liquid are all the same thing and equal h in the formula.

Now return to the text

Response 12.6   Your calculations should read as follows:

(a) $p = h \times \rho \times g$

$\qquad = 2 \text{ m} \times 1000 \text{ kg/m}^3 \times 10 \text{ m/s}^2$

$\qquad = 20\,000 \text{ Pa}$

$\qquad = \mathbf{20 \ kPa}$

where: $h = 2 \text{ m}$
$\qquad \quad \rho = 1000 \text{ kg/m}^2$
$\qquad \quad g = 10 \text{ m/s}^2$

(b) $F = p \times A$

$\qquad = 20\,000 \text{ Pa} \times 9 \text{ m}^2$

$\qquad = 180\,000$

$\qquad = \mathbf{180 \ kN} \qquad$ (Remember that $1 \text{ Pa} = 1 \text{ N/m}^2$)

where: $p = 20\,000 \text{ Pa}$ (see (a) above)
$\qquad \quad A = 3 \text{ m} \times 3 \text{ m} = 9 \text{ m}^2$

(c) p_s = pressure acting on the side of the tank. This is zero at the surface of the liquid and a maximum at the bottom of the side where it joins the bottom of the tank. Therefore we use the average pressure that occurs at the midpoint of the side of the tank:

$$p_s = \frac{p}{2}$$

$$\quad = \frac{20 \text{ kPa}}{2} \qquad \text{(using the pressure calculated in (a) above)}$$

$$\quad = \mathbf{10 \ kPa}$$

(d) $F_s = p_s \times A$

$\qquad = 10\,000 \text{ Pa} \times 6 \text{ m}^2$

$\qquad = 60\,000 \text{ N}$

$\qquad = \mathbf{60 \ kN}$

where: $p_s = 10\,000 \text{ Pa} \qquad$ (as calculated in (b) above)
$\qquad \quad A = 3 \text{ m} \times 2 \text{ m} = 6 \text{ m}^2$

(e)   The force F_s acts at the centre of the submerged area of the side, that is, $\frac{1}{2} \times 2 \text{ m} = 1 \text{ m}$ up from the bottom of the tank.

Remember that throughout this activity and its related response we use the height of the side below the surface of the liquid (submerged height) not its actual height.

Now return to the text

Response I3.1   (a)   True   Gas pressure is the sum total of all the impact forces of the gas particles on the sides, top and bottom of the container.

(b)   False   Only gases can be compressed; solids and liquids cannot be compressed.

(c)   False   As stated above, liquids cannot be compressed.

(d)   False   A fluid is a substance that can flow. Both liquids and gases can flow, so they are both fluids. Liquids cannot be compressed; only gases can be compressed.

(e)   True   See my answer to (a).

(f)   True   A gas in a closed container exerts a uniform pressure in all directions.

Now return to the text

Response I4.1   (a)   The left-hand diagram in the activity is correct because pressure is dependent on the **vertical height** of the mercury column above the surface of the reservoir, not the slant height.

(b)   Although water appears to have many advantages, its density is too low. At standard atmospheric pressure a mercury column is 760 mm high. The corresponding water column would be 10 336 mm (10.336 m) high – as high as a three-storey house! Not a very convenient size for a barometer.

Now return to the text

Response I4.2   **Mercury barometer**

Advantages

- Simplicity, there are no mechanisms nor moving parts to wear out and introduce errors.
- High level of accuracy. A laboratory instrument.

Disadvantages

- Relatively high initial cost.
- Lack of portability. Must be kept fixed to a vertical surface.

Aneroid barometer

Advantages

- Relatively low cost.
- Compact and easily portable. Will work in any position.

Disadvantages

- Not as accurate nor as sensitive as a mercury barometer.
- The many moving parts in an aneroid barometer can become worn or get out of adjustment. An aneroid barometer should be checked against a mercury barometer from time to time.

These are the main advantages and disadvantages for the two types of barometer. You may have thought of some more. Well done if you did.

Now return to the text

Response I5.1   **U-tube manometer**

Advantages

- It is simple and accurate.
- It is very sensitive and can detect small pressure changes.
- It can detect negative as well as positive pressure changes.

Disadvantages

- It cannot be used at high temperatures and pressures.
- It requires careful handling. The glass U-tube is easily broken.
- The liquid is easily spilt.
- It must be kept upright in use to give a true reading.

Bourdon-tube pressure gauge

Advantages

- It can be used at high temperatures and pressures (e.g. steam pressure of a boiler).
- It is compact and easy to read; it can be used in any position.

Disadvantages

- The mechanism can become worn or damaged; this would introduce errors.
- It is not as sensitive nor as accurate as the U-tube manometer, particularly at low pressures.

Now return to the text

Response I6.1   Your solutions should read as follows:

(a)   atmospheric pressure $(p_A) = h \times \rho \times g$

$$= 0.76 \text{ m} \times 13\,600 \text{ kg/m}^3 \times 9.81 \text{ m/s}^2$$

$$= 101\,400 \text{ Pa}$$

$$= \textbf{101.4 kPa}$$

where: $h = 760$ mm
$ = 0.76$ m
$ \rho = 13\,600 \text{ kg/m}^3$
$ g = 9.81 \text{ m/s}^2$

(b)   atmospheric pressure $(p_A) = h \times \rho \times g$

$$= 0.77 \text{ m} \times 13\,600 \text{ kg/m}^3 \times 9.81 \text{ m/s}^2$$

$$= 102\,730 \text{ Pa}$$

$$= \textbf{102.73 kPa}$$

where: $h = 770$ mm
$ = 0.77$ m
$ \rho = 13\,600 \text{ kg/m}^3$
$ = 9.81 \text{ m/s}^2$

(c)   Remember that   1 mbar $= 1 \times 10^2$ Pa $= 100$ Pa

Therefore   950 mbar $= 950 \times 100$ Pa

$= 95\,000$ Pa

$= 95$ kPa

(d) A forecaster would refer to (b) above as high pressure since it is greater than standard (normal) pressure of 760 mm of mercury. A forecaster would refer to (c) above as low pressure since it is less than standard (normal) pressure. A pressure of 950 mbar $= 95$ kPa, compared with standard pressure of 760 mm of mercury (101.3 kPa).

Now return to the text

Response I6.2   Your calculations should read as follows:

atmospheric pressure $= h \times \rho \times g$

$= 0.75 \times 13\,600$ kg/m^3 $\times 9.81$ m/s^2

$= 100\,062$

$= \mathbf{100\ kPa}$ (to nearest whole number)

where: $h = 750$ mm of mercury
$= 0.75$ m
$\rho = 13\,600$ kg/m^3
$g = 9.81$ m/s^2

absolute pressure = atmospheric pressure + gauge pressure

$= 100$ kPa $+ 400$ kPa (given)

$= \mathbf{500\ kPa}$

Well done if you got the last two activities correct. They were not at all easy.

Now return to the text

Response I7.1   Your calculations should read as follows:

(a) $F_2 \times D_1{}^2 \quad = F_1 \times D_2{}^2$

$F_2 \times 20^2$ cm $= 50$ N $\times 80^2$ cm

$F_2 \quad = \dfrac{50 \text{ N} \times 80^2 \text{ cm}}{20^2 \text{ cm}}$

$= \mathbf{800\ N}$

where: $D_1 = 20$ cm
$D_2 = 80$ cm
$F_1 = 50$ N

(b) The volume of fluid moved from the small cylinder to the large cylinder is constant. Volume transferred from smaller cylinder:

$V_\text{s} =$ piston area $\times$ piston stroke

$= \dfrac{\pi}{4} \times 20^2$ cm $\times 10$ cm (stroke)

$= \mathbf{1000\pi\ cm^3}$

(Leave π alone for the moment, it will cancel out later.)

Volume received by larger cylinder:

$$V_{\text{L}} = \text{piston area} \times \text{piston stroke}$$

$$= \frac{\pi}{4} \times 80^2 \text{ cm} \times \text{stroke of larger piston}$$

But we have already said that the volume of fluid transferred is constant. Therefore:

$$V_{\text{S}} \qquad = V_{\text{L}}$$

$$1000\pi \text{ cm}^2 = \frac{\pi}{4} \times 80^2 \text{ cm} \times \text{stroke (of larger piston)}$$

$$\text{stroke} \quad = \frac{1000 \times \pi \times 4}{\pi \times 80^2} \quad \text{(notice that } \pi \text{ cancels out)}$$

$$= \mathbf{0.625 \text{ cm}}$$

The movement of the pistons (strokes) is inversely proportional to their areas and, because π cancels out, inversely proportional to the square of their diameters. From the previous example, if the 80 cm diameter piston rises 0.625 cm then the small piston (20 cm diameter) descends:

$$0.625 \text{ cm} \times \frac{80^2 \text{ cm}}{20^2 \text{ cm}} = 10 \text{ cm}$$

(c) $\qquad F_2 \times D_1{}^2 = F_1 \times D_2{}^2$

$$2000 \text{ N} \times 20^2 \text{ cm} = F_1 \times 80^2 \text{ cm}$$

$$F_1 = \frac{2000 \text{ N} \times 20^2 \text{ cm}}{80^2 \text{ cm}}$$

$$= \mathbf{125 \text{ N}}$$

where: $D_1 = 20$ cm
$\qquad\qquad D_2 = 80$ cm
$\qquad\qquad F_2 = 2000$ N

The distance moved by the force F_1 is inversely proportional to the square of the piston diameters. Therefore the distance moved by $F_1 = 60 \text{ cm} \times (80^2)/(20^2) = 960$ cm.

I hope you managed to follow that one through without too much trouble and that you are beginning to get a feel for these problems on hydrostatics. If not remember to consult your tutor.

Now return to the text

Response I7.2 Your calculations should read as follows:

(a)   Pressure in the system is generated by the master cylinder. Therefore:

$$p = \frac{F_1}{A}$$

$$= \frac{400 \text{ N}}{0.0003 \text{ m}^2}$$

$$= 1\,333\,333 \text{ Pa}$$

$$= \mathbf{1.3 \text{ MPa}} \text{ (1 d.p.)}$$

where: $F_1 = 400$N (given)
$A = \frac{1}{4}(\pi \times (0.02 \text{ m})^2)$
$= 0.0003 \text{ m}^2$ (4 d.p.)

Note how I have changed the piston diameter from 2 cm to 0.02 m so as to give the answer in pascals.

(b)   Forces acting on the front brakes. Here we can use the ratio formula.

$$F_1 \times D_2{}^2 \quad = F_2 \times D_1{}^2$$
$$400 \text{ N} \times 5^2 \text{ cm} = F_2 \times 2^2 \text{ cm}$$
$$F_2 \quad = \frac{400 \text{ N} \times 5^2 \text{ cm}}{2^2 \text{ cm}}$$
$$= \textbf{2500 N}$$

where: $F_1 = 400$ N (given)
$D_1 = 2$ cm
$D_2 = 5$ cm

D_3 is also 5 cm, so force F_3 will also be 2500 N.

(c)   Forces acting on the rear brakes can also be found in the same way:

$$F_1 \times D_4 \quad = F_4 \times D_1$$
$$400 \text{ N} \times 4^2 \text{ cm} = F_4 \times 2^2 \text{ cm}$$
$$F_4 \quad = \frac{400 \text{ N} \times 4^2 \text{ cm}}{2^2 \text{ cm}}$$
$$= \textbf{1600 N}$$

where: $F_1 = 400$ N (given)
$D_1 = 2$ cm
$D_4 = 4$ cm

D_5 is also 4 cm, so force F_5 will also be 1600 N.

Now return to the text

Response I8.1   The water level shown in the activity consists of two open-topped transparent measuring cylinders joined by a flexible rubber or plastic pipe. The principle of connected vessels applies to this equipment. The water levels in both measuring cylinders will lie in the same plane.

In practice, both cylinders are held upright against the walls in the position shown. Water is carefully poured into the level until the water in one limb is level with the top of the wall. If the tops of the walls lie in the same plane, the water surface in both limbs of the level will be in line with the tops of the walls, as shown in the activity figure. Any error can be read off on the scales of the measuring cylinders. You will not have used the same words as I have but, if the meaning of what you have written is the same, your response is correct. Well done.

Now return to the text

Response I8.2   Your calculations should read as follows:

(a) $p = \dfrac{f}{A} = \dfrac{50 \text{ N}}{20 \text{ cm}^2} = \dfrac{50 \text{ N}}{0.002 \text{ m}^2} = \textbf{25 000 Pa}$

Note how I had to change cm^2 into m^2 in order to get my answer in pascals.

(b) $\qquad p = \rho \times g \times h$

therefore $h = \dfrac{p}{\rho \times g}$

$\qquad = \dfrac{25\,000 \text{ Pa}}{1000 \text{ kg/m}^3 \times 9.81 \text{ m/s}^2}$

$\qquad = \textbf{2.548 m}$ (3 d.p.)

where: $p = 25\,000$ Pa (from (a) above)
$\qquad\rho = 1 \text{ g/cm}^2 = 1000 \text{ kg/m}^3$
$\qquad g = 9.81 \text{ m/s}^2$

Well done if you got the correct solution. If not, I hope my response has helped you.

Now return to the text

Response I8.3   Your calculations should read as follows:

(a) $p = \rho_A \times g \times h_A$
$\qquad = 13\,590 \text{ kg/m}^3 \times 9.81 \text{ m/s}^2 \times 0.02 \text{ m}$
$\qquad = \textbf{2666.4}$ Pa (1 d.p.)

where: $\rho_A = 13\,590 \text{ kg/m}^3$
$\qquad h_A = 0.02 \text{ m}$
$\qquad g = 9.81 \text{ m/s}^2$

This is the pressure at the interface and we use it to solve part (b) of this activity.

(b) $p = p_B \times g \times h_B$ therefore:

$h_B = \dfrac{p}{\rho_B \times g}$

$\qquad = \dfrac{2666.4 \text{ Pa}}{800 \text{ kg/m}^3 \times 9.81 \text{ m/s}^2}$

$\qquad = \textbf{0.34 m}$ (2 d.p.)

where: $p = 2666.4$ Pa (from part (a))
$\qquad \rho_B = 800 \text{ kg/m}^3$
$\qquad g = 9.81 \text{ m/s}^2$

The interface pressure is common to both liquids, so the column height has to be greater for the liquid with the lower density. The ratio of the heights is in inverse proportion to the densities of the liquids. Therefore:

$$\frac{h_A}{\rho_B} = \frac{h_B}{\rho_A}$$

Let's test this ratio formula to find h_B using the previous data. Rearranging the formula we get:

$$h_B = \frac{h_A \times \rho_A}{\rho_B}$$

$$= \frac{0.02 \text{ m} \times 13\,590 \text{ kg/m}^3}{800 \text{ kg/m}^3}$$

$$= \textbf{0.34 m} \text{ (2 d.p.)}$$

where: $h_A = 0.02$ m
$\rho_A = 13\,590$ kg/m^3
$\rho_B = 800$ kg/m^3

This is the same answer as we got previously working from first principles. So the ratio formula gives us an alternative and simpler method for solving this type of problem.

Now return to the text

Response I9.1   (a)   If the ship weighs 5 MN, then the weight of water displaced by the ship must also weigh 5 MN if the ship is to float.

(b)   (i)   If 1 MN of cargo is loaded onto the ship, the water displaced by the ship must also increase by 1 MN to give a total displacement of 6 MN.

(ii)   The ship will float lower in the water so that the submerged part of the hull will displace 6 MN of water.

Now return to the text

Response I9.2   (a)   If the box weighs 20 kN then it must displace 20 kN of water in order to float:

$F = V \times \rho \times g$ therefore

$$V = \frac{F}{\rho \times g}$$

$$= \frac{20\,000 \text{ N}}{1000 \text{ kg/m}^3 \times 10 \text{ m/s}^2}$$

$$= \textbf{2 m}^3$$

where: $F = 20$ kN (given)
$\rho = 1000$ kg/m^2
$g = 10$ m/s^2

Since the box has a side length of 2 m, its base area is 2 m $\times$ 2 m = 4 m^2. To float, the box must produce a displacement of 2 m^3 as calculated above. To produce this displacement the box must be immersed in the water to a depth of 0.5 m.

$$\text{displacement volume of box} = \text{base area} \times \text{immersed depth}$$

$$2\text{m}^3 = 4 \text{ m}^2 \times \text{immersed depth}$$

$$\text{immersed depth} = \frac{2 \text{ m}^3}{4 \text{ m}^2}$$

$$= \textbf{0.5 m}$$

Therefore the height of the box above the surface of the water is 2 m − 0.5 m = **1.5 m**. If we were designing a ship, this height above the water would be called the freeboard.

(b)   This time we have to add the weight of the oil to the weight of the box:

$$2000 \text{ litres} = 2000 \text{ da m}^3 = 2 \text{ m}^3 \text{ of oil}$$

We can calculate the weight of the oil as follows:

$$
\begin{aligned}
W &= V \times \rho \times g \\
&= 2 \text{ m}^2 \times 800 \text{ kg/m}^3 \times 10 \text{ m/s}^2 \\
&= \textbf{16\,000 N}
\end{aligned}
$$

where: $V = 2 \text{ m}^3$
$\rho = 800 \text{ kg/m}^3$
$g = 10 \text{ m/s}^2$

total weight = weight of the box + weight of the oil

$$= 20\,000 \text{ N} \qquad + 16\,000 \text{ N}$$

$$= \textbf{36\,000 N}$$

This time the displacement volume (water) is:

$$V = \frac{F}{\rho \times g}$$

$$= \frac{36\,000 \text{ N}}{1000 \text{ kg/m}^3 \times 10 \text{ m/s}^2}$$

$$= \textbf{3.6 m}^3$$

where: $F = 36\,000 \text{ N}$
$\rho = 1000 \text{ kg/m}^3$
$g = 10 \text{ m/s}^2$

$$\text{displacement volume (box)} = \text{base area} \times \text{immersed depth}$$

$$3.6 \text{ m}^3 = 4 \text{ m}^2 \times \text{immersed depth}$$

$$\text{immersed depth} = \frac{3.6 \text{ m}^3}{4 \text{ m}^2}$$

$$= \textbf{0.9 m}$$

This time, the height of the box above the surface of the water (freeboard) will be 2 m − 0.9 m = **1.1 m**. The box will have sunk by an additional 0.4 m into the water to increase its displacement. This increased displacement balances the weight of the oil in the box.

Now return to the text

Response J1.1   Your completed statement should read as follows:

> As well as bonded **electrons**, metal atoms also have one or more **loosely** attached electrons. They are easily detached and become **free** electrons. There is a constant, random movement of **free electrons** within any piece of metal. The movements of the individual **electrons** cancel out and there is no current flow. When the piece of metal is connected across the terminals of a **source** of electrical **energy**, all the free **electrons** flow in the **same** direction. We now have an **electric** current.

Strictly speaking this is an 'electron current' and sometimes you will see this term used. Usually it is called an 'electric current'.

Now return to the text

Response J1.2   (a)   Since like charges repel each other and unlike charges attract each other, the negatively charged electrons will flow away from the negative terminal and towards the positive terminal of the source of electrical energy. This is shown by the arrows in the following figure.

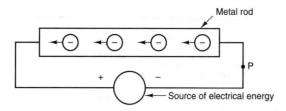

Fig. J1.2R

(b)   A flow of electric current of magnitude 1 ampere equals 6.24×10^{18} electrons passing a given point in the circuit in 1 second. Therefore a current flow of 5 amperes = $5 \text{ A} \times 6.24 \times 10^{18} = 3.12 \times 10^{19}$ electrons passing point P in 1 second, that is, 31 200 000 000 000 000 000 electrons per second.

Now return to the text

Response J1.3   (a)   The lights will become less bright because the starter motor draws a very heavy current from the battery, this in turn reduces the terminal potential difference available. Remember that the emf of the battery not only has to drive the current through the external circuit, it has to drive the current through the battery as well. Therefore, the larger the current flowing in the circuit, the greater the proportion of the emf required to drive the current through the battery. This reduces the balance of the emf available to drive the current through the external circuit, so the lights dim.

(b)   You are measuring the emf of the battery. Emf is the **no-load** voltage measured across the terminals of the battery. The current flowing in the meter is so small that it can be ignored.

(c)   heat energy (J/s) = current (A) × p.d (V)

$$60 \text{ J/s} = \text{current (A)} \times 12 \text{ V}$$

$$\text{current (A)} = \frac{60 \text{ J/s}}{12 \text{ V}}$$

$$= 5 \text{ A}$$

You will learn later that 1 J/s = 1 watt (W). Your window demister is rated at 60 W.

Now return to the text

Response J2.1   Your completed statement should have read:

There are **three** main sources of electrical energy. They are:

(a)   The **chemical** reaction that takes place in a **cell**.
(b)   The **thermal** effect that takes place in a **thermocouple** when it is heated.
(c)   The **electromagnetic effect** that takes place in a **generator** when it is rotated by an engine.

Now return to the text

Response J3.1   (a)   An electric bell is an electromagnetic device that converts electrical energy into mechanical energy. The electromagnet in the bell vibrates the clapper which strikes the bell or gong. There are many more examples you could have chosen, for example, relays, remotely operated door locks, direct on line (DOL) motor starter switches, electric razors, and grinding-machine chucks.

(b)   As well as the electric fire shown in the text, other forms of resistance heating devices include toasters, ovens, cooking hobs, furnaces, kilns, hair-dryers and electric blankets. Some heat sources do not depend upon resistance heating, for example the arc in electric arc welding. An electric arc is a prolonged spark.

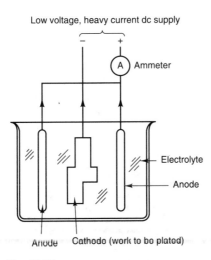

Fig. J3.1R

(c) Electroplating exploits an electrochemical reaction. A flow of electric current through a solution of chemicals is used to deposit a thin film of a valuable metal onto a component made from a cheaper and more easily worked metal. The metal deposited may be chosen for its decorative appearance, its corrosion resistance or both.

Figure J3.1R shows a typical electroplating cell. Let's assume we are going to copper plate a mild steel component. The electrolyte would be a copper sulphate solution and the anodes would be bars of pure copper. When the plating current is switched on, the electrolyte will give up its copper and deposit it on the component being plated. At the same time the electrolyte will dissolve an equal amount of copper from the copper anodes in order to maintain the strength of the electrolyte solution. The greater the current and the longer the process time, the thicker will be the film of copper deposited on the workpiece.

Now return to the text

Response J4.1 **Cable**

Copper

- low resistance to the flow of electricity
- second only to silver in terms of conductivity
- readily available and relatively low cost
- corrosion resistant and easily joined by clamping, soldering or brazing

Polyvinylchloride (PVC)

- good electrical insulation properties
- flexible yet has adequate mechanical strength
- reasonably resistant to scuffing
- can be readily colour-coded
- resistant to most solvents

Connector block

Extruded brass section

- good conductor of electricity
- more easily machined than copper
- threads less likely to strip in brass than they are in copper
- relatively low cost material that is readily available
- preformed section by the extrusion process reduces manufacturing costs

Drawn free-cutting brass rod

- good conductor of electricity
- easily turned and threaded on automatic lathes; this reduces manufacturing costs
- relatively low cost material that is readily available

Polystyrene

- easily and cheaply moulded thermoplastic material

- good insulator
- tough
- low cost material that is readily available

Now return to the text

Response J5.1   From Table J5.1 we can obtain a value for the resistivity of manganin alloy wire:

$$\rho \text{ (manganin)} = 42 \times 10^{-8} \ \Omega \text{ m}$$

$$R = \frac{\rho \times l}{A}$$

$$= \frac{42 \times 10^{-8} \ \Omega \text{ m} \times 15 \text{ m}}{1 \times 10^{-6} \ \text{m}^2}$$

$$= 42 \times 10^{(-8+6)} \ \Omega \text{ m} \times 15 \text{ m}$$

$$= 42 \times 10^{-2} \ \Omega \text{ m} \times 15 \text{ m}$$

$$= \mathbf{6.3 \ \Omega}$$

where: R = resistance (Ω)
$\rho = 42 \times 10^{-8} \ \Omega$ m
$l = 15$ m
$A = 1 \text{ mm}^2 = 1 \times 10^{-6} \text{ m}^2$

I hope you remembered to convert square millimetres into square metres before substituting in the formula. Forgetting to convert multiples and submultiples into the basic units is the most common cause of errors in all scientific calculations. Note also:

$$10^{-8}/10^{-6} = 10^{[-8 - (-6)]} = 10^{(-8+6)} = 10^{-2}$$

Now return to the text

Response J5.2   Your completed table should read as follows.

Table J5.2R

Area (A)	Length (l)	Resistivity (ρ)	Resistance (R)
1.5 mm^2	1 km	$2.7 \times 10^{-8} \ \Omega$ m	18 Ω
0.5 mm^2	12 m	$\mathbf{1.6 \times 10^{-8} \ \Omega \ m}$	0.384 Ω
0.2 mm^2	**0.1 m**	$4400 \times 10^{-8} \ \Omega$ m	22 Ω
0.01 mm²	1 m	$42 \times 10^{-8} \ \Omega$ m	42 Ω

Note the formula can be rearranged as follows:

$$R = \frac{\rho l}{A} \qquad A = \frac{\rho l}{R} \qquad l = \frac{AR}{\rho} \qquad \rho = \frac{AR}{l}$$

Did you manage to do this correctly? Well done if you did. I also hope you changed kilometres into metres in the first calculation.

Now return to the text

Response J5.3   From Table J5.1 you can find the resitivity of copper. For copper $\rho = 1.59 \times 10^{-8}$ Ωm. Next you have to find the cross-sectional area of the cable:

$$A = \frac{\pi \times D^2}{4} = \frac{\pi \times 10^2}{4} = \textbf{78.5 mm}^2$$

where: $D = 10$ mm

Resistance of the cable:

$$R = \frac{\rho \times l}{A}$$

$$= \frac{1.59 \times 10^{-8} \times 2000 \text{ m}}{7.85 \times 10^{-7}}$$

$$= \textbf{0.41 } \Omega \text{ (2 d.p.)}$$

where: $\rho = 1.59 \times 10^{-8} \ \Omega$ m (Table J5.1)
$\qquad\quad l = 2$ km $= 2000$ m (given)
$\qquad\quad A = 78.5$ mm$^2 = 7.85 \times 10^{-7}$ m^2

I hope you remembered to convert length from kilometres into metres, and to convert square millimetres into square metres. These conversions were necessary because our unit of resistivity is given as the ohm-metre (Ω m). Well done if you got this activity correct.

Now return to the text

Response J6.1   To complete the table in Activity J6.1, you will need to rearrange the basic formula thus:

$$R = \frac{U}{I} \qquad U = I \times R \qquad I = \frac{U}{R}$$

where: $R =$ resistance (Ω)
$\qquad\quad U =$ potential difference (V)
$\qquad\quad I =$ current (A)

Your completed table should read as follows.

Table J6.1R

Current (I)	Potential (U)	Resistance (R)
2 A	240 V	120 Ω
0.1875 A	30 V	160 Ω
15 A	**1500 V (1.5 kV)**	100 Ω

Response J6.2

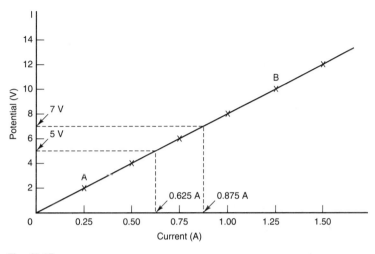

Fig. J6.2R

(a) Your graph should look like the one shown above.
(b) (i) When the potential is 5 V, the current is 0.625 A.
    (ii) When the current is 0.875 A, the potential is 7 V.
(c) The resistance equals the slope of the graph. I have calculated this over the range AB.

$$R = \frac{\Delta U}{\Delta I} = \frac{10\ \text{V} - 2\ \text{V}}{1.25\ \text{A} - 0.25\ \text{A}} = \frac{8\ \text{V}}{1.0\ \text{A}} = 8\ \Omega$$

Since the graph is a straight line, the resistance value of the resistor is constant over the range of the readings. The mathematical symbol Δ (Greek letter delta) means 'a small change in'.

Now return to the text

Response J7.1 Your completed table should read as follows.

Table J7.1R

	Potential (U)	Current (I)	Time (t)	Resistance (R)	Energy (Q)
(a)	100 V	3 A	120 s		**36 kJ**
(b)	12 V	**5 A**	15 s		900 J
(c)	**24 kV**	30 A	25 s		18 MJ
(d)	50 V	5 A	**8 s**		2 kJ
(e)		0.5 A	60 s	500 Ω	7.5 kJ

I will now work the calculations for you. Note how I rearrange the formula $Q = U \times I = t$. Note also how I use $Q = I^2 \times R \times t$ in the last calculation. Don't forget that multiples and submultiples must always be changed into base units before substituting in the formula. (The exception is the kilogram which is the base unit.)

(a) $Q = U \times I \times t$ $= 100\ \text{V} \times 3\ \text{A} \times 120\text{s}$ $= \textbf{36 kJ}$
(b) $I = Q/(U \times t)$ $= (900\ \text{J}) \times (12\ \text{V} \times 15\ \text{s})$ $= \textbf{5 A}$
(c) $U = Q/(I \times t)$ $= (1.8 \times 10^7\ \text{J})/(30\ \text{A} \times 25\ \text{s})$ $= \textbf{2.4} \times \textbf{10}^4\ \textbf{V}$ or $\textbf{24 kV}$
(d) $t = Q/(U \times I)$ $= (1.2 \times 10^4\ \text{J})/(50\ \text{V} \times 5\ \text{A})$ $= \textbf{48 s}$
(e) $Q = I^2 \times R \times t$ $= 0.5^2\ \text{A} \times 500\ \Omega \times 60\ \text{s}$ $= 7.5 \times 10^3\ \text{J}$ or $\textbf{7.5 kJ}$

If you had any difficulties with these, I hope my worked solutions have helped you.

Now return to the text

Response J8.1   Your completed table should read as follows.

Table J8.1R

	Potential (U)	Current (I)	Resistance (R)	Power (P)
(a)	200 V	5 A	**40 Ω**	**1000 W (1 kW)**
(b)	**300 V**	0.2 A	1500 Ω	**60 W**
(c)	**240 V**	2 A	**120 Ω**	480 W
(d)	1.5 kV	2 mA	**750 kΩ**	**3 W**
(e)	**147 V**	10 mA	14.7 kΩ	**1.47 W**
(f)	**2000 V (2 kV)**	5 μA	**400 MΩ**	10 mW

I will now work these calculations for you. Note how I rearrange the formulae and also how I convert the multiples and submultiples into base units before substituting the given data into the formulae.

(a) $R = U/I$ $= (200\ \text{V})/(5\ \text{A})$ $= \textbf{40}\ \Omega$
     $P = U \times I$ $= 200\ \text{V} \times 5\ \text{A}$ $= \textbf{1000 W}$ or $\textbf{1 kW}$
(b) $U = I \times R$ $= 0.2\ \text{A} \times 1500\ \Omega$ $= \textbf{300 V}$
     $P = U \times I$ $= 300\ \text{V} \times 0.2\ \text{A}$ $= \textbf{60 W}$
(c) $U = P/I$ $= (480\ \text{W})/(2\ \text{A})$ $= \textbf{240 V}$
     $R = U/I$ $= (240\ \text{V})/(2\ \text{A})$ $= \textbf{120}\ \Omega$
(d) $R = U/I$ $= (1500\ \text{V})/(0.002\ \text{A})$ $= \textbf{750 000}\ \Omega$ or $\textbf{750 k}\Omega$
     $P = U \times I$ $= 1500\ \text{V} \times 0.002\ \text{A}$ $= \textbf{3 W}$
(e) $U = I \times R$ $= 0.01 = \text{A} \times 14\,700\ \Omega$ $= \textbf{147 V}$
     $P = U \times I$ $= 147\ \text{V} \times 0.01\ \text{A}$ $= \textbf{1.47 W}$
(f) $U = P/I$ $= (0.01\ \text{W})/(0.000\,005\ \text{A})$ $= \textbf{2000 V}$ or $\textbf{2 kV}$
     $R = U/I$ $= (2000\ \text{V})/(0.000\,005\ \text{A})$ $= \textbf{400 000 000}\ \Omega$ or $\textbf{400 M}\Omega$

I could also have used the formula $P = I^2R$ in some of the examples. For instance:

(b) $P = I^2R$ $= 0.2^2 \times 1500\ \Omega$ $= \textbf{60 W}$

That should have revised some of your multiples and submultiples. I hope you remembered to convert them to base units before substituting in the various formulae.

The last one required careful thought. I hope you got it correct. Well done if you did. Consult your tutor if you are having trouble.

Now return to the text

Response J8.2   (a)   The total energy used was:

cooker	$5 \text{ kW} \times 2 \text{ h}$	$= 10 \text{ kWh}$
hob	$1.5 \text{ kW} \times 3 \text{ h}$	$= 4.5 \text{ kWh}$
radiator	$2 \text{ kW} \times 6 \text{ h}$	$= 12 \text{ kWh}$
immersion heater	$3 \text{ kW} \times 2\text{h}$	$= 6 \text{ kWh}$
lights	$0.5 \text{ kW} \times 8 \text{ h}$	$= 4 \text{ kWh}$
total		**36.5 kWh**

(b)   1 'unit' of electricity $= 1 \text{ kWh}$ and costs (at the time of publication) 7.2 p.
Therefore, the cost of $36.5 \text{ kWh} = 36.5 \text{ kWh} \times 7.2 \text{ p} = 262.8 \text{ p}$.
To the nearest whole pence this is $263 \text{ p} = £2.63$.

Now return to the text

Response J9.1   Remember, efficiency $(\eta) = \dfrac{P_{\text{out}}}{P_{\text{in}}} \times 100$ expressed as a percentage (%)   (1)

$$= \frac{P_{\text{out}}}{P_{\text{in}}} \text{ expressed as a fraction} \tag{2}$$

Your completed table should read as follows:

Table J9.1R

	Power input	Power output	Efficiency
(a)	120 W	100 W	**83.3%**
(b)	2 kW	**1.5 kW**	75%
(c)	**7.5 kW**	6 kW	80%
(d)	8.1 kW	**7.29 kW**	0.9
(e)	**51.4**	36 W	0.7

Again, this was largely an exercise in transposing formulae and converting multiples and submultiples into base units. In case you ran into difficulties, I will now work two examples for you.

(a)   Here the efficiency is to be expressed as a percentage so we will use equation (1):

$$\eta = \frac{P_{\text{out}}}{P_{\text{in}}} \times 100 = \frac{120 \text{ W}}{100 \text{ W}} \times 100 = \textbf{83.3\%}$$

(b)   Here the efficiency is expressed as a decimal fraction so we will use equation (2):

$$\eta = \frac{P_{\text{out}}}{P_{\text{in}}}, \text{ so } 0.7 = \frac{36 \text{ W}}{P_{\text{in}}} \text{ and } P_{\text{in}} = \frac{38 \text{ W}}{0.7} = \textbf{51.4 W}$$

Now return to the text

Response K1.1 Your completed statement should read as follows:

An electric **current** consists of a source of electrical **energy**, an **appliance** to convert the flow of current into useful work, a **switch** to control the **flow** of **current** and **connecting** leads. Most circuits are also fitted with an overcurrent protection device such as a **fuse** or a miniature circuit-breaker (MCB).

Now return to the text

Response K2.1 (a) In a series circuit the current has the same value at all points around the circuit. Therefore the current flowing through R_3 is 2A.

$$R_3 = \frac{U_3}{I} = \frac{12 \text{ V}}{2 \text{ A}} = 6 \text{ }\Omega$$

(b) Similarly:

$$R_2 = \frac{U_2}{I} = \frac{8 \text{ V}}{2 \text{ A}} = 4 \text{ }\Omega$$

(c) $R_{total} = R_1 + R_2 + R_3 = 10 \text{ }\Omega + 4 \text{ }\Omega + 6 \text{ }\Omega = 20 \text{ }\Omega$ ($R_1 = 10 \text{ }\Omega$ given)
(d) Terminal pd $= I \times R_{total} = 2 \text{ A} \times 20 \text{ }\Omega = \textbf{40 V}$
(e) Power dissipated by $R_1 = I^2 \times R_1 = 2 \text{ A} \times 2 \text{ A} \times 10 \text{ }\Omega = \textbf{40 W}$
(f) Heat energy (Q) radiated by $R_1 = P_1 \times t = 40 \text{ W} \times 10 \text{ s} = \textbf{400 J}$

Well done if you got all those. If you had any difficulties, I hope that my solutions have helped you.

Now return to the text

Response K3.1 The given data is $R_1 = 8 \text{ }\Omega$, $R_2 = 12 \text{ }\Omega$, $R_3 = 24 \text{ }\Omega$, $U = 36 \text{ V}$.

In a parallel circuit, the potential difference has the same value across each limb of the circuit:

(a) $\dfrac{1}{R_{total}} = \dfrac{1}{R_1} + \dfrac{1}{R_2} + \dfrac{1}{R_3}$

$$= \frac{1}{8 \text{ }\Omega} + \frac{1}{12 \text{ }\Omega} + \frac{1}{24 \text{ }\Omega}$$

$$= \frac{3 + 2 + 1}{24}$$

$$= \frac{6}{24}$$

Thus $R_{total} = \dfrac{24}{6}$

$$= 4 \text{ }\Omega$$

(b) $I_1 = \dfrac{U}{R_1} = \dfrac{36 \text{ V}}{8 \text{ }\Omega} = \textbf{4.5 A}$ (if $R = U/I$ then $I = U/R$)

$$I_2 = \frac{U}{R_2} = \frac{36 \text{ V}}{12 \text{ }\Omega} = \textbf{3 A}$$

$$I_3 = \frac{U}{R_3} = \frac{36 \text{ V}}{24 \text{ }\Omega} = \textbf{1.5 A}$$

(c) Total current $= I_1 + I_2 + I_3 = 4.5\text{ A} + 3\text{ A} + 1.5\text{ A} = \mathbf{9\ A}$

(d) Power dissipated by $R_3 = I_3{}^2 \times R_3 = 1.5\text{ A} \times 1.5\text{ A} \times 24\ \Omega = \mathbf{54\ W}$

Well done if you got all or most of this correct. The ability to manipulate formulae and to be able to solve series and parallel circuits is very important if you are involved in electrical or electronic engineering.
Consult your tutor if you have any difficulties.

Now return to the text

Response K3.2   We begin to solve this network of resistors by tackling the parallel groups.

Group (i)

$$\frac{1}{R_{(i)}} = \frac{1}{R_1} + \frac{1}{R_2} + \frac{1}{R_3}$$
$$= \frac{1}{20} + \frac{1}{10} + \frac{1}{20}$$
$$= \frac{1+2+1}{20}$$
$$= \frac{4}{20}$$

Thus $R_{(i)} = \mathbf{5\ \Omega}$

Group (ii)

$$\frac{1}{R_{(ii)}} = \frac{1}{R_4} + \frac{1}{R_5}$$
$$= \frac{1}{15} + \frac{1}{30}$$
$$= \frac{2+1}{30}$$
$$= \frac{3}{30}$$

Thus $R_{(ii)} = \frac{30}{3}$
$$= \mathbf{10\ \Omega}$$

We can now replace the two groups of parallel resistors with a single 5 Ω resistor and a single 10 Ω resistor respectively.

- Replace the group of three resistors in parallel with a single 5 Ω resistor.
- Replace the group of two resistors in parallel with a single 10 Ω resistor.
- The two parallel groups were connected in series with each other, so:

$$R_{total} = R_{(i)} + R_{(ii)} = 5\ \Omega + 10\ \Omega = \mathbf{15\ \Omega}$$

The most complex networks can be solved in this way. First reduce all the parallel groups to single resistors. This invariably leaves the single resistors connected in series. The series resistors are then added together to give you a final resistance value.

Now return to the text

Response K4.1 For series connected cells:

$$E_{total} = E_1 + E_2 + E_3 \ldots E_n$$

If all the cells have the same emf, (as in this activity) then we can say:

$$E_{total} = E_C \times n$$
$$= 2\ V \times 12$$
$$= \mathbf{24\ V}$$

where: E_C = emf per cell
$\qquad n$ = number of cells

Now return to the text

Response K5.1 From the activity, we know that the emf of each of the cells is 2 V and that their current-handling capacities are $I_1 = 20\ A$, $I_2 = 25\ A$, $I_3 = 35\ A$.

(a) For cells connected in parallel, $I_{total} = I_1 + I_2 + I_3$
$$= 20\ A + 25\ A + 35\ A$$
$$= \mathbf{80\ A}$$

(b) In a parallel circuit, the potential is the same across each limb of the circuit. Similarly, the emf must be the same across each cell connected in parallel. Therefore the emf across each cell and for the battery as a whole is 2 V (given).

Now return to the text

Response K6.1 Since the lamps have a common current rating of 0.2 A they can be connected in series. Remember that current is constant at all points in a series circuit.

Since the lamps have an identical current **and** power rating, they will also have an identical voltage rating. We can calculate the voltage rating as follows:

$$U = \frac{P}{I}$$
$$= \frac{5\ W}{0.2\ A}$$
$$= \mathbf{25\ V}$$

where: U = pd across each lamp (V)
$\qquad P$ = 5 W (given)
$\qquad I$ = 0.02 A (given).

To operate the 10 lamps in series at their 'ideal' power rating of 5 W would require a supply potential of:

$$U_{supply} = 25\ V \times 10\ lamps = \mathbf{250\ V}$$

Since the actual supply potential is 240 V, it is safe to operate these series-connected lamps from it. It is always safe to operate from a supply potential slightly **below** the ideal for the appliance. In this instance all that will happen will be that the lamps will be rather less bright. However, they will last considerably longer.

Warning: Never operate an appliance from a supply with a higher potential than it is designed to use. To do so could be highly dangerous.

Now return to the text

Response K7.1   The circuit consists of three lamps connected in parallel. The lamps are rated at 4 W, 6 W and 10 W respectively, and they are connected across a 6 V supply. We now have to calculate the current demand on the battery if the 4 W bulb is switched off:

remaining load = 6 W + 10 W = **16 W**

current $I = \dfrac{P}{U} = \dfrac{16 \text{ W}}{6 \text{ V}} = \textbf{2.5 A}$

That shouldn't have caused you too much trouble.

Now return to the text

Response L1.1

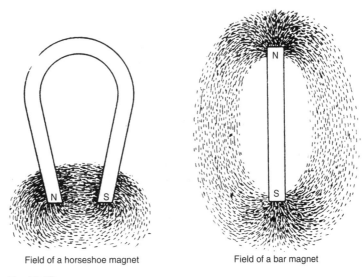

Field of a horseshoe magnet   Field of a bar magnet

Fig. L1.1R

The figure shows the patterns the iron filings should take up for a horseshoe magnet and a bar magnet. They not only show the shape of the force field but also how the field is strongest close to the poles.

Now return to the text

Response L1.2   (a)   The end marked * is a south pole. We know this because unlike poles attract each other and the flux field 'flows' between them.

(b) The end marked * is again a south pole. This time we have like poles repelling each other. Their flux fields are also repelled.

(c) The left-hand pole (*) is a south pole and the right-hand pole (**) is a north pole. We know this from the arrowheads on the 'lines' of magnetic flux in the diagram. It is always assumed that magnetic flux 'flows' from north to south.

(d) The north pole of a magnet will always attract the south-seeking pole of a compass needle and repel the north-seeking pole of a compass needle. Therefore the pole of the compass needle marked * is a north-seeking pole.

(e) The piece of soft iron is attracted to the magnet. A magnetic field will be induced in the soft iron by the magnet. The polarity of this induced field will depend upon whether the soft iron is attracted to the north pole or the south pole of the magnet. Therefore the end of the soft iron marked * will have a south pole induced in it (unlike poles attract each other). The end of the soft iron marked ** will have a north pole induced in it. This is because opposite ends of a magnet have opposite poles. Similarly, opposite ends of a piece of soft iron in a magnetic field also have opposite poles. A piece of soft iron placed in a magnetic field will behave as a magnet as long as it is in the magnetic field.

Now return to the text

Response L1.31

(a) You close the switch to complete the circuit and enable the current to flow through the solenoid.

(b) I have now added arrowheads to the figure to show the direction of current flow. This is 'conventional' current flow (positive to negative) as used in electromagnetic theory and practice.

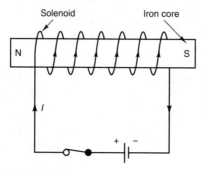

Fig. L1.3R

(c) With reference to the figure, close the fingers of your right hand round the solenoid (coil) in the direction of current flow (direction of the arrowheads). The thumb of your right hand, extended sideways, will indicate the north pole of the solenoid and its iron core (right-hand grip rule).

(d) The current flow would be reversed, therefore the north and south poles of the solenoid and its iron core would also be reversed.

Now return to the text

Response L2.1   (a) Yes, It appears to behave like a magnet because it attracts one end of the compass needle and repels the other end. If it were not magnetised, it would attract both ends of the compass needle.

(b) South, the north pole of the steel rod will be in contact with the south pole of the magnet because the induced pole is always opposite the inducing pole. This is proved by the fact that the remote end of the steel rod repels the south-seeking pole of the compass.

(c) The polarity of * is also reversed and it becomes a north pole. It now attracts the south-seeking pole of the compass.

(d) No, once the magnet is removed the piece of mild steel no longer retains any appreciable magnetism. Both poles of the compass are attracted to both ends of the rod.

(e) Mild steel (low carbon steel) is a soft magnetic material; it becomes easily magnetised in the presence of a strong magnetic field but loses virtually all its magnetism when the field is removed.

Note

If you use a piece of mild steel that has been cold drawn, or a steel nail made from cold-drawn mild steel, it may not lose all its magnetism when the energising field is removed. There may be some **residual** magnetism. This is because the cold-drawing process work-hardens the steel. For this reason it is always best to anneal (soften) the piece of steel before using it for this experiment. To soften the steel, heat it up until it is red-hot then allow it to cool down very slowly.

Now return to the text

Response L2.2   (a) Yes, the blade of the screwdriver behaves as a magnet because it attracts one end of the compass needle and repels the opposite end.

(b) North pole, the south pole of the magnet will induce a north pole in the end of the screwdriver marked *. The handle end of the screwdriver blade will become a south pole. This can be tested with a compass. The blade end of the screwdriver is a north pole and will repel the north pole of a compass. The handle end of the screwdriver is a south pole and will repel the south pole of the compass.

(c) Yes, the screwdriver blade remains strongly magnetised after the energising bar magnet has been removed.

(d) It is a hard magnetic material because it retains its magnetism after the energising field has been removed.

Now return to the text

Response L3.1   (a) (i)   Increasing the strength of the magnetic field cut by the conductor increases the emf induced in the conductor.

(ii) Reducing the speed of rotation reduces the velocity with which the conductor cuts the magnetic field. This, in turn, reduces the magnitude of the induced emf.

(b) (i)   Reversing the polarity of the field magnets reverses the direction of current flow in the conductor loop.

(ii) Reversing the direction of rotation also reverses the direction of the current flow. Reversing the polarity of the field magnets and simultaneously reversing the direction of rotation at the same time, leaves the current flowing in the original direction. Think about it!

Now return to the text

Response L3.2

(a) $\text{frequency (Hz)} = \dfrac{\text{number of cycles}}{\text{time (s)}}$

$= \dfrac{1000 \ \text{cycles}}{5 \ \text{s}}$

$= \mathbf{200 \ Hz}$

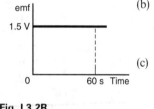

Fig. L3.2R

(b)   In a single-loop generator, one cycle is completed every complete revolution (360°). To generate a current with a frequency of 50 Hz, the loop would have to rotate 50 times per second or $50 \times 60 \ \text{s} = 3000$ times per minute, that is, 3000 rev/min.

(c)   A 1.5 V dry cell produces a constant, unidirectional current. Its emf, over a short period of time is a straight line parallel to the time axis, as shown in the figure. The straight line would eventually start to droop as the cell becomes exhausted (run down).

Note

An alternating current (ac) reverses its direction continually, whereas a direct current (dc) flows uniformly in one direction all the time. A direct current is required for such purposes as:

- The charging of accumulators.
- The electroplating of metal components.
- Powering radios and computers.

Direct current is obtained from an alternating current by a rectifier circuit.

Now return to the text

Response L4.1

(a) $\dfrac{\text{input voltage}}{\text{output voltage}} = \dfrac{\text{primary turns}}{\text{secondary turns}}$

$\dfrac{415 \ \text{V}}{U_{\text{output}}} = \dfrac{2490 \ \text{turns}}{144 \ \text{turns}}$

$U_{\text{output}} = \dfrac{415 \ \text{V} \times 144 \ \text{turns}}{2490 \ \text{turns}}$

$= \mathbf{24 \ V}$

(b) $\dfrac{\text{input voltage}}{\text{output voltage}} = \dfrac{\text{primary turns}}{\text{secondary turns}}$

$\dfrac{415 \ \text{V}}{45 \ \text{V}} = \dfrac{2490 \ \text{turns}}{\text{secondary turns}}$

$$\text{secondary turns} = \frac{2490 \text{ turns} \times 45 \text{ V}}{415 \text{ V}}$$

$$= \textbf{270 turns}$$

Now return to the text

Response L4.2 Remember that the symbol for efficiency is the Greek letter eta (θ). Efficiency is a ratio and has no units:

$$\eta = \frac{I_{secondary} \times U_{secondary}}{I_{primary} \times U_{primary}} \times 100$$

$$84\% = \frac{I_{secondary} \times 24 \text{ V}}{2 \text{ A} \times 415 \text{ V}} \times 100$$

$$I_{secondary} = \frac{84\% \times 2 \text{ A} \times 415 \text{ V}}{100 \times 24 \text{ V}}$$

$$= \textbf{29.05 A}$$

In an ideal transformer ($\eta = 100\%$) the current would be:

$$I_{secondary} = \frac{2 \text{ A} \times 415 \text{ V}}{24 \text{ V}}$$

$$= \textbf{34.6 A}$$

I will again emphasise why I have used $I \times U$ instead of power in watts. When dealing with alternating current (and transformers will only operate on alternating current), the formula $P = I \times U$ only applies to resistive loads. Examples of resistive loads are lamps and heaters. In resistive loads the voltage and current curves are in step with each other. They go up and down together and the current and voltage reverse direction at the same time; they are in phase. For devices such as induction motors and transformers, the current and voltage curves do not go up and down together. They are out of step; they are **out of phase**. The formula $P = I \times U$ does not apply; instead we simply refer to volt-amperes (VA) or kilovolt-amperes (kVA) for the power rating of such devices.

Now return to the text

Response M1.1 Remember: for equilibrium the clockwise moments must equal the anticlockwise moments:

$$W \times l_W = F \times l_F$$

$$2 \text{ kN} \times 0.3 \text{ m} = F \times 1.5 \text{ m}$$

$$\text{Therefore} \quad F = \frac{2 \text{ kN} \times 0.3 \text{ m}}{1.5 \text{ m}}$$

$$= \textbf{0.4 kN or 400 N}$$

Now return to the text

Response M1.2   Your completed illustrations should appear as shown in the figure.

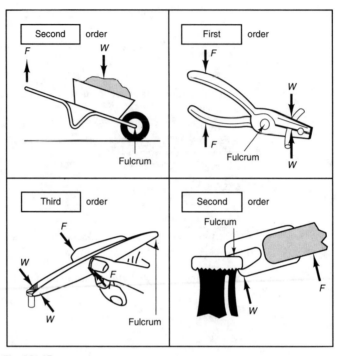

Fig. M1.2R

I hope you managed to identify the effort force and load force, and from their positions relative to the fulcrum, the order of lever for each example.

Now return to the text

Response M1.3   *Shearing force F_1*

clockwise moments = anticlockwise moments

$$F_1 \times 15 \text{ mm} = 20 \text{ N} \times 180 \text{ mm}$$

$$F_1 = \frac{20 \text{ N} \times 180 \text{ mm}}{15 \text{ mm}}$$

$$= \textbf{240 N}$$

Shearing force F_2

clockwise moments = anticlockwise moments

$$F_2 \times 50 \text{ mm} = 20 \text{ N} \times 180 \text{ mm}$$

$$F_2 = \frac{20 \text{ N} \times 180 \text{ mm}}{50 \text{ mm}}$$

$$= \textbf{72 N}$$

Again, you can see that the shears work more efficiently when cutting close to the pivot rather than at the tips of the blades. This was a practical example of the theory you studied in an earlier module. There will be another practical example of the application of moments of forces in the next activity.

Now return to the text

Response M1.4

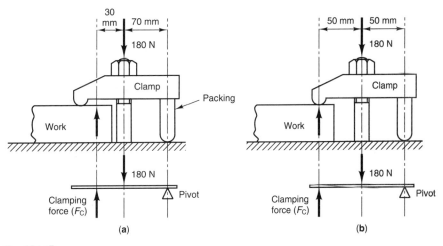

Fig. M1.4R

(a) The first part of the activity asks us to calculate the clamping force F_c when the stud and nut are moved 10 mm nearer to the workpiece and 10 mm further from the packing. These new conditions are shown here.

clockwise moments = anticlockwise moments

$$F_c \times (30 \text{ mm} + 70 \text{mm}) = 180 \text{ N} \times 70 \text{ mm}$$

$$F_c \times 100 \text{ mm} = 180 \text{ N} \times 70 \text{ mm}$$

$$F_c = \frac{180 \text{ N} \times 70 \text{ mm}}{100 \text{ mm}}$$

$$= \textbf{126 N}$$

Compared with the example in the text, moving the stud and nut nearer to the workpiece and further from the packing has increased the clamping force.

(b) The second part of the activity asks us to calculate the clamping force F_c when the stud and nut are moved 10 mm further from the workpiece and 10 mm nearer to the packing. These new conditions are shown here.

clockwise moments = anticlockwise moments

$$F_c \times (50 \text{ mm} + 50 \text{ mm}) = 180 \text{ N} \times 50 \text{ mm}$$

$$F_c \times 100 \text{ mm} = 180 \text{ N} \times 50 \text{ mm}$$
$$F_c = \frac{180 \ N \times 50 \ \text{mm}}{100 \ \text{mm}}$$
$$= \textbf{90 N}$$

Compared with the worked example in the text, moving the stud and nut away from the workpiece and nearer to the packing has reduced the clamping force.

(c)   Thus we can see that the most effective clamping occurs when the stud and nut are as close as possible to the work and as far as possible from the packing under the heel of the clamp.

Now return to the text

Response M1.5   From the text we have the relationship:

$$F \times r_1 = W \times r_2$$
$$F \times 600 \text{ mm} = 1000 \text{ N} \times 150 \text{ mm}$$
$$F = \frac{1000 \ N \times 150 \ \text{mm}}{600 \ \text{mm}}$$
$$= \textbf{250 N}$$

where: $r_1 = 600$ mm
$r_2 = 150$ mm
$W = 1$ kN $= 1000$ N

Thus a force of 250 N can raise a load of 1000 N. This is a force magnification of $4:1$.

Now return to the text

Response M1.6   From the text we have the relationship:

$$F \times r_1 \times \frac{T_2}{T_1} = W \times r_2$$
$$F \times 600 \text{ mm} \times \frac{90 \ t}{45 \ t} = 1000 \text{ N} \times r_2$$
$$\text{Therefore:}\quad F = \frac{1000 \ N \times 150 \ \text{mm} \times 45 \ t}{600 \ \text{mm} \times 90 \ t}$$
$$= \textbf{125 N}$$

where: $W = 1$ kN $= 1000$ N
$r_1 = 600$ mm
$r_2 = 150$ mm
$T_1 = 45$ teeth
$T_2 = 90$ teeth

I hope you noticed that introducing the $2:1$ gear ratio halved the effort force required. Had we used T_2 180 teeth, in place of 90 teeth, we would have had a gear ratio of $4:1$. This would have reduced the effort force to 62.5 N.

The gears enable us to raise heavier loads while keeping the radius of the crank handle to a convenient length. We cannot reduce the drum as this would damage the rope by bending it too sharply. The figures we have calculated are for an ideal winch. As I have mentioned in the text, introducing the gears also increases the friction losses so, in practice, we do not gain fully from their introduction.

Now return to the text

Response M2.1   (a)   The number of falls of rope equals the sum of the pulleys in the top and bottom sheaves.

2 pulleys + 3 pulleys = 5 pulleys = 5 falls of rope

$$= \frac{W}{n} \quad \text{effort force } (F)$$

$$= \frac{2000 \text{ N}}{5}$$

$$= \textbf{400 N}$$

where: $W = 2$ kN $= 2000$ N

$n = 5$ falls of rope

(b)   If the load is raised by 2 m, the tail rope will have to be hauled through the tackle by an amount given by the expression:

effort distance = distance moved by load × number of falls of rope

= 2 m × 5 falls of rope

= **10 m**

(c)   The reaction force (F_R) at the beam equals the sum of the forces acting downwards. We will assume that the effort force (F) is also acting vertically downwards, therefore:

F_R = load + weight of tackle + effort

= 2 kN + 0.5 kN + 0.4 kN

= **2.9 kN**

I hope you managed to work out the number of pulleys and falls of rope correctly. The table preceding this activity should have helped you.

Now return to the text

Response M2.2   For a set of Weston differential pulley blocks, the expression relating load and effort is:

$$F = W \times \frac{D_1 - D_2}{2 \times D_1}$$

$$= 3000 \text{ N} \times \frac{300 \text{ mm} - 200 \text{ mm}}{2 \times 300\text{mm}}$$

$$= 3000 \text{ N} \times \frac{100 \text{ mm}}{600 \text{ mm}}$$

$$= \textbf{500 N}$$

where: F = effort force (N)
     W = 3 kN = 3000 N
     D_1 = 300 mm
     D_2 = 200 mm

Now return to the text

Response M3.1   For an inclined plane, we are given the relationship:

$$F \times l_F = W \times l_w$$

$$F \times 500 \text{ mm} = 4000 \text{ N} \times 10 \text{ mm}$$

$$\text{Therefore } F = \frac{4000 \text{ N} \times 10 \text{ mm}}{500 \text{ mm}}$$

$$= \mathbf{80 \text{ N}}$$

where: F = effort force (N)
     W = 4 kN = 4000 N
     l_F = 500 mm
     l_W = 10 mm

Note how the load only moves a very short distance compared with the effort force. Let's see how we can make our inclined plane more compact and convenient to use.

Now return to the text

Response M3.2   Given that lead = pitch × number of starts, your completed table should read as follows.

Table M3.2R

Pitch	Number of starts	Lead
4 mm	1	**4 mm**
4 mm	3	**12 mm**
3 mm	2	6 mm
2.5 mm	**4**	10 mm
6 mm	**1**	6 mm

Now return to the text

Response M3.3   (a)   For a simple screw-jack the following facts hold true for one revolution of the screw. The effort force (F), acting tangentially against the handle, moves through a distance (l_F) equal to one complete revolution of the handle. That is, $l_F = 2 \times \pi \times r$ where the radius (r) is the distance from the axis of the screw to the point on the handle where the effort force (F) is acting. For one revolution of the screw, the load (W) will move through a distance equal to the lead of the screw thread. So the following relationship again holds true:

$$F \times l_F = W \times l_W$$

$$F \times 2 \times \pi \times 250 \text{ mm} = 2000 \text{ N} \times 8 \text{ mm}$$

$$F = \frac{2000 \text{ N} \times 8 \text{ mm}}{2 \times \pi \times 250 \text{ mm}}$$

$$= \mathbf{10.19} \text{ N} \text{ (2 d.p.)}$$

where: F = effort force
$l_F = 2 \times \pi \times 250$ mm
$l_W = 4$ mm $\times$ 2 starts
$= 8$ mm
$W = 2$ kN $= 2000$ N

(b) $$F \times l_F = W \times l_W$$

$$F \times 2 \times \pi \, 200 \text{ mm} = 2000 \text{ N} \times 4 \text{ mm}$$

$$F = \frac{2000 \text{ N} \times 4 \text{ mm}}{2 \times \pi \times 200 \text{ mm}}$$

$$= \mathbf{6.37} \text{ N} \text{ (2 d.p.)}$$

where: F = effort force
$l_F = 2 \times \pi \times 200$ mm
$l_w = 4$ mm
$W = 2$ kN $= 2000$ N

(c)   The use of a two-start thread in (a) halved the movement ratio compared with the worked example in the text, therefore the load moved twice as far for the same movement of the effort force. Correspondingly, the force ratio is also halved and twice the effort is required to move the load. In (b) the use of a shorter handle also reduced the movement ratio and increased the effort required to raise the load compared with the worked example. Remember that in (b), as in the worked example, we are using a single-start thread. Therefore in (b), the lead equals the pitch of the screw.

Now return to the text

Response M3.4   This time side b is **opposite** angle B and side a is **adjacent** to angle B. Side c is still the *hypotenuse*. Your ratios should now read:

$$\text{tangent (tan)} \; B = \frac{\text{opposite}}{\text{adjacent}} = \frac{b}{a}$$

$$\text{sine (sin)} \; B = \frac{\text{opposite}}{\text{hypotenuse}} = \frac{b}{c}$$

$$\text{cosine (cos)} \; B = \frac{\text{adjacent}}{\text{hypotenuse}} = \frac{a}{c}$$

You must be absolutely sure of these ratios and how to use them before moving on.

Now return to the text

Response M3.5   The text gave you the relationship $c^2 = a^2 + b^2$ for the triangle shown in Fig. M3.7. Therefore:

(a) $c^2 = 5^2 + 12^2$
  $= 25 + 144$
  $= 169 \text{ cm}^2$
  $c = \sqrt{(169)}$
  $= \textbf{13 cm}$

(b) $a^2 = c^2 - b^2$
  $= 50^2 - 40^2$
  $= 2500 - 1600$
  $= 900 \text{ mm}^2$
  $a = \sqrt{(900)}$
  $= \textbf{30 mm}$

You may find these transpositions useful:

$c = \sqrt{(a^2 + b^2)}$
$b = \sqrt{(c^2 - a^2)}$
$a = \sqrt{(c^2 - b^2)}$

Now return to the text

Response M3.6   (a) From the text we have the relationship:

$F = W \times \sin \theta$
  $= 400 \text{ N} \times \sin 15°$
  $= 400 \text{ N} \times 0.25882$
  $= \textbf{103.53 N}$ (2 d.p.)

where: $W = 400 \text{ N}$
  $\theta = 15°$

(b) work done = force × distance moved by the force
  $= W \times l_w$
  $= 400 \text{ N} \times 1 \text{ m}$
  $= \textbf{400 J}$

where: $W = 400 \text{ N}$
  $l_w = 100 \text{ cm} = 1 \text{ m}$

I hope you remembered to convert centimetres into metres so that you could obtain your answer in joules. This is because 1 joule (J) = 1 newton-metre (N m).

Now return to the text

Response M4.1   If you revised Section I7 as I suggested, you will have come across the basic relationship:

$$\frac{F_1}{A_1} = \frac{F_2}{A_2}$$

which we can use (after a little rearrangement) to solve part (a) of this activity and so find the effort force (F_1).

(a) $F_1 = \dfrac{F_2 \times A_1}{A_2}$

$= \dfrac{5000 \text{ N} \times 0.05 \text{ m}^2}{0.5 \text{ m}^2}$

$= \mathbf{500 \text{ N}}$

where: $F_2 = 5 \text{ kN} = 5000 \text{ N}$
$A_1 = 0.05 \text{ m}^2$
$A_2 = 0.5 \text{ m}^2$

(b) The volume of water displaced from the small cylinder equals the volume of water received by the large cylinder, therefore:

$l_F \times A_1 = l_w \times A_2$

$l_F \times 0.05 \text{ m}^2 = 0.4 \text{ m} \times 0.5 \text{ m}^2$

$l_F = \dfrac{0.4 \text{ m} \times 0.5 \text{ m}^2}{0.05 \text{ m}^2}$

$= \mathbf{4 \text{ m}}$

where: l_F = movement of effort force
$A_1 = 0.05 \text{ m}^2$
$A_2 = 0.5 \text{ m}^2$
$l_w = 0.4 \text{ m}$

To make a cylinder 4 m long with a cross-sectional area of only 0.05 m² would be very difficult. It would also be very inconvenient to use. We will now look at a way of reducing the length of the small cylinder without losing the movement ratio of the system.

Now return to the text

Response M4.2 This activity revised quite a number of facts concerning the theory behind engineering tools.

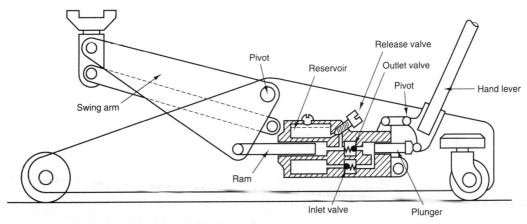

Fig. M4.2R

(a)   I have marked the position of the inlet and outlet valves for you on the drawing of the trolley-jack.

(b)   The sequence of operations for using the jack is as follows:

- Close the release valve.
- Operate the hand lever, this drives the pump plunger backwards and forwards in its cylinder.
- On each outward stroke of the plunger, oil is drawn into the cylinder from the reservoir.
- On each inward stroke of the plunger, oil is forced into the ram cylinder, raising the load slightly.
- Continuous pumping keeps raising the load in small steps (increments). The outlet valve of the pump prevents oil returning to the pump cylinder during each backward stroke. Thus the load remains stationary during the suction (return) stroke of the pump plunger.
- Pumping is continued until the load has been raised to the required height.
- To lower the load, stop pumping and open the release valve carefully so that the load does not drop suddenly. Oil in the ram cylinder flows back into the reservoir.

(c)   The hand lever has its fulcrum (pivot) lying between the effort force and the load. It is also a force magnifier (see (d)). Therefore it is a lever of the **first order**.

(d)   The distance between the effort force and the pivot is greater than that between the load and the pivot, therefore the hand lever is a **force magnifier**.

(e)   The swing-arm is pivoted so that the load moves further than the effort, therefore the swing-arm is a **distance magnifier**.

(f)   Since the swing-arm is a distance or movement magnifier, it is a lever of the third order.

Now return to the text

Response N3.1   Using the relationship given in the text:

$$\text{percentage elongation} = \frac{L_U - L_0}{L_0}$$

$$= \frac{95.2\ \text{mm} - 56\ \text{mm}}{56\ \text{mm}} \times 100$$

$$= \frac{39.2\ \text{mm}}{56\ \text{mm}} \times 100$$

$$= \mathbf{70\%}$$

where: $L_0 = 56$ mm
           $L_U = 95.2$ mm

Now return to the text

Response N4.1   First we have to calculate the areas from the diameters that we have been given:

$$A_0 = \frac{\pi D_0{}^2}{4} = \frac{\pi \times 10^2}{4} = 78.54\ \text{mm}^2 \qquad (D_0 = 10\ \text{mm diameter})$$

$$A_U = \frac{\pi D_U^2}{4} = \frac{\pi \times 8.5^2}{4} = 56.75 \text{ mm}^2 \qquad (D_U = 8.5 \text{ mm diameter})$$

We can now calculate the percentage elongation:

$$\psi = \frac{A_0 - A_U}{A_0} \times 100$$

$$= \frac{78.54 \text{ mm}^2 - 56.75 \text{ mm}^2}{78.54 \text{ mm}^2} \times 100$$

$$= \frac{21.79 \text{ mm}^2}{78.54 \text{ mm}^2}$$

$$= \mathbf{27.74\%}$$

where: ψ = percentage reduction of area
$A_0 = 78.54 \text{ mm}^2$
$A_U = 56.75 \text{ mm}^2$

Now return to the text

Response N5.1 From the text we are given the expression:

$$\text{tensile stress } (\sigma_t) = \frac{\text{tensile force } (F_t)}{\text{cross-sectional area } (A)}$$

First we must find the cross-sectional area of the 25 mm diameter rod:

$$A = \frac{\pi D^2}{4} = \frac{\pi \times 25^2}{4} = \mathbf{491 \text{ mm}^2}$$

Since we are working in millimetres, we must also work in newtons, so 35.7 kN = 35 700 N. Substituting in our original expression, we get:

$$\sigma_t = \frac{35\,700 \text{ N}}{491 \text{ mm}^2}$$

$$= 72.7 \text{ N/mm}^2$$

$$= \mathbf{72.7 \text{ MPa}} \qquad (\text{Remember that } 1 \text{ N/mm}^2 = 1 \text{ MPa})$$

Now return to the text

Response N5.2 (a) Steel Q is the more ductile because its ductile range (curved length) is greater than for steel P.
(b) Steel P is the more rigid because the straight-line portion of its curve (elastic range) is more upright than that for steel Q.
(c) Steel P has the higher elastic limit because the kink in its curve has a higher value measured on the stress axis of the graph.
(d) Steel Q has a lower UTS because the top of its curve is lower than the top of the curve for steel P measured up the stress axis.
(e) Steel P is the stronger because it has a higher value of ultimate tensile stress (UTS).

Now return to the text

Response N6.1   (a)   Inspection of the graph shows the UTS value for the steel to be 400 MPa to the nearest 100 MPa. Since we are given a safety factor of 3.2, we can calculate the safe working tensile stress:

$$\text{safe working tensile stress} = \frac{\text{UTS}}{\text{safety factor}}$$

$$= \frac{400 \text{ MPa}}{3.2}$$

$$= \textbf{125 MPa}$$

(b)   Inspection of the curve shows this value for the safe working tensile stress to be approximately 50% of the elastic range of the steel. This is what we would expect and is the value that must not be exceeded under normal service conditions.

Now return to the text

Response N7.1   The workpiece (1) is in compression because it is being squeezed (compressed) between the clamp and the machine table.
The packing (2) is also in compression because it is being squeezed (compressed) between the clamp and the machine table.
The stud (3) is in tension because it is being stretched when the nut is tightened up.

Now return to the text

Response N7.2   (a)   From the text we see that the safe compressive stress can be calculated from the relationship:

$$\bar{\sigma}_c = \frac{\sigma_{c,max}}{s}$$

$$= \frac{400 \text{ MPa}}{4}$$

$$= \textbf{100 MPa}$$

where: $\sigma_{c,max} = 400$ MPa
$s = $ safety factor
$= 4$

(b)   To find the safe working compressive load (F_c), we use the safe working compressive stress that we have just calculated. (Remember that 1 MPa = 1 N/mm².)

$$\bar{\sigma}_C = \frac{F_C}{A}$$

$$F_c = \bar{\sigma}_C \times A$$

$$= 100 \text{ N/mm}^2 \times 5420 \text{ mm}^2$$

$$= 542\ 000 \text{ N}$$

$$= \textbf{542 kN}$$

where: $\bar{\sigma}_C = 100$ MPa $= 100$ N/mm^2
$A = 5420$ mm^2 (given)

The sums are not difficult, especially with the help of a calculator. I expect your biggest difficulty is in sorting out and applying the rather strange-looking symbols. It's all just a matter of practice making perfect.

Now return to the text

Response N8.1   (a)   First we have to calculate the cross-sectional area (A) of the rivet:

$$A = \frac{\pi D^2}{4}$$

$$= \frac{\pi \times 12^2}{4}$$

$$= \textbf{113 mm}^2 \text{ (3 s.f.)}$$

where: $D = 12$mm

From the text:

$$\text{shear stress } (\tau) = \frac{F_s}{A}$$

$$= \frac{11\,300 \text{ N}}{113 \text{ mm}^2}$$

$$= 100 \text{ N/mm}^2$$

$$= \textbf{100 MPa}$$

where: $F_S = 11.3$ kN $= 11\,300$ N
$A = 113$ mm^2

I hope that you remembered to convert kilonewtons (kN) into newtons (N) since we are working in millimetres and square millimetres. Remember that:

1 Pa $= 1$ N/m^2
1 MPa $= 1$ MN/m$^2 = 1$ N/mm^2.

(b)   The safe working shear stress is given as 0.5 times the safe working tensile stress. Therefore we must first find the safe working tensile stress ($\bar{\sigma}_t$), given that the UTS for the rivet material is 400 MPa and the tensile safety factor is 4:

$$\bar{\sigma}_t = \frac{\sigma_{t,\,max}}{s}$$

$$= \frac{400 \text{ MPa}}{4}$$

$$= \textbf{100 MPa}$$

where: $\sigma_{t,\,max} = 400$ MPa
$s = 4$

Safe working shear stress $(\bar{\tau}) = 0.5 \times$ safe working tensile stress $(\bar{\sigma})$

$$= 0.5 \times 100 \text{ MPa}$$

$$= \textbf{50 MPa}$$

I hope you managed to get that one correct. Well done if you did. Remember to work through the calculations a step at a·time; don't take short cuts and show all the working. That way you can always check back to see where you have made an error.

Now return to the text

Response N8.2   First we have to calculate the area in shear, where:

area (A) = perimeter of blank × thickness of material

$\qquad$ = 50 mm × 50 mm × 2 mm

$\qquad$ = **5000 mm^2**

To find the blanking force (F_s) we multiply the shear stress for the metal by the area in shear:

blanking force $(F_s) = \tau \times A$

$\qquad$ = 300 MPa × 5000 mm^2

$\qquad$ = 1 500 000 N

$\qquad$ = **1.5 MN**

where: τ = 300 MPa

That's the final activity completed. I hope you managed it successfully.

Now return to the text for the final assignment

Index